MAN'S CONQUEST OF THE STARS

PIERRE ROUSSEAU

Translated from the French by
MICHAEL BULLOCK

W · W · NORTON & COMPANY · INC · *New York*

ENGLISH TRANSLATION
COPYRIGHT © 1959 BY JARROLDS PUBLISHERS (LONDON) LTD.

FIRST AMERICAN EDITION 1961

Library of Congress Catalog Card No. 61-13045

PRINTED IN THE UNITED STATES OF AMERICA

Contents

Roemer subjects light to mensuration—Death of Cassini, eclipse of physical astronomy—The founding of positional astronomy—Huygens, the father of precision horology—The first inventory of the stars—Bradley establishes the position of the stars—Resumption of planetary exploration—The Moon, the first step in surveying the planets—Cassini stretches the surveyor's chain from the Earth to the Sun—The transit of Venus: adventures and misadventures

Foreword

Is there any more thrilling epic than that of the discovery of the universe?

The branch of humanity at first confined to a corner of the Mediterranean was moved by the spirit of adventure to extend its domain along the whole coastline of the inland sea, then to launch out into the interior of the continent, establishing colonies at various points, conquering Asia and Europe, massing along the Atlantic seaboard, setting out from here to conquer the New World and finally, in our own day, gaining a foothold in all the countries of the globe and planting its flag at the two extremities of the axis, the Arctic and the Antarctic. What a victory of energy and determination, and what booty this victory yielded!

Yet this conquest is only a tiny fraction of the conquest of the universe.

Imagine a microbe gifted with intelligence in a drop of dew. This microbe has succeeded in forming an idea of the flower on which the drop rests, of the garden in which the flower grows, of the town in which the garden stands, of the country, of the continent. . . . It has even managed to vizualize the earth as a whole, to ascertain its shape, to measure its dimensions.

This is roughly the significance of Man's discovery of the universe. This universe, which has been slowly, patiently, laboriously enlarged, was initially limited to the immediate horizon, then progressively widened till it embraced the solar system, spread to the nearest stars, enveloped the Milky Way and finally included those nebulae that appear like scattered dust on the photographs taken from Mount Palomar.

The story of this prodigious conquest accomplished by a thinking microbe attached to one of the most insignificant stars of one of the humblest spiral nebulae in the cosmos is indeed a tribute to human intelligence.

This story, moreover, is not merely a thrilling adventure, but a matter of vital importance to the very foundations of our society. From the very outset, astronomy proves to have 'taught civilization' to mankind. By compelling Man to raise his face to the skies, it made him acquainted with the earth and assured his mastery over it. Every stage in the enlargement of the world of heavenly bodies is accompanied by an enrichment of the world of men. If progress in the field of astronomy has frequently owed a debt to technical progress, the conquest of the skies has even more frequently given birth to the most important discoveries and inventions in the material domain.

It is the phases of this conquest that are outlined here—not from a purely descriptive point of view, but in an effort to bring to light the processes that brought them about: in a word, in an effort to *understand* them.

Even if he has not succeeded, the author will be forgiven for having, as a good Cartesian, made the attempt.

P.R.

I

Primitive man between the
gods and the heavenly bodies

Man conquered the Earth by looking up to the sky—Cro-Magnon
Man confronts the gods and the heavenly bodies—Having turned
to agriculture, Man consults the Sun—Each people constructs its
own astronomy—The Sun god of the Egyptians—The birthplace
of astronomy—Babylon reads the omens in the sky—Beneath
the vagaries of astrology are laid the first foundations of
astronomy—Man, the central figure on the celestial stage

THIS book opens with a picture from twenty thousand years ago,
a man of the Magdalenian era crouching in fear and trembling at
the mouth of his cave. It ends with that of a modern scientist busy
either with some calculation in his study, or at the eye-piece of a giant
telescope. Around the former stretches a vast and hostile universe, in
which he is menaced by beasts of prey, the hidden dangers lurking in
impenetrable thickets and behind every rock, thunder and lightning
and the invisible powers manifested when the arrow soars into the air,
when death strikes or when an eclipse blots out the Sun. To the latter
this universe has yielded. Not only has the cloak of its mystery been
torn from it, not only has the secret mechanism of its most impressive
phenomena been dismantled and demonstrated, but the scientist has
even made himself master of this mechanism. The Magdalenian
sorcerer tried, by means of propitiatory rites, to conciliate the
capricious divinities governing the world; the contemporary scientist
embodies his power in a series of equations. A few mathematical
symbols scribbled on a scrap of paper may, as he wishes, either
describe the orbit and course of some double star on the periphery of
the Milky Way, or touch off the explosion of a hydrogen bomb that
will echo the most terrifying volcanic eruptions.

This comparison between our palaeolithic ancestor and the

twentieth-century physicist or astronomer may seem rather facile. But the wonderful thing, to which the reader's attention should be drawn, is that no more than twenty thousand years lie between the one and the other. Twenty thousand years—perhaps the thirtieth part of our race's age. That is all it took to progress from the drawings in the Lascaux cave to photographs with an electron microscope enlarging a hundred thousand times; from the Eyzies spear-thrower, a bone engraved with mystical figures, to the rocket plane that passes 2,000 m.p.h.; from the narrow domain of dense undergrowth full of savage beasts and pitfalls of all kinds, into which Cro-Magnon man did not venture without a shudder, to the realm, now several thousand million light-years in extent, that has been progressively mapped out by his successor.

Victory over disease—thanks, for example, to antibiotics; over geography—since he is now able to divert rivers and shape mountains; over space—through his means of locomotion; over matter—as the result of so many atomic discoveries; over the whole of blind and inert Nature: these are the advances Man has made during the last twenty millennia. A succession of battles won, which it would be an over-simplification to attribute solely to the continuous perfecting of the human brain.

Man conquered the Earth by looking up to the sky

The giant Anteus recovered his strength every time he touched the Earth. Conversely, as this book sets out to show, Man has seen his genius and power expand every time he renewed his contact with the starry sky. His intelligence would have been poor indeed if this sky had been for ever concealed from him. However exact his reasoning, however broad his imagination, they would not have counterbalanced the deficiencies of his vision. Caged between the earth and the dark vault above, how could he have obtained the elementary data on the external world? The movement of the heavenly bodies would have escaped him. The path of the planets would not have afforded him that demonstration of determinism without which no science is possible, and Cartesian logic, the basis of all rational knowledge, would never have passed beyond its first rough outline. A hidden sky would have kept Man for ever ignorant of the great natural laws. It would have been impossible to explain such things as weight, since observation of the Moon would not have led Newton to the idea of universal gravitation. It would have been equally impossible to plumb the world of atoms, since it was the chemistry of the Sun and stars that guided physicists in their investigation of the nucleus.

The invention of determinist logic, the discovery of universal attraction, the conquest of atomic energy, these are three prime stages in the formation of the modern world that could nct have been accomplished except hand in hand with advances in the exploration of the heavens. It was by looking more and more keenly at the heavenly bodies that Man became increasingly able to expand his own kingdom. Throughout the centuries the stars served him as guide marks, and science, today the very essence of our civilization, could not have developed if astronomy had not first broadened its horizons.

It is because Man was revealed by himself to be smaller and smaller in face of a more and more overpowering universe that he has finally found himself once more so great. In the world of Homer's day—a flat Earth roofed by a starry dome—he was a personage of some importance in an environment made on his own scale and for his benefit. In the universe of Hubble or Baade—a supposedly hyper-spherical volume extending over thousands of millions of light-years— he is simply nothing. Yet who would venture to compare the intellectual and material power of a hero of the Trojan War with those of a present-day scientist? That our field of activity should have expanded the more rapidly and more precisely we were able to visualize our own smallness is only an apparent paradox: in proportion as astronomy shed light around us, we became increasingly aware of our potentialities and our real powers, and it is these latter that endow us, in our struggle against encroaching Nature, with arms less and less unequal to hers. Henri Poincaré once said: 'Astronomy has equipped us with a soul capable of understanding Nature,' and he added: 'Nowadays we no longer petition Nature—we command her, because we have uncovered some of her secrets and are uncovering fresh ones every day. We command her in the name of laws which she cannot repudiate because they are her own.' Since Poincaré wrote these lines over half a century has passed, during which we have perceived more and more clearly that technology and civilization have always advanced in step with the progress of astronomy. The latter was at one time pictured as a beautiful but cold goddess, whom men contemplated from a distance in all her magnificence, but who never deigned to stoop down to them. Now we see her in a truer light—as a guide who walks ahead of us along the road of the ages and with whom we feel ourselves to be on more and more familiar terms.

Only yesterday the awe-inspiring story of Man's penetration, century by century, into the mystery of the stars seemed glorious but devoid of practical significance. Today, on the contrary, we realize how closely the most down-to-earth of human preoccupations are inter-linked with disinterested knowledge. The rise of agriculture in ancient Egypt appears to us bound up with the observation of Sirius; the birth of democracy in Greece, seven centuries before our era, related to the disinterested study of the heavenly bodies; the enrichment of Europe, at the time of the great nautical expeditions of the sixteenth century, dependent upon the development of navigational techniques based on astronomy; the fear of atomic reactions, that took the world by the throat not so very long ago, inseparable from relativity, that supremely theoretical law of the infinitely large.

The story of the gradual conquest of the skies is only another side, unfamiliar to most people, of the story of civilization. This story shows the ever-increasing part which the science of the heavens plays in our earthly undertakings, and it is also the most splendid symbol of the growing powers of the human intelligence.

It is true that our attention was long since drawn to the perpetually expanding circle enclosing the explored universe—first the Earth, then the solar system, then the near stars, then the Milky Way; but it was only a few years ago that this ever more rapid conquest acquired its full importance—since the time when the main laws of logic, mathematics and physics were found to be valid as far as the limit reached by the great telescope at Mount Palomar, and the scientist felt entitled to regard the stars as so many adjuncts to his laboratory.

Thus the conquest of the sky by astronomy has not only raised

Man to the supreme dignity of a thinking being, but has also furnished him with the means of conquering his earthly domain and exploiting it to the full.

Cro-Magnon Man confronts the gods and the heavenly bodies

We may seek the origins of this conquest of the sky no further back than the Upper Palaeolithic—twenty thousand years ago. This is the period of the rock paintings in the Lascaux cave—the Versailles of prehistory, Abbé Breuil has called it—of the steatopygous Venuses of Laussel and the numerous bracelets, necklaces and spear-throwers recovered from Magdalenian deposits. It is also the age of Cro-Magnon Man, a tall, broad-shouldered figure with a high forehead, the prototype of *Homo sapiens* and the direct ancestor of our race.

This means that Man was already far removed from his genesis. Hundreds of thousands of years had passed since he invented stone tools and learnt how to make fire. By the end of the Palaeolithic era he had acquired the same level of intelligence as ourselves. He drew, painted, engraved and carved—though it was in obedience to the demands of religion, rather than out of pure feeling for art. Nevertheless, in the midst of a Nature that no force had yet attempted to discipline, how weak and unprovided he was! Naked and hungry, in the face of animals clad in warm furs and armed with terrifying claws and fangs, he scarcely dared emerge from the cave which he had made his home. Everything around him was a chaos of dark forces seeking only to harm him. He submitted, marvelled, resigned himself, implored the occult powers to cease doing him harm or to show him favour.

He saw the Sun rise every morning and go down every night; he observed the imperturbable course of the Moon and the periodic succession of its phases. These were powers whose implacable regularity ordered his life. Occasionally an unexpected occurrence would upset this regular course of events—thunder, lightning, the fall of a meteor, the sudden darkness of an eclipse, the fantastic apparition of a comet, the furtive passage of a shooting star. Far from wondering what these phenomena might really be, Man confined himself to enduring them, to noting them as manifestations of the divine. His sole concern was to obtain food and preserve his life. Nothing mattered to him except, by means of magic rites and with the aid of wizards, to avoid suffering excessively from the caprices of the powers dwelling in the skies. Not until his material situation had become somewhat more secure and he himself was no longer completely at the mercy of Nature, did he begin to observe instead of merely submitting, to make a bold attempt to profit from out-of-the-ordinary events instead of passively turning his back.

Having turned to agriculture, Man consults the Sun

The end of the Ice Age, fifteen thousand years ago, heralded the end of the Palaeolithic period. With the advent of the Neolithic period, mankind entered upon totally new conditions of life.

The mitigation of the climate allowed the tribes to emerge from their caves. They established themselves in favourable positions in the open, flocking to the shores of the Mediterranean, the banks of the Nile, the Euphrates and Tigris, the Indus and the Yellow River. They looked for water and sometimes sought its protection, going so far, in Europe, as to erect their villages on piles in the midst of lakes. As their perpetual worry was always the quest for food, and as hunting no longer brought sufficient, they had to turn to herbs, berries and grains. The day on which someone, tired of the never-ending search for these grains, thought of sowing and reaping them represents a cardinal date in the history of mankind. When they opened the era of agriculture, men ceased to regard themselves as Nature's victims and sought her collaboration. On leaving their dens for the bright sunshine of the fields, they offered her a sort of pact, and instead of glancing at her with suspicious hostility they raised their eyes and gazed at her openly.

Corn-growing goes back ten to fifteen thousand years, and we owe it to Mesopotamia or Egypt. Those who undertook it were naturally led to pay more heed to the major events affecting the weather and the heavenly bodies, since upon them depended the harvest. It was certainly for very practical reasons that they learned to distinguish the seasons, especially those of sowing and harvest, discovered that they returned in the same order after a certain number of days, noted that the Sun rose more or less high in the sky according to the season and, at the same time, that it came up and went down at different points on the horizon.

These are facts that the citizen of today has little opportunity of observing for himself. He would have to be in the country from one year's end to the other to notice that in December the Sun comes up quite near the south, drags languidly across the sky without rising much above the horizon and goes down still quite close to the south; whereas, in June, the high, wide arc it describes compels it to rise and set much nearer the north. It is only at the spring and autumn equinoxes (around 21 March and 23 September) that it rises in the east. It is easy to understand that Neolithic Man, paying close heed to the vegetation upon which his life depended, should have observed that the annual growth of this vegetation was correlated with the variation in the daily course of the Sun. Hence there is nothing surprising in the fact that the people of those days constructed a sort of calendar which, by indicating the beginning of the seasons according to the path of the Sun, kept them informed of the correct rhythm of work in the fields.

Some of these prehistoric 'calendars' have survived down to the present—huge constructions now an object of curiosity to sightseers. The two most notable are the megalithic 'alignments' at Carnac in Brittany and the cromlech at Stonehenge, Wiltshire. The former consisting of three series of parallel lines of menhirs, the latter of menhirs arranged in circles. Both these monuments seem at first to have a religious significance, and even to have served as tombs; nevertheless, one cannot help being struck by the discovery that one of the three alignments at Carnac runs exactly east and the other two north-east (the direction in which the Sun rises at the summer solstice), while the geometrical axis of the Stonehenge ring also points towards the north-east. In the latter case, incidentally, the direction seems inaccurate by about $1°$ $12'$. This difference might have arisen from a mere error, very pardonable in view of the date at which the structure was erected; but in 1901 the astronomer Norman Lockyer ascribed to it a far more interesting significance. He supposed that Stonehenge had been oriented by its builders with no less precision than Carnac, and that if the Sun no longer rose on 21 June in the direction established by these builders, it was because the position of the solstitial sunrise had changed. Since the only possible cause of change is the infinitesimal, but regular, variation in the obliquity of the ecliptic, it is possible to calculate how many years were required for this variation to reach 1° 12'. In this way Lockyer dated Stonehenge from the year 1840 B.C. (plus or minus 200 years). This figure was confirmed in 1952 by the American physicist W. F. Libby: traces of charred wood found in the soil provided him with radiocarbon 14, which, when examined by modern methods of analysis, yielded the date of 1848 B.C. plus or minus 275 years.

This date of *circa* 1800 B.C. is generally regarded as marking the end of the Neolithic period (that is to say, the age of polished stone) in Western Europe, and the beginning of the Bronze Age. But the essentially relative character of this chronology must be borne in mind. When bronze appeared in Europe it had been in everyday use for at least 700 years in Egypt and Mesopotamia. For the transition from prehistory to proto-history did not take place at the same time everywhere. In Egypt and Mesopotamia it occurred in about the fifth millennium B.C.; in India, around 2500 B.C.; in the Aegean, around 2300 B.C.; in China, around 2000 B.C.; among the Mayas, Aztecs and Incas, at about the beginning of the Christian era . . . and there are tribes in Africa and South America who are still waiting for it.

In other words the demarcation of the ages—Palaeolithic, Neolithic, Copper, Bronze, Iron—cannot serve as a criterion for the antiquity of a civilization. When iron was introduced into Gaul, in c. 700 B.C., the Great Pyramids were already some twenty-one centuries old and the Sumerian ceramics of Tepe Giyan over thirty centuries old. Europe was still in the darkness of savagery when civilization and the systematic observation of the heavenly bodies were evolved on the shores of the Mediterranean and, more generally, in all regions where a pastoral and nomadic life had given way to an agricultural and sedentary one.

Again, there is no cause for surprise at seeing astronomy, that soaring towards the skies, born at the same time as agriculture, that earthbound drudgery with a harshly material aim. Both are daughters of the Sun and of clear skies. The latter was bound to give birth to the former; the periodical nature of work in the fields was bound to lead men to seek guidance regarding the passage of time in the movements of the heavenly bodies; these observations, in turn, were bound to steer human intelligence in the direction of rational knowledge and to create civilization. Hence it was only to be expected that the latter should come into being in sunny latitudes, and that the cold and misty lands of Northern Europe should not have awakened until much later.

Astronomy was not created everywhere at the same time, and those who first devoted themselves to it were also the authors of our civilization.

Each people constructs its own astronomy.

A poetic tradition, possibly derived from the Bible, shows us the first observers of the skies as Chaldean shepherds keeping watch on mild nights and gazing with interest at the stars, whose brilliance was dulled by no mist and no dust. In reality this picture applies equally well to Egypt, China, the land of the Mayas or Sumeria. For if conditions of life varied from one region to another, and if the purpose of observing the heavens was not the same everywhere—being purely agricultural in some places and elsewhere more mystical or astrological —the phenomena observed did not change.

Since the dawn of prehistoric times, since Man became a conscious being, he had naturally grown familiar with the chief of these phenomena, the daily course of the Sun, the phases of the Moon, the starry sky. But he scarcely began to look at them before Neolithic times, and then it was the daily and yearly movements of the Sun, so intimately linked with agricultural tasks, which he studied most systematically. To say that observation of nocturnal phenomena did not begin till later may sound a misleading over-simplification. Nevertheless, a great deal of time must have passed before a grain of disinterested curiosity was mingled with the exclusively practical concern of the farmer, before the latter looked at the stars and discovered, for example, that throughout the night they moved gradually from one side of the horizon to the other, while remaining fixed in relation one to another, as if they were pasted on to the interior of a huge hemispherical dome pivoting slowly about its axis.

It must certainly have taken many centuries before facts that seem to us so simple, such as the diurnal rotation of the celestial sphere about its axis, were recognized, before the celestial pole at the extremity of this axis was visualized in the material shape of a polar star. People must eventually have noticed that at the first light of day the heavenly bodies, instead of suddenly disappearing, faded imperceptibly away, and that some of them, like the morning star, remained visible even after the sun had risen. This perhaps suggested that the sky might, in spite of superficial appearances, be filled with stars during the day as well as during the night and that there was no abrupt break between the two.

Observers also noticed that day by day the visible stars changed and gradually succeeded one another as the year passed. The little group of the Pleiades, for instance, doubtless caught men's attention early on, and they must quickly have appreciated that its first appearance in the course of the year signalled the approach of winter and meant it was time to bring in the harvest, while its disappearance heralded the season for ploughing.

And there was the Moon, the orb of cool nights after burning hot days, the light of shepherds and travellers. Since the beginning of Palaeolithic times men were familiar with the succession of its phases, they could foresee them and knew the number of days that passed between two consecutive full Moons or first quarters. The number is twenty-nine and a half. This constitutes a lunation, or what modern astronomers call a synodical month. The lunation furnished the most primitive of calendars, before men were capable of defining the year by the movement of the Sun.

Such are the phenomena that must have been observed and recorded almost everywhere when the curtain of proto-history was raised—among the Egyptians and the Sumerians, among the Chinese, the Hebrews and the Hindus. At the same time men of such different types and subject to such varied conditions of life necessarily put this common fund of knowledge to different uses. Thus astronomy assumed very diverse forms as between one people and another.

India, which had previously attained a very high level of civilization, as the astonishing urban remains of Mohenjo-Daro and Harappa (c. 2500–1500 B.C.) attest, was invaded around 1500 B.C. by Aryan nomads. The knowledge of these Aryans is codified in the *Vedas*. Like all sacred books, the *Vedas* contain many astronomical references, but they are used to furnish a universe that is extremely naïve in conception. The flat Earth floats on the cosmic ocean; above it are set two skies, one above the other; the first is the domain of the clouds, winds and thunder, the second of the heavenly bodies. In this cosmology the observation of eclipses, solstices and equinoxes served merely as prop for the development of religious ideas, and the few accurate data were drowned in a welter of mysticism. In fact Hindu astronomy did not acquire any value until several centuries after Christ, when it came into contact with Greek science.

It was much the same with Israel, but here observation of the heavenly bodies played an even smaller role. The Hebrews were organized as a theocracy, in which the conduct of life was dominated by considerations of ritual. Though they founded monotheism, the Jews proved incapable of providing themselves with a calendar, and after the Exodus (c. 1400 B.C.) they were compelled to adopt the Babylonian calendar.

From the outset, Chinese astronomy followed a different path. Unlike that of the ancient Hebrews and the Hindus, the Chinese mind is meticulous and practical. As the religion practised in those days taught them that there was a continuous and reciprocal interaction between Heaven and Earth, a knowledge of the former was indispensable to the emperor in governing the latter. Hence certain officials were entrusted with the task of observing the firmament, forecasting the movements of the heavenly bodies and noting any unusual events that might take place among them. They practised 'judicial' astrology, applying to the community as a whole, not 'horoscopical' astrology— still, alas, fashionable in the twentieth century of our era—which claims to deduce the destiny of the individual from the position of certain heavenly bodies.

That the sovereign attached the greatest importance to astrological predictions in the conduct of public affairs is borne out by an anecdote dating, according to the *Annals of China,* from the year 2159 B.C. In this year there occurred an eclipse of the Sun not foreseen by the official astronomers Hi and Ho. It caused such panic that the emperor took serious measures—he had the two unfortunate astronomers beheaded.

The date quoted must be treated with the greatest reserve. The Chinese pride themselves on their great antiquity, and their classics refer to events said to have taken place five thousand years ago. But, in reality, the principal source of these accounts, the *Chou-King* or *Book of History,* gives no reliable information of anything prior to the first millennium. No doubt at this period the Chinese had divided the night sky into 284 constellations; no doubt they could plot the annual path of the Sun and the monthly path of the Moon in relation to the celestial equator[1]; no doubt they were able, with the aid of a little instrument known as the *siun-ki,* to demarcate equal hour angles in the sky and so calculate the time of day[2]; no doubt they were capable of predicting eclipses; but the Mesopotamians had known all this and more, over a thousand years earlier—and they had irrefutable documentary evidence to prove it.

The Sun-god of the Egyptians

Astronomy showed yet another face when it appeared in Egypt. 'Egypt is a gift of the Nile', Herodotus wrote later. Without the Nile, there would be no Egypt—nothing but a torrid valley, its soil cracked by the heat, infertile and uninhabitable. But the Nile is there; every summer it rises from its bed and spreads out over the countryside;

---

[1] The sky surrounding us is regarded as forming the 'celestial sphere' (Fig. 1). The observer occupies the centre O of this sphere, which the horizontal plane cuts along a great circle HH' which is the horizon. A vertical line OZ pierces it at the zenith Z. The axis round which the diurnal rotation takes place is PP'. P is the northern celestial pole, indicated by the Pole Star. The celestial equator is the great circle EE' perpendicular to PP'. The meridian is the vertical great circle PZEH. Let us suppose a star at S; the circle PSP' is the star's 'hour circle'. The angle between this hour circle and the meridian plane PZP' is the star's 'hour angle'.

[2] H. Michel, 'Du prisme méridien au *siun-ki*' (*Ciel et Terre,* January-February 1950).

when autumn comes it retires again, leaving the earth overflowing with moisture and carpeted with fertile mud on which cereals grow abundantly.

They were already growing there thousands of years ago, and the subjects of the very earliest Pharaohs already knew that they owed life and fortune to the beneficent floods of the river. Their fate

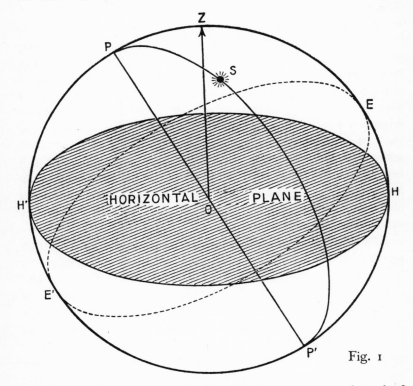

Fig. 1

depended upon them; naturally these floods were among their chief preoccupations. The three seasons of the year were called 'flood', 'emersion' (sowing time) and 'harvest'; and Heliopolis, the principal centre of the corn trade well before 3000 B.C., was also the residence of the main body of officials charged with supervising and regulating the advance of the floodwaters.

This agricultural turn of mind moulded the astronomic patrimony

inherited from Neolithic times, just as it had been moulded in different
ways by the mystic bent of the Hindus and the astrological trend of the
Chinese. Thus the Egyptians noticed very early on that the lunation,
hitherto the basis of every people's calendar, did not correspond at all
to theirs, which was drawn up according to the flooding of the Nile.
Since a lunation is 29½ days, it produced a 'lunar year' of 354 days.
This was naturally in flagrant contradiction to the 'solar year' marked
by the periodical return of the floods.

To tell the truth, other peoples, too, had noticed that the lunar
year did not coincide with the growth of vegetation. This is easily
understood: it varies by eleven days from the solar year, the year of
living nature. At the end of ten years the variation amounted to 106
days or almost four months—the lunar calendar showed summer
when it was still winter! To rectify this awkward fact a compromise,
the 'luni-solar year' containing twelve months of thirty days, had been
adopted in various places, notably Babylonia and China. But this
compromise did not suit the Egyptians, who asked everything of the
Sun and among whom the Moon was only a minor deity. In the fifth
millennium they arrived, by counting the days from one flood to the
next, at the year of 365 days.

Obviously, the rise of the Nile is not a mathematical phenomenon
that occurs unerringly every year on a fixed date. The date may vary
widely around 15 or 20 July. But the officials whose duty it was to
announce this date had a more accurate means of determining the
duration of the solar year: they noticed that on the first day of the
floods the Sun rose immediately after the star Sothis, our present-day
Sirius.[1] This 'heliacal rising' of Sothis afforded a less vague chronological landmark than the overflowing of the waters of the Nile, and
the Egyptians became accustomed to reckon the year from one
heliacal rising of Sothis to the next.

On the other hand, what might be called the 'natural year', the
year that runs from one spring equinox to the other, for example, is not
365 days, but 365 days *and a quarter*. The 'Sothiac year' was therefore

[1] According to Antoniadi, the name Sothis comes from the verb *sothi*, meaning 'to
carry in one's breast' and translated into Greek as *cuein* (κύειν). A curious alteration is
said to have changed *cuein* into *Kuôn* (κύων), meaning 'dog', which finally gave its name
to the constellation of which Sirius is part, Canis Major, the Great Dog.

too short by a quarter of a day in one year, one day in four years, one month in a hundred and twenty years. The shift was slight, but it did not escape the officials at Heliopolis. These men, invested with a task so vital as the control of the floods, carried it out with a conscientiousness and solemnity that had long endowed them with priestly status. Mystical, uncommunicative, subject to age-old rites and discipline, they were true priests who, freed from material cares and led by their functions to study Nature closely, had already amassed a rich store of observations several millennia before our era.

It was these priests who came to grips with the problem of this discrepancy and worked out the exact duration—365¼ days—of the 'tropical year'. For this they employed the *gnomon*. It is quite possible that this instrument was devised simultaneously in Egypt, Mesopotamia, China and elsewhere. However, in view of the importance accorded by the Egyptians to the Sun, we may justifiably suppose that it was invented by them. It consists of a vertical shaft (a rod, mast or obelisk) set in the ground, which, when struck by the light of the Sun, casts a shadow whose length varies according to the luminary's height in the sky. It is shortest at midday, and of all the midday shadows that of the summer solstice is the smallest. Measurement of the shadow therefore makes it possible not only to tell the time, but also, by counting the days from one solstice to another, to calculate the exact duration of a tropical year. It also provides a means of tracing the Sun's diurnal arc and noting that it falls between two extreme arcs, that of the summer solstice, the highest and widest, and that of the winter solstice, the lowest and narrowest.

It is curious to note that in spite of the accuracy of measurement thus attained by the Egyptian astronomer-priests, the year of only 365 days continued to be used in everyday life. The result was a growing discrepancy between the real agricultural year and the official year, and a point was reached where the religious festival of the harvest was celebrated while the fellaheen were starting to sow. At the rate of about one month in 120 years, the discrepancy rose to twelve months in 1,460 years, at the end of which period the Sothiac year momentarily coincided once more with the tropical year. Modern astronomers have made use of this fact in seeking to establish the earliest date at which this coincidence occurred—a date which must, of course, tally with the findings of Egyptology. The date proved to be 4245 B.C. Hence it was probably in this year that the heliacal rising of Sirius was officially adopted as a chronological landmark and that the first solar calendar in history was put into use.

This immense antiquity seems to be confirmed by Egyptian legends and by a mass of evidence. 'The Egyptians,' writes Diodorus of Sicily, for example, 'preserved for an incalculable number of years registers to which their observations are consigned.' We cannot doubt that such an accurate determination of the heliacal rising of Sirius, more than six thousand years ago, could only have been made possible by the comparison of a large number of earlier observations. A further proof is to be found in the pyramids of Gizeh. We know that they stand almost exactly on the thirtieth parallel, that they are oriented strictly towards the cardinal points and that they contain internal passages so inclined that they point at the pole star of the period,[1] that is to say c. 2800 B.C. Such precision of construction could only have been achieved on the basis of sound knowledge of the movements of the heavenly bodies obtained with the aid of sighting instruments. The American Egyptologist J. H. Breasted came across one of these in a London antique shop in 1924. It is a piece of ebony 10 inches long by 1 inch wide and ½ inch thick; it is pierced by a hole at one end, and opposite the centre of the hole a line marks the position of a lead wire. An inscription states that this instrument was made with his own hands by King Tutankhamon (1352–1320 B.C.). No doubt it long served for the observation of such things as the instant a particular star reached the meridian.

The history of Egyptian astronomy plunges us into a world of immense durations of time, quite out of proportion to the scale of our national histories. Faced by this chronology extending over four thousand years, from the Scorpion King to Cleopatra, we may feel a certain sense of inferiority, when we think that modern science dates, at most, from Descartes, Galileo and Newton.

[1] The celestial pole, a prolongation of the terrestrial pole subject to the 'precession of the equinoxes', moves slowly across the sky. Today it is close to the star α Ursae Minoris, which is therefore our pole star. In 13,000 years it will be near Vega; 4,800 years ago (the age of the great pyramids) it was near α Draconis.

Yet any such feeling is unjustified. What is surprising is not that Egyptian astronomy should have been so advanced, but that it should not have been more so. For the sighting instrument manufactured by Tutankhamon proves that the technique of the years around 1300 B.C. was the same as that of the time of the pyramids, that is to say around 2800 B.C. and perhaps the same as at the time of the invention of the calendar, fifteen hundred years earlier still. It is as though our astronomy had remained unchanged since the Middle Ages. But Egyptologists have long ago opened our eyes to the extraordinary conservatism to which the history of this country bears witness, and the history of its astronomy provides further proof of it. Is it not astonishing, for example, that the discrepancy between the agricultural year and the Sothiac year should have been allowed to go on increasing for 1,460 years, and that the same error should have been permitted to perpetuate itself for several Sothiac periods, from 4245 to 29 B.C.?

It is no less strange that in spite of the instruments which enabled them to orient their monuments, the Egyptians failed to notice that Sirius was not at exactly the same point in the sky at the beginning and end of a Sothiac period. The distance between the two points is admittedly not great, but the priests of Heliopolis would certainly have detected it if they had not been conservatives to whom every novelty seemed heretical. Then they would have noticed that, if the year of 365 days was too short, the year of $365\frac{1}{4}$ was too long—and they would have discovered the phenomenon of the precession of the equinoxes.

Finally, it is equally hard to understand how, after hundreds and thousands of years of assiduous observation, the Egyptians could have retained the same rudimentary conception of the universe as a flat Earth encircled by a vast river and covered by the sky as by a bell, a conception then current from one end of the world to the other.

The birthplace of astronomy

Which country was the birthplace of astronomy? This question may appear both idle and unanswerable. The foregoing remarks seem to imply that there was no one birthplace and that, around the second millennium B.C., every people had roughly the same idea of the external world.

Yet there is a radical break between this naïve notion and the almost modern conception that was to see the light in Ionia a few centuries later. An abyss separates the priests of Heliopolis from Thales, and we instinctively seek to know how this abyss was crossed and who provided the bridge by which science passed from the narrow empiricism of the Egyptians to the pre-rationalism of the Greeks.

To explain this transition, and at the same time to account for the astonishing accuracy of constructions like the pyramids, the suggestion was at one time advanced that there existed a secret science, transmitted to one another by the priests of Egypt from age to age. Eugène Antoniadi (1870–1944), a scrupulous astronomer as well as an erudite Hellenist, championed this theory. He distinguished between the superior knowledge of the initiates and the childish anthropomorphic beliefs of the people—the only ones that have come down to us. This superior knowledge seems to have been so secret that not a trace of it is to be found in any Egyptian text. Antoniadi based his thesis on the texts of Greek historians such as Herodotus or Strabo; more recently the Egyptologist Alexandre Varille claimed to find it expressed symbolically in certain architectural structures; but it must be said that these were both purely speculative hypotheses, almost unanimously contradicted by experts. Nowadays it seems clear that ancient Egypt was in possession of considerable technical ability, tested working methods and a body of astronomical observations extending over thousands of years, but that she was incapable of synthesizing them, of extracting from them an explanatory theory; in a word, of rising from the utilitarian plane to that of disinterested science.

We may also note that Egyptian astronomy, based, above all, on the motion of the Sun, was perforce very incomplete, since it was led to neglect nocturnal phenomena, the stars and planets. Yet the study of nocturnal phenomena seems also to be very ancient. From the earliest times, the astronomy of the most diverse peoples concerned itself with the constellations. The English astronomer A. C. D. Crommelin (1865–1939) attributes the grouping of the stars in constellations to the Egyptians of 4000 B.C., but there is sound evidence for a still earlier origin.

In fact the origin of the constellations is lost in the mists of time. We find them among the Chinese and among the Sumerians, among the Egyptians and among the Incas, and it is noteworthy that certain figures are the same everywhere. The Bear and the giant Orion are recognized on the banks of the Nile as on those of the Yellow River, so it is possible that this celestial topography sprang from a common fund of knowledge, to which every people made its contribution. These immensely ancient constellations, which are alluded to in the oldest documents, are forty-eight in number, but they cover only a negligible part of the heavens. This undoubtedly means that the remainder of the celestial vault was unknown to the first astronomers and hence invisible to them. This 'ungrouped' section of the sky forms a zone centred roughly on the star Achernar in the constellation of Eridanus. At the time when it was invisible from Egypt, Mesopotamia and China, this zone must have been situated in the middle of the southern firmament, and we may guess that Achernar was, at this moment, close to the South Pole. Now, the slight displacement due to the precession of the equinoxes indicates that this must have happened in about 2800 B.C. Since Achernar was the south polar star, it was out of sight from any latitude beyond the thirty-eighth northern parallel. Thus, following the British astronomers E. W. Maunder, R. A. Proctor and Crommelin, we may very roughly outline the zone of the earth in which preoccupation with the heavens first made its appearance. This zone passes through the Mediterranean, Asia Minor, Iran, Northern India and China. It is even possible to localize the birthplace of the science of the heavens less approximately, if we note that the most ancient constellations form a zoo in which figure the lion and not the tiger, the bear and not the elephant, the dog and the bull and not the camel or the crocodile, and if we consider that the only region where this zoological distribution prevails is Asia Minor.[1]

Babylon reads the omens in the sky

Asia Minor means, in essence, Mesopotamia, a land which, unlike Egypt, has left an abundance of written documents. This is where the

[1] After Peter Doig, *A Concise History of Astronomy* (London, 1950).

stars were first grouped in constellations and where contemplation of the night sky gave birth to the science that is devoted to it. Occupied by the Arabs at the time of Mahomet's first conquests, the country is now nothing but a waste land, a lifeless desert smelling of petrol and crossed by the muddy waters of the red Tigris and the yellow Euphrates. But, two thousand years before our era, we must imagine Man achieving its conquest by successive feats of skill and determination, draining its marshes, irrigating its sandy wastes with a system of canals that conveyed life and abundance in all directions, mapping out and registering its fields and governing the society that was established there by a strict and sensible set of rules. The country of Sumer, which had already amalgamated with that of Akkad, had just fallen into the Babylonian sphere of influence. In the grip of powerful kings, the whole unified complex was consumed with a tremendous need for order—an order which the great king Hammurabi (1848–1805 B.C.) was to codify down to the minutest details. Once the empire had been inventoried, surveyed, divided into plots duly registered for purposes of agriculture—and taxation—how could the authorities allow the night sky to remain in a state of disorder, its stars scattered at random, its wandering orbs appearing sometimes at sunrise and sometimes at sunset?

To say that the organization of the land for administrative purposes brought with it the organization of the sky, and that the division of the country into local government areas—Ur, Larsa or Nippur—was copied, during the twenty-first century B.C., when the heavens were divided into constellations—the Wain, the Plough or the Shepherd— may sound far-fetched. It is, nevertheless, understandable, when we recall the importance ascribed to celestial phenomena in that part of the world. Like Egypt, Babylonia owed its existence to agriculture, and it was, in fact, enormously fertile. But this fertility was not due to natural irrigation; the floods of the Tigris and Euphrates produced not fruitful humidity, but devastation and death. It was a miracle of technology, an artificial irrigation system established by bold engineers, that enabled the inhabitants to cover with cereals a land baked by the sun. For here the sun was the enemy. It dried up the vegetation, released the miasmas from the swamps, impeded work and trade.

Night alone brought relaxation and rest, made it possible for travellers to go on their way and shepherds to take their flocks to pasture.

With what avidity and disquiet they questioned this night sky! With what anxiety they watched for the slightest portent of rain or a change in the weather! With what fear and trembling they scrutinized the stars, since this dark sky might let fall resurrection or ruin! Hence observation of the heavens was not the affair of shepherds peacefully musing as they gazed carelessly at the heavenly bodies, but of attentive watchers, conscious of the importance of their task and endeavouring, by ceaseless prayers, to procure the good will of the gods.

It is not surprising that these watchers should at an early stage, as in Egypt, have been endowed with a sacred character, at an epoch impregnated with mysticism, when the human mind did not yet distinguish between the chain of causality and the caprices of chance, and the influence of divine beings was seen in the most everyday events. In all probability, therefore, it was the Babylonian astronomer-priests who, to bring order into the chaos and facilitate the reading of its portents, divided the firmament into constellations. Complete lists of these have been found on clay tablets, written in Sumerian—the language of science and religion, rather as Latin was in Europe. They include the *Wain* (our Great Bear), the *Wagon of the Sky* (our Little Bear), the *Yoke of the Sky* (the Dragon), the *Yoke of the Earth* (the Wagoner), the *Plough* (the Triangle), the *Shepherd* (Orion), the *Old Man* (Perseus), the *Lion*, the *Scorpion* and so on.[1]

Just as every city had its god, so had every constellation, and of this god it was the attribute and possession. The whole complex is said in the great poem of the Creation to have been arranged by Marduk himself, the supreme god of the first dynasty of Babylon.

Thus the starry sky was no less than the world of the gods made visible to all mortals. This world was by no means all order and immobility, since the frontiers of the constellations were crossed by 'wandering stars' that roamed about in the most freakish fashion, stopping for a day and then setting off in the opposite direction; since every now and then a comet threaded its way amongst them, falling

[1] After Andre Florisoone, *Ciel et Terre* (November–December 1950 and September–October 1951).

31

stars occasionally rained down and at times the Sun and the Moon were even blotted out.

Accustomed as they were to receiving from the sky pitiless heat, rather than the rain they begged for, the Babylonians could not help attaching a cardinal importance to these various phenomena. It was their destiny that they read in the heavens. Since one set of events foretold the continuation of the drought, while another heralded a flood, it was inevitable that they should seek to interpret them all in terms of earthly disasters and suspect any unusual configuration—the conjunction of two planets, the occultation of a star—of foreboding catastrophe, a military defeat, an epidemic, or the death of a great personage.

The reader will have seen that after consulting the sky for the purely utilitarian purposes of agriculture, Mesopotamian observers were led to extend their curiosity and consult it on far more general matters. As Sir Leonard Woolley has said: 'Astrology was one of the most important branches of the magic art. The Sumerians had already by observation acquired a little astronomical knowledge, and since the Sun and Moon and the planets were identified with gods the changes in the face of the heavens reflected the dispositions of the gods and were directly responsible for events on Earth: the student of the stars therefore might hold the key of the future in his hands.' [1]

Thus astrolatry was followed by astrology, both of them having their roots in astronomical observation.

Astrology occupied an important place in Mesopotamian civilization, much more important than in Egypt or even China. Nothing was done without consulting the astrologer-priests. The latter, by predicting future celestial phenomena, simultaneously foretold the terrestrial events that would accompany them, and provided time in which to prepare for them or take counter-measures. Tradition shows these astrologers scanning the heavens from the tops of many-storeyed towers that were at once temples and observatories. That at Babylon, dedicated to Marduk, rose in seven storeys to a height of 295 feet: this was the famous Tower of Babel. From this retreat suspended between heaven and earth, the soothsayers interpreted the

[1] C. Leonard Woolley, *The Sumerians* (Oxford 1928).

message of the skies with the aid of ancient tomes and were able to issue such warnings as these:

'On the 14th of the month there will occur an eclipse. There will be misfortunes for the lands of Elam and Suria, but good luck for the king. May the king be unperturbed.'

'When a halo encircles the moon and Jupiter is within it, the king of Akkad will be besieged.'

Most of these predictions were based on the movements of the mobile bodies—the Moon and planets—and on their positions in relation to the fixed stars. It was noted very early on that among the constellations, formed of luminaries that never shifted in relation one to the other, a few luminous points moved hither and thither. Prehistoric Man already distinguished the evening and the morning star, but it was probably not until the onset of proto-history that they came to be thought of as a single orb, the goddess Ishtar, our beautiful planet Venus. The planet Jupiter, symbol of Marduk himself, which is scarcely less brilliant and shines not only at dawn and dusk, but the whole night through, was also not slow in attracting attention. Then there was Mars, the maleficent personification of the god Nergal, master of the nether regions, Saturn, and finally Mercury, which is more difficult to discern and is lost sometimes in the red glow of sunrise and sometimes in that of sunset.

It was then noted that these five heavenly bodies do not wander at random over the celestial vault, but follow a predetermined route, the same for all, the same as that taken by the Sun in the course of the year. For it had been observed many centuries earlier that the Sun shifts slightly, day by day, in relation to the stars. Naturally, the latter are completely blotted out by its brilliance and it is impossible to ascertain the position of the Sun among its stellar followers by direct observation, but instead of asking oneself which stars are in its vicinity at midday, it is enough to see which come into view just before it rises. It is easy enough to see that these stars change day by day. The one that today shines before dawn was a few days earlier drowned in its effulgence after remaining invisible in the fires of the rising Sun. This explains why the night sky is transformed as the year passes, why the constellations that are visible on a spring evening are not the same as those visible in autumn, and why those that light our winter nights are identical with those that pass the meridian in full daylight during the summer.

The fact that the starry sky changes completely in twelve months shows that the Sun moves right across it during this same span of time. In other words, it moves imperceptibly day by day amongst the stars in the opposite direction to its daily movement across the sky. The Mesopotamians early succeeded in determining the arc it thus described among the stars. They marked it out by the constellations of the Pleiades, Taurus, Orion, Perseus and so on, and promptly identified the 'path of the sun' that we call the *ecliptic*.

Beneath the vagaries of astrology are laid the first foundations of astronomy

Once they had drawn on the celestial sphere the great circle that is the ecliptic, it was easy for the Babylonians to establish the precise position of the planets in relation to it. They learnt to calculate the duration of the revolution of each of them according to the time it took to return to the same point, and were able to tabulate this knowledge. They located the position on the ecliptic of the Sun and planets on the first day of each season, and were able to deduce from this the equinoxes of spring and autumn and the solstices of winter and summer, periods credited by their astrological teachings with especial influence. As Sin, the Moon god, enjoyed particular esteem—did not the Moon, as the orb of night, evoke coolness and rest?—they took great care in plotting its path and drawing up tables of its phases. The latter were of prime importance, for upon the course of the Moon depended the calendar. The beginning of the month, defined by the new Moon, had to be established with the greatest exactitude. Methods of observation and calculation were gradually perfected and reached their maximum efficiency in the first millennium B.C.

Around this period, moreover, great historical upheavals led Babylonian astronomy to change its aspect. In 612 B.C. the Medes took possession of Niniveh. Assyria, which had so long bent the peoples under a yoke of iron and blood, was destroyed, and Babylon, previously eclipsed by the rival capital, recovered its former splendour thanks to Nebuchadnezzar. But war and vengeance dogged these old civilizations. In 539 B.C. the Persian king Cyrus entered Babylon as a conqueror. Unlike the fanatical and cruel Assyrian sovereigns, who had pillaged, tortured, deported and slain, he showed himself just and tolerant, repatriating the Jews to Jerusalem, compelling the sects to live together in peace, whether they worshipped Marduk, Assur, Yahveh or Ahuramazda, and evinced a very unusual concern for the well-being of his subjects. Religion thus ceased to reign like a tyrant possessed of absolute power. It had less of a hold on men. Observation of the sky was no longer directed exclusively towards providing tables for astrological predictions. An increasing number of astrologer-priests were content to register the movements of the heavenly bodies, without feeling obliged to draw horoscopes from them. Some of them, such as Naburiannu (*c*. 500 B.C.) and Kidinnu (*c*. 380 B.C.), studied the firmament out of purely disinterested curiosity and almost deserve to be looked upon as scientists.

What a wealth of information these observers had at their disposal! They possessed clay tablets on which details of celestial phenomena had been entered for hundreds of years. Some were only a few centuries old—the oldest reliable record of an eclipse of the Sun, for example, dates only from 15 June, 763 B.C.—but some of them, such as the astronomical table of Venus drawn up in the reign of Ammizaduga, went right back to the second millennium. To extract from these works the laws governing the courses of the heavenly bodies and effective means of foretelling their movements was the obvious thing to do.

The neo-Babylonian astronomers gathered together all the studies left by their predecessors regarding the position and circulation of the Moon and planets. They broke down the most complicated motions into their elementary components, submitted them to mathematical analysis and succeeded in obtaining from them astronomical tables covering the near future. This achievement was made possible by the state of mathematics, which was much further advanced in Mesopotamia than anywhere else, and by the system of sexagesimal numeration that had just been created. Remember that it is to this country we owe the division of the hour into sixty minutes and the circumference of a circle into 360 degrees.

We must also not forget, however, that if the Mesopotamians were able to calculate in advance the location of the planets in the sky, it was not because they knew their real elliptic orbit and Keplerian path round the Sun, but because they had derived an empirical rule-of-thumb for predicting from their knowledge of past positions. They had noticed, for example, that eclipses, especially eclipses of the Moon, were repeated in the same order and with the same characteristics at the end of eighteen years. Did they know that this cycle is due to the fact that, for an eclipse to come about, the Moon must first be new or full and second lie in the plane of the ecliptic? It is very probable that they did not, and that they merely applied the rule-of-thumb without seeking to explain it. In any case, this discovery of the period between eclipses, a period known as the *saros*, was one of the principal achievements of neo-Babylonian astronomy and ensured it great prestige.

We must credit neo-Babylonian astronomy with establishing the 'zodiac', the band that encircles the sky from one side of the ecliptic to the other and within which move the Sun, Moon and planets. We have seen above (page 34) that the Mesopotamians marked out the imaginary circle of the ecliptic by constellations such as the Pleiades, Taurus, Orion and Perseus. Around the sixth century B.C. it occurred to them that it would be useful to mark on this circle each of the stages annually passed through by the Sun. As there were 360 days in their solar year—and the same number of degrees in their full circle—they divided the ecliptic into twelve equal parts of thirty degrees and assigned to each of them, as a symbol, the constellation roughly corresponding to it.

In an interesting study published in the Belgian review *Ciel et Terre*, M. André Florisoone dates the first appearance of the twelve signs of the zodiac on a tablet from the seventh year of Cambyses (522 B.C.). Its origin or zero point was in the sign-constellation Aries the Ram, which the Sun reached on the first day of spring. From this supposedly fixed point the Babylonians henceforth measured, right along the ecliptic, the celestial 'longitude' of the planets.[1]

[1] *See* note on p. 64.

Man, the central figure on the celestial stage

When, after calculating the position of the heavenly bodies century by century, the astronomers of Mesopotamia noticed the emergence of an ever-increasing discrepancy between their calculations and reality, they naturally imputed it to some error of observation. It certainly never occurred to them that if the longitude of the planets slowly changed, it was because the point of origin itself was shifting. They were no more capable than their Egyptian colleagues of detecting the cause of this discrepancy, the precession of the equinoxes. This simple observation is sufficient to assess at its true value the progress we owe to Babylon. Justice demands that we should recognize the effort, the scrupulosity, the objectivity that guided its astronomers: we must not forget the ingenuity they employed in applying the mathematical weapon to the immense mass of information inherited from the astrologers, and in this respect they, far more than the Egyptians or the Chinese, are the true ancestors of the Greek scientists. But we cannot overlook the essential fact that their knowledge was, above all, empirical. By observing and noting down the eclipses of the Sun and Moon throughout a number of years, the empiricist finally discovers that they recur after eighteen years, and he can then predict that the total eclipse of the Moon on 26 September, 1950, for example, will be reproduced, under exactly the same conditions, on 6 October, 1968. The scientist, on the contrary, traces the orbit of the Earth round the Sun and that of the Moon round the Earth, shows that an eclipse of the Moon can take place only when the three spheres are in a straight line; employing Kepler's laws and the formulae of spherical trigonometry, he ascertains when this situation will occur; he then arrives, among other dates, at that of 6 October, 1968. The difference of method is the same as that which distinguishes the engineer from the handy-man, the physician from the bone-setter; it is the difference between an empirical rule-of-thumb drawn from practical experience, and reasoning based on logic.

We will ask no more from these magi of the last epoch of Babylon, noting without censure that they were content with appearances and very little concerned to know what lay behind them. The Sun, Moon and planets were mere patches or points of light that moved across the starry vault. To their movements religion attached an astrological significance. It was enough for the priests to observe them and locate them against the immovable setting of the stars. For the starry sky was no more than that—a background dotted with fixed points that were most convenient in marking out the slow journey of the moving stars. The universe was in the first place the Earth, a seven-storey tower resting on the terrestrial ocean and lodged in a kind of egg, itself surrounded by the celestial ocean. The heavenly bodies were only luminous signals by means of which there were transmitted to humans the divine messages that it was the business of astrologers to decipher. Man had not yet realized that he inhabited a minute island suspended in the abyss. He took this abyss for a background and remained obedient to the will of the gods while he watched with satisfaction as the radiant Sun, the gentle Moon, the mysterious planets and the eternal constellations gravitated round his dwelling.

2

Greek genius sees the Sun
as the centre of the universe

The spirit of trade gives birth to the critical spirit—Thales expels
the gods—The Earth becomes a planet—The Pythagoreans prove
the sphericity of the Earth—Does the Earth rotate?—It is
certainly the universe which revolves round the Earth—The
mechanism of the crystalline spheres—Aristarchus places the Sun at
the centre of the cosmos—The geocentric universe of Apollonius,
or the omnipotence of error—Hipparchus, a great retrograde
scientist—The sky becomes an object of measurement—First
step into the sky: Hipparchus measures the distance of the Moon—
Measurement of the Earth—Hipparchus makes the epicycles
revolve round the Earth—Ptolemy's luck—A counter-blow to
the conquest of the skies

A ND divine Ulysses, full of joy, spread his sails to the propitious
wind; and seating himself at the helm he steered skilfully,
without sleep weighing down his eyes. And he contemplated the
Pleiades, and the Wagoner that was going to rest, and the Bear which
is called the Plough and which rotates in its place as it looks at Orion,
and alone does not bathe in the waters of the ocean.' But when Homer
composed the *Odyssey* (in the second half of the eighth century B.C.)
the stars had already served as a guide to mariners for many centuries.
The Phoenicians in particular, those 'kings of the sea', began to utilize
the Little Bear at an early stage, and it was this constellation which
showed them the way during their long voyages on behalf of the
Pharaohs or Solomon. The role of the heavenly bodies was generally
beneficent, but concern about weather conditions and the everlasting
fear of the gods introduced a powerful element of superstition. Orion
was held to be a baneful influence, Aquila was thought to presage
storm when it rose from the horizon at the end of the night and Arcturus
to herald rain, while at the end of the eighth century Hesiod feared 'the

period when the Pleiades, fleeing impetuous Orion, plunge into the ocean, for then the breath of all the winds is let loose'.

Thus, a thousand years before our era, the stars were observed with a practised eye and utilitarian purpose by the pilots of innumerable vessels ploughing the Mediterranean. After the legendary expedition of the Argonauts, which took Jason to Colchis in pursuit of the Golden Fleece around 1230 B.C., this sea had become a sort of great lake around which civilization developed. In about 500 B.C. Scylax sailed all round it, covering some 15,000 miles. At least half a millennium earlier Cornish tin, Irish gold and amber from the Baltic coast had begun to flow into it through the Phoenician trading centre of Gades (Cadiz) and the Pillars of Hercules (Gibraltar). And the memory of a yet earlier naval power was not entirely forgotten, that of the Aegeans from the island of Crete, who had radiated art and peaceful trade throughout the whole Mediterranean area.

Ever since the fabulous times in which the great empires were born, the Mediterranean had served as their point of contact. One after the other the Egyptians, the Cretans and the Phoenicians had exercised maritime supremacy over it, while from the eighth century B.C. onwards the latter were outpaced in their turn and forced to dispute the monopoly of Eastern trade with the Greeks of Asia Minor, who were boldly advancing towards a leading position in the world.

The spirit of trade gives birth to the critical spirit

Trading in the north and west with barbarian Europe, in the east with the ancient Mesopotamian civilization and in the south with the venerable civilizations of Crete and Egypt, Aegean Greece was then at the centre of world activity. An unprecedented colonial expansion had peopled the islands of the Sporades and Cyclades and the shores of Asia Minor with quick-witted, enterprising, astute men whose bent lay in the direction of trade rather than mystic meditation. The stretch of coasts called Ionia, in particular those between Smyrna and Halicarnassus, emerged as a mart, a place of exchange, of hitherto unequalled importance. Ephesus or Miletus are today no more than ruins, among which one may search in vain for vestiges of their former glory, but we must picture their harbours, around 600 B.C., filled with sunshine, tumult and movement, the unshipping of merchandise, the arrival of caravans bringing textiles, pottery, spices and corn. We must imagine the intense activity of the merchants who went to Byblos for the pines and cedars of Syria, to Naucratis for Egyptian wheat, to Babylon for cloth and articles of gold and silver, pushed as far as the Caucasus to buy tin and all the way to India to bring back ivory and precious stones. How could the discovery of such varied lands, intercourse with such different peoples and the alert and realistic mind demanded by commerce have failed to forge in these tireless travellers a basically new mentality? In addition to economic wealth they brought back to Ionia from every trip fragments of the whole spiritual heritage of the ancients—the fabulous knowledge of the Egyptians with its geometrical formulae, its methods of taking bearings and working out the calendar, the vast farrago of Sumero-Babylonian learning with its rudiments of algebra, its lists of eclipses extending over thousands of years, its observations of planets, its sexagesimal numerical system, all of them bound up with magical beliefs and astrological prescriptions and traditions rendered sacrosanct by their antiquity. A heterogeneous patrimony, but one of inestimable importance because, in addition to the empirical foundations of geometry, algebra and astronomy, it contained the alphabet, which the Ionian Greeks thus received from the Phoenicians. The alphabet made it possible to transmit in writing all the manifestations of thought, to avoid oral transmission with the excess of imagery and religious themes introduced into it by the bards; it permitted the intelligence henceforth to make use of a rational means of expression.

A merchant just back from a fortnight's trip for the acquisition of furs, jewels or spices would remain unimpressed by rhetoric and eloquent metaphors. If he were not a realist, who would be? We may imagine him receiving with cynical amusement the ancient beliefs that attributed night, storms, eclipses or the outcome of a battle to the wrath or benevolence of a god. That Atlas bore the skies on his shoulders, that Poseidon stirred up the fury of the waves from his palace beneath the sea, that the Sun and Moon were deities who acted towards men according to their shifting moods, were so many fables which the merchant judged good for old men and children, but at which he himself smiled incredulously. What a gulf separated the Babylonian priest-astrologer, solemn, austere, full of faith and respect for sacred things, from this sceptical and mocking Ionian business-man, who believed only what he saw and attributed to the most majestic phenomena nothing but humble natural causes. For this man was highly materialistic in his outlook. He considered that the rising and setting of the heavenly bodies, the phases of the Moon, the appearance of Venus either in the morning or the evening, were the result not of the comings and goings of restless gods or charming goddesses, but of simple mechanisms minutely regulated once and for all. He was convinced that if there was an eclipse of the Sun it was not because furious Apollo was veiling his face, but simply because the Moon had interposed itself like a screen between this luminary and the Earth. If he had travelled in Mesopotamia he would even have brought back with him knowledge of the *saros*, and could therefore predict future eclipses to the great astonishment of his fellow citizens.

Thales expels the gods

Let us, for example, take a look at Miletus, then the most com-mercially active city in the world. She had scattered colonies and trading posts along the shores of the Hellespont, the Propontis and the Euxine, her power extended from the Bosphorus to the Danube, and she was the place of exchange for slaves and metals, products of the Black Sea and furs from Scythia. The city was filled with the perpetual bustle of caravans and traders of all kinds on their way to buy and sell in Egypt and Mesopotamia. One of these traders was called Thales. Because of his intimate knowledge of the weather, this businessman was able, if we are to believe Aristotle, to foresee a rich olive harvest; he therefore hired all the oil presses in the region, so that when the harvest had been brought in he was able to sub-rent them at an appreciable profit. . . .

A practical-minded man, he supervised the digging of a canal in Lydia and edited a manual of astronomy for the use of mariners. An influential citizen, he held public office and seems to have nourished political ambitions. As we can see, he had nothing in common with the dreamy astrologer—with whom Plato nevertheless identified him —who fell down a well through gazing at the sky!

It was men like Thales who introduced into Ionia the knowledge they had acquired in the Orient and subjected it to critical examination. They rejected any mystical interpretation of nature. They admitted the existence of a supernatural realm, but on condition that it should be strictly confined to religious matters, and they did not tolerate its encroachment, to however slight a degree, upon anything susceptible of rational explanation. They refused to believe blindly and demanded reasons. As J. H. Breasted has said, these people, 'by gradually breaking away from the ancient myths, took the world from the failing hands of the gods'.

To this stimulation of the critical spirit must be added a lively curiosity, itself developed by the bustle of commercial traffic. Among the majority, this curiosity remained a simple instinct, more or less fully satisfied by looking about observantly. In a few people it was transformed into a higher need. These latter wanted to know not merely for the pleasure of picking up information, not even because this information might be useful to them, but because, without the incentive of any practical considerations, their thinking minds experienced a perpetual desire to learn. Unlike the Egyptians, the Mesopotamians, the Chinese and the Hindus, for whom knowledge *served a purpose*—whether a religious or utilitarian one—the knowledge sought by the Ionians was disinterested, free from any thought of advantage. Critical spirit, curiosity, disinterested research—what are these but the characteristics of true science?

Thales of Miletus (born *c.* 637 B.C., died *c.* 548 B.C.) remains for us the prototype of those first scientists who, serving the apprenticeship of reason, set about dismantling the machinery of the skies. That he knew the duration of the year, the inequality of the seasons, the position on the celestial vault of the solstices, the equinoxes and the zodiac, need not surprise us since he had travelled much and learnt much. Nor are we surprised that he was able to predict an eclipse of the Sun in the year 585 B.C.—the Babylonians had long been doing the same by applying the *saros*. Nor does he deserve our admiration for his conception of the universe—he stuck to the notion of the flat Earth floating on water, covered by a hemispherical bubble like a bell.

This universe was only a piece of stage scenery, as in the days of the ancient empires; but Thales's picture did not include the gods. The heavenly bodies were no longer mere patches of light, but solid bodies; the Moon only shone because it reflected the light of the Sun and the stars were made of fire. Eclipses sank to the level of common optical phenomena, eclipses of the Sun resulting from the interposition of the Moon between the luminary and the Earth, eclipses of the Moon from the shadow of our globe falling across it. These interpretations were rudimentary, certainly, but they nevertheless took the machinery of the planets out of the hands of occult powers and placed it in those of dispassionate reason. Indeed this was the first time such an idea had been promulgated—the idea that the movement of the heavenly bodies was governed not by the caprice of deities, but according to impersonal laws, in obedience to an immutable order and an unfailing determinism.

The Earth becomes a planet

Thales had shown the way that should be taken in order effectively to embark on the conquest of the skies. But for him the starry firmament remained a mere piece of scenery, while the Earth alone represented the universe. The first hole was knocked in this stage setting by another Milesian, his friend Anaximander (610–545 B.C.). The latter was the first man who dared to visualize the celestial vault not as a surface, but as a three-dimensional volume, in which the heavenly bodies must be spaced out at various distances.

It is said to have been Anaximander who introduced into Europe the Babylonian gnomon and sun-dial. It was also he who, in Sparta around 580 B.C., first used them to assess the obliquity of the ecliptic. Such claims to fame are of little moment, however, by comparison with the major notion we owe to him—that the Earth is not the whole universe, but isolated and freely suspended in space.

Once more, of course, we have to take into account the childish views of the period. Anaximander conceived of the Earth as a cylinder three times as wide as it was high, while the Sun and Moon were merely apertures that revealed flaming masses revolving around it like wheels. But it is nevertheless true that the philosopher had withdrawn from the Earth its traditional supports: it was no longer borne by pillars, nor by an elephant, nor was it floating on the celestial ocean. It was poised in space and did not fall because it was at the centre of the cosmos. The boldness of this conception becomes evident when we ourselves, civilized people of the twentieth century to whom the isolation and spherical shape of the planet have been familiar since childhood, look at the landscape around us and try to imagine it as a tiny fragment of an enormous ball, which itself rests in the heart of a space that has neither top nor bottom nor limits.

Anaximander was therefore the first to depict the Earth as occupying the centre of the universe, while the sky round about it is the interior of a complete sphere and not merely of a hemispherical dome. Thales had regarded the Sun, Moon and stars as solid bodies; his friend went further still and ascribed to them varying distances. The wheel of the Sun was the most remote, at 27 or 28 terrestrial diameters; then came that of the Moon, at 19 diameters; the wheels of the stars were the closest.

We must note that reality played no part in these original ideas. They still consisted of theoretical schemata, and the figures just quoted were drawn not from observation or experiment, but from religious myths which made them the basis of every cosmology. This shows that, in spite of Thales, human minds were still far from skilful in handling the tool of reason. Too often they continued to yield to old mystical impulses, which caused them to lend an esoteric tinge to the most materialistic preoccupations.

In fact the school of Miletus gradually abandoned the path mapped out by its founder and became bogged down in a metaphysic from which reality was increasingly excluded. After Anaximander, it is scarcely worth mentioning Anaximenes (c. 553–499 B.C.), who made of the Earth a table supported by the pressure of the air and compared the movement of the sky round it to the movement of a nightcap round the head. We may bear in mind that he was the originator of a belief which persisted down to the Middle Ages—the idea that the firmament consisted of a crystal sphere in which the stars were set like jewels.

As to Heraclitus (570–480 B.C.), an Ephesian generally regarded as the last member of the Ionian school, the contempt in which he held both his predecessors and the facts may be judged from a brief statement of his view of the universe. He held the Sun to be as big 'as a human foot', explained the alternation of day and night by alternating light and dark exhalations, and pictured the heavenly bodies as blazing troughs. . . .

The Pythagoreans prove the sphericity of the Earth

One of those Ionian philosophers in whom the mystical instinct fought more and more victoriously against the rationalist trend inherited from Thales was called Pythagoras. He was born around 572 B.C. on the island of Samos, and the American mathematician E. T. Bell summed up his personality pretty accurately when he described him as 'one-tenth genius, the rest illuminatus'. When he left his homeland at the age of forty to found a school in Italy, at Crotona in Calabria, he had already made the rounds of virtually all religions. He began by spending twenty-two years in Egypt, in order to be initiated into the secret beliefs of the priests of Heliopolis. Then, following a Persian invasion, he was taken into captivity, which brought him into contact with the astrologers of Babylon and the magi of Persia. This was followed by other initiations, on Crete and at Delphi, the exact nature of which is wrapt in mystery, but which added to the strangeness of the school he created, with its religious and magical teaching hedged about with rites and taboos.

Pythagoras became a legendary, semi-divine figure to the generation that came after Plato. In our own day many people, on the strength of memories of their school-days, are more inclined to think of him as an outstanding geometer. The truth probably lies somewhere between the two. Pythagoras was undoubtedly a religious reformer before all else, but his doctrine, based on the conviction that all the processes of nature are governed by harmony, order and measure, soon led to the study of numbers and forms. It was claimed that number is the essence of all substance, that all things have their number and that the perfect number is 10 because $10 = 1 + 2 + 3 + 4$. The regular pentagon was credited with mystic significance, circular and uniform movement was held to be the perfect form of motion and the sphere to be the perfect physical body. From this it was deduced that since the heavenly bodies—which included the Earth—were perfect creations, they must be spherical in shape.

Recognition of the sphericity of the Earth was therefore not a scientific discovery, but a conclusion drawn from theological speculations to which experiment was totally alien. It is not certain, incidentally, that this conclusion was advanced by Pythagoras himself; according to Theophrastus it was put forward by his follower Parmenides (born c. 520 B.C.), who taught at Elea, to the south of Naples. Stated like this, the theory that the Earth was round did not cause as much indignation as might have been expected. At a time when religious sects existed in profusion and gave free rein to the most far-fetched cosmological hypotheses, it seemed no more absurd to believe that the Earth was round than to believe that it was flat, as Anaxagoras and Democritus were teaching at the same period, or cylindrical, as Anaximander had claimed.

Pythagoras died around 500 B.C. Hence the idea that the Earth was spherical dates from the fourth century B.C. It was not generally accepted, however, until a century later, when Plato, in his *Phaedo* (380 B.C.), showed the terrestrial sphere in the centre of the universe not borne by the air or by any force. Then Aristotle, in his treatise *On the Sky* (c. 350), supplied this hitherto theoretical hypothesis with the necessary experimental proofs. He pointed out that the shadow cast by the Earth during eclipses of the Moon is circular, that the stars change according to the latitude, that a ship appearing on the horizon comes into view progressively, from the tip of the masts to the hull. Nothing less than these irrefutable arguments could persuade people that, contrary to what everyone had hitherto believed, the vast domain in which they lived was a ball and that, consequently, at the two extremes of a diameter men stood feet to feet.

Does the Earth rotate?

Thus less than two centuries were enough to knock down the stage scenery it had taken the methodical and conscientious observers of Babylon thousands of years to erect. At the beginning of the sixth century B.C. our globe assumed the place in the centre of the cosmos which it was to occupy for so long, and the celestial vault with its fixed stars and moving planets began to revolve around it. Naturally, minds as brilliant as the Pythagoreans, or the first Eleatic philosophers such as Parmenides, could not fail to wonder whether it was really the sky that rotated and not the Earth, appearances being the same in both cases. On this point, too, the school of Pythagoras had the distinction of casting light. It was the first to explain the diurnal revolution of the heavens by rotation of the globe. Whose name can we link with this great discovery? Perhaps that of Parmenides once more, or else, more probably, that of Heracleides Ponticus (388–315 B.C.). Whichever it was, this discovery was not accepted as readily as the first. Aristotle in particular, that powerful and universal genius, while recognizing that 'the Pythagoreans assert that the Earth, being one of the wandering stars, produces night and day by turning on itself', refused to regard the diurnal revolution as a mere appearance; he considered it to be real and pictured the celestial sphere, whose magnitude filled him with wonder, as rotating around a tiny planet.

How could such a profound thinker have failed to see the insurmountable difficulties created by the theory that the Earth was stationary? For if it was easy to envisage the crystalline sphere, in which the stars were set at unvarying distances from one another, as revolving round the Earth, it was a great deal less easy to explain the movements of the wandering stars, that is to say the Sun, Moon and planets. There were at first believed to be six of the latter—*Hermes* (Mercury), *Vesper* (the evening star), *Lucifer* (the morning star), *Ares* (Mars), *Zeus* (Jupiter) and *Chronos* (Saturn); they were reduced to five when the Pythagoreans showed that, as had already been suspected, Vesper and Lucifer were one and the same star, our planet Venus.

This classification was by no means arbitrary. It had long been observed that, since the Moon can eclipse or occult any star in its

48

path, it must be closer than all of them. It had also been noted that certain planets—Mercury and Venus—always accompany the Sun, and that the three others change position more and more slowly as we go from Mars to Jupiter and Saturn. The Pythagoreans therefore pictured the universe as consisting of the terrestrial globe in the centre surrounded by eight concentric transparent spheres. These spheres, the closest of which bore the Moon, the next the Sun, the third Mercury and so on to the fixed stars, rotated at various speeds round different axes, so as to explain the peculiarities of the motion of each of the heavenly bodies.

At what distance from one another were these spheres spaced out? The school of Crotona reckoned 126,000 stadia[1] from the Earth to the Moon—a purely arbitrary figure, as may be imagined. The other intervals were calculated in such a way as to account for the apparent speeds, and they happened to correspond to the sound-intervals between the strings of the lyre. . . . The Pythagorean cosmology culminated in that *harmony of the spheres* which is unfortunately inaudible to our poor ears, but was the delight of later commentators.

Nowadays, we find it hard to understand how men of such remarkable intelligence as these Greek thinkers could have accepted such figments of the imagination unsupported by any tangible fact. And we are astonished that their esoteric bent should have impelled them to believe in the real existence of these crystal spheres revolving one inside the other and animated by varying movements. Some of them did indeed refuse to be imposed upon, discovered that the principal difficulties arose out of the immobility of the Earth at the centre of the universe and sought to escape from the dilemma.

A Pythagorean named Philolaeus (second half of the sixth century) solved the problem and published his theory in a book entitled *The Bacchantes* (c. 400 B.C.). He had the audacity to make of the Earth a planet like the rest, that is to say revolving round a central body. Only this central body was not the Sun—it was an unspecified fiery mass. The Sun itself revolved around this Central Fire just like the planets. Finally, since nothing was perfect save the number 10, the moving stars had to be increased to this number. To reach the figure

[1] On the value of the stadium *see* p. 71.

10, Philolaeus felt obliged to add to the Central Fire, the Earth, the Moon, the Sun and the five planets a further planet, *Anti-Earth*.

Philolaeus's system took no more heed of observable facts than its predecessors. No one had ever seen the Central Fire? That was because the Earth always turned towards it the same hemisphere, which was precisely the uninhabited hemisphere. Anti-Earth was not visible either? This was because the latter, being always on the opposite side of the Central Fire to the Earth, was drowned in its effulgence. The main point was that the movements described by the heavenly bodies should be perfect movements, that is to say circular and regular, that the shape of these bodies should be perfect, that is to say spherical, and their number a perfect number, that is to say 10.

All the same, this theory dislodged our globe from its position at the centre of the universe and reduced it to the level of an ordinary planet. This was a tremendous achievement on the part of Philolaeus, if we consider that the world had to wait very nearly two thousand years before Copernicus timidly ventured to imitate him. We can understand that the bold Pythagorean's reputation spread, becoming so great that Plato actually paid one hundred Athenian minae (about £900) to acquire a copy of his book.

It is certainly the universe which revolves round the Earth

The name of Plato, which we have just written, takes us straight to the heart of a new world very different in atmosphere from that of Ionia and the Pythagoreans. During Philolaeus's day a considerable ferment stirred the peoples of the Mediterranean. The individualism of the Greek cities of Asia Minor had proved fatal to them. Undisciplined and turbulent, incapable of agreeing amongst themselves and allying against the watchful enemy, they were destined to succumb to him. How could this enemy, the Persia of Darius, have failed to be tempted by their wealth? The outbreak of the Median Wars heralded the end of Ionia. In 495 B.C. Miletus was taken by assault, pillaged and laid waste, its inhabitants reduced to slavery and deported. One after the other, the remaining towns of the Aegean coast and sea were destroyed. Around 475 B.C. the last Ionian philosopher, the last representative of the school of Thales, emigrated and took up his abode in continental Greece, at Athens, whose prosperity was at its height and which had been saved from invasion by its victory at Marathon (490 B.C.).

This philosopher was Anaxagoras (500–428 B.C.), a native of the town of Clazomenae (now Vurla, west of Smyrna). He is of little interest to us except as a chronological landmark. He carried to Athens the ideas of the Milesian school, that strange hotchpotch of rationalism and mystical speculation, which made him unpopular with the Athenians. He probably supported the views of Anaximander and Philolaeus, for he taught that the stars were not gods, but solid bodies, and that the Sun itself was only a white-hot block of metal, so large that it was perhaps bigger than the Peloponnesus. Such a heretical doctrine would have cost him his life if he had not been protected by his friend Pericles.

For, after long enjoying unbridled liberty and licence, after hearing sophists and rhetors of all kinds preaching, with equal virtuosity, the most varied and heterodox philosophical and moral theses, the Athenians had lost patience. Socrates, who, as a free rationalist, had criticized religion, the gods and venerable traditions, had been condemned in 499 B.C. to drink hemlock. And his follower Plato (428–337 B.C.) bent his rationalism to a philosophical doctrine in which reality and experience no longer had any place.

In his dialogues (the *Theaetetus*, *Sophist* and *Timaeus*) this great philosopher presented a picture of the world that owed everything to pure idea. He did not consider for a moment that there could be any use in first observing phenomena—the movements of the planets, for example—and then evolving a theory that would explain them. Convinced of the existence of a general idea embracing all possible particular cases, he taught that this general idea obeyed the supreme law of the Good, the Beautiful and the Perfect—rather as though, when we draw a circumference on the blackboard, we visualized behind this circle roughly drawn in chalk the ideal circumference corresponding to the rigorous definition given by geometry. The way to understand the system of the cosmos must therefore be, according to Plato, not to look around, to observe or experiment, but to discover what ideal imperatives things must conform to. This was a view close to that of the Pythagoreans, and it ended, like theirs, by formulating a picture of the universe modelled on an imagined perfection.

As may be seen, there was nothing scientific about Platonic thought. The study of the cosmos became once more an eloquent discussion of the Good and the Beautiful, in which facts were adapted to theories, rather than the other way about. In conformity with these principles, the universe must perforce be spherical, because the sphere was the perfect volume, and, for the same reason, the movements of the heavenly bodies must inevitably be circular and uniform. Unfortunately, although it led to the view that the Earth was round,

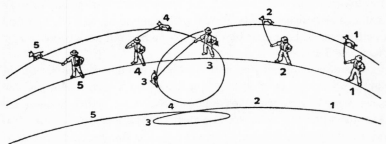

Fig. 2. HOW THE APPARENT MOTION OF THE
PLANETS ARISES

The Sun appearing to revolve round the Earth may be compared to a man walking round us holding a dog on a lead. The dog rotating round him like a planet round the Sun presents to us exactly the same apparent motion as the planet (after Henry Michel).

the rest of this fanciful conception—the Earth as the centre of the universe and the existence of a series of spheres each of which accounted for the movement of a planet—remained incompatible with the facts.

As already mentioned, it was easy to account for the diurnal revolution by the combined rotation of all the spheres in twenty-four hours; it was also possible to explain the annual displacement of the Sun and Moon by the existence of additional spheres revolving in the opposite direction to the first spheres; but it was impossible to picture the irregular motions of the planets in the same way.

To understand the anomaly presented by these motions, let us suppose that the facts are as they seem, that is to say that it is the Sun which revolves round the Earth. Employing the ingenious comparison devised by M. Henri Michel, let us imagine the Sun symbolized by the man in Fig. 2 who is holding the dog. He occupies successively the positions 1, 2, 3, 4 and 5, and the dog revolves around him at the same time (as a planet revolves around the Sun). This means that the dog-planet describes a curve, the curve at the top of the figure, known to geometers as an *epicycloid*. Seen in profile, that is to say from the Earth, this curve looks exactly like the lower one, with halts and retrogressions. We can imagine how Plato must have racked his brains in attempting to explain these curious evolutions in terms of uniform circular motions.

In actual fact, his attitude represented a backward step as compared with the Babylonians'. The latter noted the results of a long series of observations and strove to find an empirical formula consistent with all of them. Plato, on the contrary, started from a preconceived postulate and sought some device by means of which he could prove that the heavens bowed to this postulate. We need not be surprised that he failed to find one.

The mechanism of the crystalline spheres

A device of this kind was put forward by one of his pupils, Eudoxus of Cnidus (408–353 B.C.). This brilliant geometer imagined a sphere bearing the fixed stars, which accounted for the diurnal revolution of the starry sky. For the Sun he supposed a second sphere, which imparted to this orb its daily movement from east to west; then a third, which gave it its annual retrograde motion around the zodiac; and a third, charged with explaining its deviations to one side or other of the ecliptic. The movement of the Moon was also explained by three spheres, and that of each of the planets by four. This made a total of twenty-seven *homocentric* spheres.

The system was ingenious—'a prodigy of elegance and geo-metrical subtlety', Bigourdan has called it—but in spite of its com-plexity it accounted for appearances only imperfectly. In proportion as the Greeks came into possession of a greater number of Babylonian observations, in proportion as they came to observe on their own account, the movements of the heavenly bodies lost their initial simplicity and proved to be affected by numerous minor irregularities. Eudoxus, for example, had overlooked the inequality of the seasons. Callipus of Cyzicus calculated it with sufficient exactitude to ensure that the error did not exceed 0·44 of a day in winter. The increased precision thus obtained enabled him, between 336 and 323 B.C., to add two new spheres for the Moon and one for each planet, bringing the total up to thirty-four.

It is probable that in the minds of these forerunners, and particularly of Eudoxus, these spheres had no real existence; they were probably no more than a mathematical device by which to break down a complex motion into its elementary components. Aristotle, it seems, was the first to attribute to them an objective reality. Then, as he admitted that these material spheres must react one upon the other, he added twenty-two more intended to serve as a kind of buffer between them.

It may appear paradoxical to say that the more genius a scientist possessed, the greater the obstacle he presents to subsequent progress. Nevertheless, it is a fact observed more than once. Did not the Cartesian vortices long stand in the way of Newton's theories? Was not the progress of human palaeontology blocked for half a century by the authority of Cuvier? As relativity was blocked by the united authority of Euclid, Newton and Lavoisier? In each case the obstacle arose out of a discovery of considerable importance—so considerable that it seemed like the last word in the science and an impassable frontier. It was the same with Aristotle. His works, which constituted an admirable synthesis of science and philosophy three centuries before Christ, assumed, as hundreds and even thousands of years passed, such status that they froze intelligence into sterile immobility. Until, in 1637, Descartes shook off the yoke and opened up a new issue to investigation, Aristotelianism was identified with science itself, and it became all the more dangerous to deviate from it because, from the time of St. Thomas Aquinas onwards, it was supported by the lofty authority of the Church.

The mechanism by which Aristotle explained the universe, the

fifty-six crystalline spheres at the centre of which our Earth sat in
motionless state, was to hinder the conquest of the skies until Copernicus. Yet it was far from accounting faithfully for observed phenomena! Why were Venus and Mars more brilliant at certain times of the
year? Since these orbs described circles round the globe, was it not
logical to suppose, on the contrary, that they would preserve all the
time the same radiance and the same appearance? And were not the
halts and retrogressions represented in Fig. 2 an even worse stumbling-
block?

We are surprised to see so many men of talent or genius groping,
when the solution to the problem was so simple. Are not all these
phenomena explained by supposing that the planets revolve around the
Sun? But this idea had to be thought of, and before that could happen
theory had to be submitted to observation, instead of observation
being moulded on theory. Now, docilely to register observations and
compare them objectively without preconceived notions was an
attitude of mind which, since Plato and Aristotle, had become less and
less possible in Athens. Philosophical discussion, hairsplitting, the
erudite formalism of a rhetoric that was nothing but a torrent of words
—all this empty phraseology devoid of any real content had replaced
the study of Nature and initiated the period of decadence that was
brought to a close by the defeat of Chaeronea (338 B.C.).

The part Athens had to play in the epic of the conquest of the
heavens was finished. After its discoveries, as after those of Ionia, the
sceptre of science passed into other hands. The city of Pericles,
Socrates, Herodotus, Thucydides, Aeschylus and Phidias had grown
senile and there was no longer any vigour behind its actions.

This is the impression left by the work of Plato's follower
Heracleides Ponticus, who has already been referred to on p. 48. In
about 345 B.C. he advanced the hypothesis that Venus revolved around
the Sun. It was the beginning of the truth, but why did Heracleides stop
there? Why Venus alone? Why did he not extend his supposition to
all the planets? It was reserved to another people to take over the
relay from this expiring philosophy, as it was reserved for another
younger, bolder, more enterprising capital to succeed Athens on the
throne of the world.

Athens drowsing in its former glory, surrounded by the effulgent halo of its schools of philosophy, its monuments, its marvellous past, and, 600 miles to the south, Alexandria, waking to its youthful fame, active, industrious, hungry for money, pleasure, knowledge—what symmetry and what a lesson! Alexander the Great founded this latter city, and on his death it became the capital of one of the fragments of his empire. The sovereigns who reigned there, the Ptolemies, made it the world centre of trade and the world centre of intelligence. A harbour seething with ships, warehouses stuffed with goods, and beside them palaces dedicated to research, the Museum, the Library, the Serapeum, bursting with teachers, students and books—this was a juxtaposition perhaps unique in history. It was here that a new episode in the history of science was enacted, the episode called *Hellenistic*, a science entirely impregnated by Greek thought but rendered realistic by the mercantile outlook, rendered living by the drive of the Ptolemies, and rendered disinterested by the extraordinary conjunction, at the same time and in the same place, of some of the greatest men who have honoured the human race: Euclid, Apollonius, Eratosthenes, Aristarchus and, surpassing them all, the profound genius Archimedes. A brilliant constellation, to which no equivalent arose until the twentieth century A.D.

It was in this constellation that there shone, from the first years of the third century, Aristarchus of Samos (310–230 B.C.). At Athens he had studied at the Lyceum, the school founded by Aristotle. Strato, the principal, who had been tutor to one of the Ptolemies, had spoken enthusiastically of the warm welcome given to scholars at that time by Egypt, and it was this which encouraged him to go to Alexandria.

We can guess the favour with which Ptolemy Philadelphus must have received Aristarchus, when we know this scholar's wonderfully nimble and lucid intelligence. And what better proof of these qualities could we have than the masterly way in which, around 265 B.C., he attacked the problem of measuring the distance of the Sun and Moon?

It was not the first time the ancients had tackled this problem, the first true stage in the conquest of the heavens. But it is hardly necessary to stress that they had done so in a highly unscientific spirit. When Anaximander, for example, estimated the distance of the Moon at 19 terrestrial diameters and that of the Sun at 27 or 28, or when the Pythagoreans reckoned the latter at 126,000 stadia, it must not be forgotten that they did so on the basis of mystical considerations and

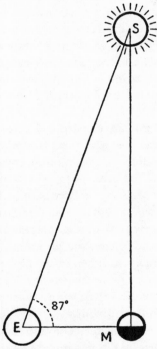

Fig. 3. HOW ARISTARCHUS MEASURED THE DISTANCE OF THE SUN

When the Moon M is seen from the Earth E in the shape of a semi-circle, the angle EMS (S being the Sun) is a right-angle. The construction of a similar triangle then enables us to find the relation of distance MS to distance ME.

had no means of calculating the terrestrial diameter. Aristarchus, on the contrary, made use of a strictly geometrical procedure. He considered that at the moment of first or last quarter we see from the Earth E (Fig. 3) only half the Moon M, the half illumined by the Sun S.

Hence the angle EMS is a right-angle. If we know the angle MES, nothing is easier than to construct on paper a right-angled triangle similar to the triangle EMS and to deduce from it the relationship of the distance EM to ES.

Aristarchus then worked out the angle MES formed by the directions of the Moon and Sun at the time of first or last quarter, estimating it at 87 degrees. Having constructed a similar right-angled triangle, he concluded that the distance from the Earth to the Sun was nineteen times that from the Earth to the Moon. Then, estimating that the width of the Earth's shadow was double the width of the Moon at the distance of the Moon, he calculated that the lunar diameter was 0·36 of the terrestrial diameter, which gave a diameter of 6·75 for the Sun.

Although these results are erroneous, let us not be niggardly in our admiration. It was the first time that a rigorously scientific method, not based on dubious considerations, had been employed in surveying the heavens. The error in the results arose out of the procedure itself: the angle MES should have been measured at the precise moment when EMS was a right-angle, that is to say at the exact instant of the dichotomy[1]. Now, the Alexandrian scientist had no means of determining this instant, and the error of time he committed was reflected, considerably enlarged, in the final result. In reality the angle MES is 89° 50', not 87°, which gives a distance between the Sun and Moon of 388 instead of 18 to 20, with a lunar diameter of 0·27 and a solar diameter of 109 terrestrial diameters.

But what does the result matter! The essential thing is to note that Aristarchus was a man who did not rest content with words, and to understand that when he set about explaining the cosmic system he looked for a theory consistent with observations, not observations that would fit in with a theory. Having examined one after another the ideas of his predecessors—the Ionians, the Pythagoreans, Philolaeus, Heracleides, Eudoxus, Aristotle—he decided, after mature reflection, to adopt that of Philolaeus. We have no evidence of this written by Aristarchus himself—the only treatise by this scientist we possess is

[1] Dichotomy occurs when the lunar disc is divided exactly into two semicircles, one luminous, the other darkened.

his book *On the Magnitudes and Distances of the Sun and Moon*—but we have an irrefutable witness to it in his contemporary Archimedes (287–212 B.C.).

Aristarchus first supposed the celestial sphere to be absolutely fixed. Then he placed the motionless Sun in the centre and sent the planets circling round it, with the Earth in its place between Venus and Mars. The axis of the globe was inclined to the plane of its annual revolution; the Moon revolved round it and all its movements were circular and uniform. We must add that the radius of the starry sphere was infinite in relation to that of the terrestrial orbit, to account for the fact that the perspective of the stars does not change during the course of the year. Such was Aristarchus's system, the same that Copernicus was to rediscover and appropriate to himself eighteen centuries later (p. 101).

Copernicus is generally credited with this major revelation, a vast flight of the mind that extended man's kingdom to the confines of the planetary world. We shall speak of the Polish astronomer again, but we may state at once that the term *Copernican* applied to our heliocentric system is a misnomer. Copernicus does not shine for his originality, since he merely rediscovered what Aristarchus had found out long before him; nor by his honesty, since in propounding his theory he mentioned neither Aristarchus nor the majority of his forerunners; nor by his courage, since, for fear of getting into trouble, he deferred publication of his book till he was on the verge of death. Aristarchus had originality, honesty and courage. We may well understand that a hypothesis which banished the Earth from the centre of the universe, to make of it a body wandering in the same way as the planets, might be regarded as sacrilege. It was also a defiance of the all-powerful Aristotelian doctrine, according to which, by virtue of the 'theory of places', the Earth's 'place' was the centre of the universe. In short, Aristarchus was accused of impiety and denounced by the Stoic Cleanthes, because 'he supposed the sky to be at rest while the Earth circled on the oblique sphere at the same time as it rotated about its axis'. He missed by a hair's breadth being condemned to death by hemlock, as had happened to Socrates some 170 years earlier, for very similar reasons.

Yes, Aristarchus's system is called today the 'Copernican system', an injustice that the centuries have not corrected. Posterity, whatever people may say, is not always equitable, indeed it happens frequently that one man is deprived of his heritage so that it may be improperly attributed to another. Was the originator of the theory of evolution Darwin, or Lamarck who preceded him by half a century? Was the cinema invented by the Lumière brothers, whose *L'Arroseur arrosé* dates from 1895, or by Marey, who filmed the sea, a horse and a singlestick match in 1891? In Aristarchus's case, however, if this system was stifled at birth by the indignation of the devout and the enthusiastic followers of Aristotle, it must be admitted that even in the eyes of scientists this rejection was not entirely unfounded.

What actually was it the Alexandrian astronomer set out to do? He wished to explain the motions of the heavenly bodies, to account for celestial phenomena, as Philolaeus, Eudoxus and their successors had sought to do before him. Now, this search for a theory of the cosmos was rather like a race. No sooner had an astronomer evolved a theory than some new phenomenon was discovered, some little irregularity in the movements of the planets, which made it necessary to recast the whole theory. Ever since the Pythagoreans, theory had thus run ceaselessly after observation without ever catching up with it. And Aristarchus's system did not escape this unlucky fate.

If the Earth and planets describe circular orbits round the Sun at uniform speeds, it was objected, why are the seasons of unequal duration? Why does the Sun seem to pursue its retrograde movement on the zodiac faster in winter than in summer? Why does its apparent diameter vary slightly in the course of the year?

We now know the answer to the riddle. It is that the planets do not describe circles, but ellipses; their movements are not uniform, but of variable speed, in conformity with the second law of Kepler (p. 113). But in Aristarchus's time Plato's postulate—everything must be explained in terms of circular and uniform motions—was in its heyday, and we can understand that the best-intentioned partisans of Aristarchus resigned themselves to the abandonment of his system when they noted that it left these curious phenomena unexplained. Only one of them remained faithful, a Babylonian named Seleucus—the same who, if Plutarch is to be believed, connected the tides with the movement of the Moon and the rotation of the Earth.

Once Aristarchus's system had fallen into oblivion, would there be a return to the crystalline spheres with the Earth at the centre of the cosmos? Basically, the two systems were equally unacceptable. If the brightness of Venus and Mars varied, if the apparent diameter of the Sun changed, it proved that these orbs did not remain at the same distance from the Earth and therefore that they did not follow spherical courses. All at once the Aristotelian hypothesis of material spheres began to look startlingly inadequate. An illustrious Alexandrian mathematician, Apollonius of Perga, younger than Aristarchus by perhaps half a century, rejected it completely and looked for a purely geometrical solution.

It is possible to reconstruct the stages in the development of his ideas. The Earth remained motionless, therefore he had to admit that the path described around it in one year by the Sun, that is to say the ecliptic, was centred not exactly upon it, but slightly to one side; in other words, he had to suppose the ecliptic eccentric (Fig. 4) in such a way that the changing distance of the orb accounted both for the apparent variations in its diameter and the inequality of the seasons.

In the case of planets varying greatly in brilliance, such as Venus and Mars, things were more complicated. Observation showed that they passed through their greatest brilliance when they were aligned with the Sun and the Earth. This meant that the centre of their orbit was on the straight line Sun-Earth. But the difficulty arose from the fact that the Sun revolved round the Earth, so that the line Sun-Earth also revolved. Must he, then, suppose that the centre of the planetary orbit, which must rest upon this straight line, revolved with it? This was, in fact, the conclusion to which Apollonius came at the beginning of the second century and which is presented by Fig. 4. Here we see the Earth, the Sun following its eccentric orbit, and a planet at its maximum brilliance. Paradoxically enough, this terribly artificial system was more consistent with appearances than Aristarchus's heliocentric system!

Apollonius died in c. 200 B.C. After this date the demands of the astronomical theorists grew side by side with accuracy of observation. Astronomers asked themselves, for example, at what distance from the Earth lay the centre of the ecliptic and what eccentricity would explain the complex movements of the Moon, not to mention the halts and retrogressions of the planets, which remained the supreme enigma. In short, the disheartening race between theory and observation continued, as scientists handed on the torch one to the other. After

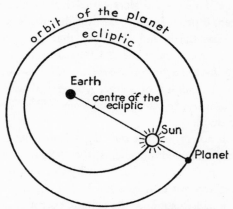

Fig. 4 APOLLONIUS'S SYSTEM

The Earth was supposed at the centre of the universe and the variations in the brightness and apparent diameter of the Sun and planets were accounted for by assuming that they described round the Earth eccentric circles.

the death of Apollonius, however, ten years elapsed before the birth of the man who took up the relay.

Hipparchus, a great retrograde scientist

Imagine reading in manuals of the history of science two thousand years from now, say around A.D. 4000, a passage like this: 'The greatest scientist of the first two millennia of our era was Einstein. Unfortunately, all his works have been lost with the exception of a speech delivered at a prize-giving which, by reference to historical events, we can date from the twentieth century. We know his works only by constant reference to them in many treatises found in the ruins of ancient Europe.'

It is under rather similar conditions that we come to know the works of the scientists of antiquity. Most of the time their works have disappeared for good and we can judge them only by quotations given by their commentators and the use made of them by their successors. Occasionally, the name alone survives, recopied through the centuries by one compiler from the other and linked with the mention of some invention or discovery. We are fortunate when we possess a date of birth, the name of a place of residence, a fragment of writing. The fame of a Greek astronomer called Hipparchus thus comes to us out of the past, embellished by a flattering reputation forged by Pliny, Ovid and Ptolemy. Who was this Hipparchus? Where did he live? At what period precisely? The answers that can be given to these questions are very inexact. It is thought that his whole life passed within the second century B.C., that he first saw the light at Nicaea in Bithynia, Asia Minor, and lived at Rhodes or Alexandria; but if we confine ourselves to the more or less concordant statements of his biographers, that is as far as we can go. As for his works, the only original piece remaining to us is the *Commentary on Phenomena*, a youthful book devoted to the criticism of a poem on the heavens written a century earlier by the physician Aratus.

Hipparchus carried out his observations on Rhodes between 161 and 126 B.C., and he was, alas! the greatest astronomer of antiquity. The meaning of this surprising 'alas!' will be clear if we imagine a great astronomer like Lyot or Hubble, whose worth nobody contests, deciding that the Earth did not rotate and sending all opinion off along this retrograde path. This is what Hipparchus did, a scientist of great value, who took up the cudgels on behalf of militant geocentrism and thereby set science off on the wrong track for sixteen centuries. . . .

Upon what achievements did such authority rest?

Let us say that he codified, clarified, perfected and developed all the knowledge acquired up to then regarding the movements of the heavenly bodies. To be exact, he created *positional astronomy*, the form of astronomy that teaches us how to predict the course of the heavenly bodies, to foretell eclipses and calculate the time. That is to say, to his mind the celestial sphere was merely a backcloth on which luminous objects—the Sun, Moon and planets—came and went, whose circulation was a far more interesting subject of study than their intrinsic nature.

As these movements could be examined only by comparing the greatest possible number of observations, Hipparchus was led to study the records of ancient astronomers, going right back to the best of the Babylonian astrologers. To these he added his own observations. Did he accomplish this double task at Rhodes or Alexandria? As Louis Figuier has written, it is hard to believe that a scientist of this calibre could have cloistered himself on his island without the king of Egypt moving heaven and earth to attract him to his capital. It seems, too, that Hipparchus would have had infinitely fewer facilities for the successful completion of his task on Rhodes than at Alexandria, where instruments, books and records of observations lay to hand.

Hipparchus's intellectual stature is made clear to us as soon as we realize the material means with which he worked. His predecessors down to Aristarchus had used the most rudimentary appliances: the gnomon and clepsydra to tell the time, the alidade to take bearings and the armillary sphere to identify the heavenly bodies and note their movements. With Hipparchus the latter grew more complicated. It was furnished with graduated circles (Hipparchus had borrowed from the Babylonians their division of the circumference into 360 degrees, the degree into 60 minutes and the minute into 60 seconds). One of these circles represented the ecliptic; a second, the meridian; a third, which was movable and bore alidades equipped with sights, was used for sighting the heavenly bodies. As may be seen, this instrument made it possible to measure at one and the same time the angular distance from a heavenly body to the ecliptic (that is to say its celestial latitude) and its angular distance to the meridian or any hour circle (that is to say its right ascension or celestial longitude[1]). With its

[1] To locate a heavenly body on the celestial vault, two systems of co-ordinates may be employed. One takes as its plane of reference the celestial equator. The declination is then the angular distance from the heavenly body to this plane, and the *right ascension*, the angle of the body's hour circle (*see* note p. 36) to a fixed hour circle taken as origin (the one which passes through the point on the sky at which the Sun is situated at the spring equinox). The other system has as its plane of reference the ecliptic, that is to say the Sun's apparent annual arc. The corresponding co-ordinates are the celestial *latitude* and *longitude*, the latter being counted, like the right ascension, from the equinoctial point of spring. This is also called the *vernal point*, symbolized by the sign of Aries (not by the Greek letter γ, as is commonly supposed).

bronze circles fifteen or sixteen feet in diameter the apparatus was huge, and we can understand that it was the basic appliance in every observatory, rather as the meridian instrument is today.

To study the movement of the Sun, Hipparchus made use more particularly of a meridian armilla, a vertical ring graduated every five minutes of arc and fixed in the meridian plane. Inside this armilla was a second, concentric to the first and mobile around its vertical diameter. This second armilla could therefore be directed towards any heavenly body, the direction of which was exactly located on the graduation by means of an alidade with sights that moved upon it. It was thus possible to determine the position of the Sun at the winter and summer solstices and, by means of these, the celestial equator.

The course of the Sun could equally well be followed with the *plinth*. This was a block in the shape of a parallelepiped, one of whose vertical faces was placed in the meridian plane. A rod was placed upon it perpendicularly, the shadow of which passed through one graduation.

To measure angles, Hipparchus specially invented the *diopter*. This consisted essentially of an alidade with sights that moved on a graduated circle. We can confidently admire the care and precision with which armilla, plinth, diopter and the instruments derived from them must have been constructed for Hipparchus to have been able, at a time when sighting was done with the naked eye and without reticles, to measure positions in the sky to within a few minutes of arc —the thickness of a pencil at fifteen feet from the eye.

The sky becomes an object of measurement

In the year 134 B.C. a new star appeared one fine evening in the constellation Scorpio. For a star to be suddenly born in the sky and added to the luminaries known since time immemorial is no rarity, and scarcely a year passes in which astronomers do not observe such an event, either with the naked eye or through the telescope, at least a dozen times.

But the star of 134 B.C. must have been especially brilliant, for it made a great impression upon the peoples of the world. Incidentally, the English astronomer J. K. Fotheringham proved in 1919 that it was not a new star, a *nova*, but a comet. The Latin historian Justin mentions it in his *Philippic Histories*, so do Julius Obsequens and the Chinese Sse-Ma-Ts'ien. We have not previously referred to comets, but we know what importance was attached to these bearded and curiously shaped objects in astrology. The Sumerians already spoke of them as 'vultures' or 'birds of death' and all later peoples regarded them as omens of grave or disastrous events. The comet of 394 B.C. marked the defeat of Sparta by Athens at Cnidus; that of 371 B.C. was followed by the earthquake and tidal wave at Achaea, as well as the battle of Leuctra; that of 343 B.C. served as a guiding torch for the fleet of Timoleon the Corinthian as it made for Syracuse. As for the comet of 134 B.C., it was hailed by Justin as announcing the conception of a child who would be born as the mighty conqueror Mithridates (who was, in fact, born the following year), and it reappeared in 120 B.C. to greet his accession to the throne.

This unexpected apparition made a tremendous impression on Hipparchus. He asked himself whether any similar prodigy had occurred before in the course of the ages, and he thought it would be interesting for future astronomers to possess a catalogue of stars by means of which they could easily detect any newcomer.

The idea was not entirely new. It had already occurred to two Alexandrian astronomers named Aristylles and Timocharis. Between 295 and 269 B.C., these two had actually determined the positions of certain brilliant stars. But Hipparchus resumed this project on quite a different scale. In about 128 B.C. he undertook to list all the stars visible to the naked eye, to measure their celestial latitude and longitude and to estimate their brightness. He thus drew up the first catalogue of stars, the same which, after being revived by Ptolemy, survived unchallenged until after the Renaissance and led to a wealth of discoveries.

This catalogue, like all Hipparchus's works, is lost. All that has come down to us is the copy made by Ptolemy. It comprises 1,026 stars, in other words about a third of those visible without a telescope in one terrestrial hemisphere. It gives for each the longitude, the latitude and an estimate of the brilliance termed the *magnitude* (the most luminous stars being referred to as of the first magnitude and the least luminous as of the sixth magnitude). Here, for example, is an extract from this catalogue dealing with the constellation Gemini, the Heavenly Twins:

Star	Constellation	Longitude	Latitude	Magnitude
The star at the tip of the tail	Twins	$\frac{1}{6}°$	$66°$	3rd
The star that follows, underneath the tail	Twins	$2\frac{1}{2}°$	$70°$	4th
The star next to this, at the beginning of the tail	Twins	$16°$	$74\frac{1}{3}°$	4th

This method of locating the stars naturally meant that celestial globes had to bear drawings of the mythological beings symbolized by the constellations. We may gain a slight idea of the work involved in identifying a star, under these conditions, by opening one of those splendid celestial atlases of the sixteenth or seventeenth century, teeming with minutely engraved figures on which are dotted the stars. More than seventeen centuries passed before astronomers decided to adopt a more practical system of designation (p. 105).

Whatever its shortcomings, Hipparchus's work created a stir. Some 180 years later, Pliny (A.D. 23–79) gave vent to his enthusiasm thus: 'Hipparchus was led to undertake what a god would have judged rash and to count the stars for the benefit of posterity; he therefore gave names to all of them and devised instruments for noting the position and magnitude of each star. His work makes it possible not only to recognize which stars have disappeared or newly appeared, but also to know if one or other of them moves, or increases or decreases in brilliance. He thus bequeathed the heavens as a heritage to all men capable of profiting from such a gift.' It is a fact that it was through comparing with his own the co-ordinates furnished by Hipparchus that the great astronomer Halley discovered, in the eighteenth century, the proper motion of the stars (p. 214).

It was natural enough that, after obtaining his positions for the stars, Hipparchus should have felt curious to compare them with those of Aristylles and Timocharis. He then noticed that the beautiful star Corn-Ear of the Virgin no longer had the same longitude. The discrepancy might, of course, have been due to an error. But it was a curious fact that all the stars which figured both in Hipparchus's list and in that drawn up by Aristylles and Timocharis showed the same error, a difference of minus 2 degrees. Evidently, then, the change of longitude was perfectly real, that is to say, the two observations had been made from different starting points. As this starting point was, in both cases, the equinoctial point of spring, it must be this point which had shifted. Hipparchus had no difficulty in calculating that since his two predecessors' day, that is to say in the course of 150 years, it had actually moved back 48 seconds of arc a year. This meant that the plane of the terrestrial equator cut the ecliptic at two points (the equinoxes) which were imperceptibly shifting; Hipparchus had thus discovered the *precession of the equinoxes*, which was later explained by the fact that the axis of the Earth describes a complete circle in 26,000 years.

Hipparchus was thus responsible for the first catalogue of the stars, the discovery of the precession of the equinoxes and a number of other not unimportant achievements, such as the determination of the obliquity of the ecliptic, of the lunar orbit and of the duration of the year; all this undoubtedly gave Hipparchus the right to advance, in his turn, a theory of the cosmic system. Had he not the most accurate instruments of the period with which to trace the motions of the planets and describe them most truthfully? Did he not employ a strikingly original method of calculating distances and angles on the celestial ephere, the method of *trigonometry*? We know that with this method calculations are worked not with the angles themselves, but with their *trigonometrical functions*. Perhaps inspired by Apollonius, Hipparchus took the angles as being drawn in the centre of a circle of unit radius, and characterized them not, as nowadays, by their sine, cosine or tangent, but by the chord of the double arc. He worked out a table of chords for every angle from zero to 180 degrees at half-degree intervals, and was thus able to begin the systematic study of the movements of the planets.

The first problem was to place the planets, Moon and Sun in the order of their distance from the Earth, which was still assumed to be the centre of the universe.

To be strictly accurate, there was no means of solving it. How can we tell that object A is farther away than object B? Imagine that we are looking out into the street from one of the windows of a room. On the edge of the pavement opposite the house there is a post which, as seen by us, stands out against the corner of a certain shop-front. Let us look at it through a different window. The post now stands against the centre of the same shop-front. This shift is, of course, due to the distance between the two windows and is called the *parallax*. It is all the more marked the greater the distance between the two windows and the closer the post. If, instead of observing a post situated at, say, 10 yards, we observe an electric pylon 2 miles away, the effect of the parallax will be almost imperceptible, that is to say the pylon will not appear to move appreciably against the background of the horizon. The difference between the parallaxes in the two cases can be very exactly calculated. If the two windows are 3 yards apart, they are seen from the post at an angle of 17° and from the pylon at an angle of 2' 56". The parallax of the post is then said to be 17°, while that of the pylon is 2' 56".

It may thus be seen that the parallax of a distant object may give an indication of its distance. In fact this is precisely how surveyors work. Trigonometry shows that if a base measuring 100 yards is seen from, say, a distant steeple to subtend an angle of 1°, it must be 5,729 yards away. The same method may be applied in the domain of astronomy . . . on condition that a base of sufficient length is available. It is obvious that, looking out in turn from each of our two windows, we shall not see the Moon, or the Sun, or any planet shift in relation to the background of the sky. Even if, instead of a base of 3 yards, we take one of 30 miles, or even 300, or even 3,000, the effect of parallax will remain imperceptible. The planets are much too far away and even for the closest celestial body, the Moon, the base must be not less than 5,600 miles (the length of the chord joining Paris to the Cape of Good

Hope, as will be explained on page 174). The lunar parallax—that is to say the angle which a radius of the terrestrial sphere would subtend from the Moon—is still only 57 minutes of arc.

In Hipparchus's day there was clearly no possibility of measuring a base of this length, and since no parallax effect was available as a means of judging the respective distances of the stars, astronomers were reduced to gratuitous hypotheses. Eclipses and occultations alone had made it possible to establish the following order: Earth, Moon, Mercury, Venus, Sun, Mars, Jupiter, Saturn. As for the absolute distances, expressed in terrestrial diameters, we may recall that Aristarchus was the first to attempt to measure them scientifically. Yet the sole result he arrived at, 9·5 terrestrial diameters for the distance of the Moon, was a long way out (the distance is really 30 diameters).

To Hipparchus belongs the honour of being the first to reach an acceptable figure. He observed eclipses of the Moon and noted their duration, that is to say the time the planet took to pass through the shadow of the Earth. He rightly supposed that the cone of the shadow was long enough to be about the same, at this small distance, as a cylinder having the diameter of our globe. He then found that the lunar diameter went three times into the width of the shadow. This meant that the diameter of the Moon was one-third of the diameter of the Earth (in reality it is 0·27, not 0·33).

Having reached this result, it became possible to work out the distance. The question trigonometry had to answer was how many terrestrial spheres away must the lunar sphere be in order to appear to us as having an apparent diameter of 30 minutes. Hipparchus found 33·66. Once again, this figure was close to the truth. The great astronomer then made the mistake of going on from the Moon to the Sun. We can see the extent of his temerity when we recall that where the parallax of the Moon is 57 minutes that of the Sun is scarcely more than 8 seconds. He thus made an enormous mistake in estimating the diameter of this latter body as 12·33 terrestrial diameters (it is really 109) and putting its distance at 1,245 (it is really 11,739). But how could he have suspected such a distance at a time when the known world was scarcely more than a band 1,300 miles wide running from Spain to India?

We have several times referred to the terrestrial diameter as a unit of astronomical distance, and the reader may justly wonder how accurately this unit was then known. For the credit due to Hipparchus's measurements would be very slight if he had based them on a unit vitiated by 50 per cent error!

The spherical shape of the Earth had long been almost beyond dispute, Aristotle's first proof having seemed overwhelming. The great navigators, such as Pytheas of Marseilles in the fourth century B.C., invariably reckoned with this sphericity in taking bearings. But the size of this sphere had been the subject of the wildest and most various estimates. In his book *On the Sky* Aristotle attributed 400,000 stadia to the circumference of the Earth—perhaps following a calculation by Eudoxus. His pupil Dicaearchus of Messina (died 285 B.C.), inventor of the geographical system of rectangular co-ordinates, spoke of 300,000. The difference is even greater than it seems because the value of the stadium varied.

The royal surveyors of Egypt employed one of 520 feet, but the Attic stadium of 586 feet, the Olympic stadium of 607 feet and even a stadium of 693 feet were equally common.

With the stadium of 610 feet, which seems to have been the one utilized by Aristotle, the latter's 400,000 stadia made 46,000 miles, while Dicaearchus, using a stadium of 586 feet, reached the figure of 33,000 miles, which is still excessive. Archimedes adopted this figure in his *Arenarius* or *Sand Reckoner* without giving the evidence for his opinion.

The principle of a rational measurement was, however, very simple, though difficult to translate into practice. Since the circumference of the Earth may be divided into 360 degrees, all that was required to ascertain its length was to measure one degree and multiply it by 360. The practical application of this principle constitutes the claim to fame of Eratosthenes, custodian of the Library at Alexandria.

Eratosthenes (276–192 B.C.) was not only an archivist, but also a grammarian, orator, philosopher, poet and above all a geometer. 'Unfortunately,' says Doublet ironically, 'public opinion accorded him only secondary status in all these fields, which led to his being surnamed β' (the Greek letter beta, the second in the alphabet).

It was around 230 B.C. that he addressed himself to the task of measuring a meridian arc of one degree. The way he set about it may be regarded as a model of ingenuity and even, by virtue of the mingled strictness and imagination it displays, as a prototype of scientific research. He started from the established fact that Alexandria was on the same meridian as the village of Syene, now Aswan. This village was held to stand exactly on the tropic of Cancer, so that on the day of the solstice, the Sun appeared there precisely at the zenith. Eratosthenes made sure of this by observing that a well (now proudly exhibited to tourists) was lit up at this moment right down to the bottom. At the same instant, at Alexandria, the luminary was at 7° 12′ from the zenith. This difference of 7° 12′ therefore corresponded to the difference in latitude between Alexandria and Syene. As the distance between these two places was 5,000 stadia, a simple rule of three showed that one degree of latitude equalled 694·56 stadia, and the 360 degrees of the Earth's circumference 250,000 stadia. Since the stadium used was that of 520 feet, this gave approximately 24,560 miles—an error of about 1·5 per cent.

As a matter of fact, this wonderful accuracy was due eighty per cent to genius and twenty per cent to luck. It so happened that all the erroneous data (Alexandria and Aswan do not share exactly the same longitude, the difference between their latitude is not exactly 7° 12′, nor is the distance between them exactly 5,000 stadia) operated in his favour. But we can imagine the outburst of enthusiasm aroused by such a measurement, obtained by a method so simple and yet so scientific. Pliny, a benevolent troubadour of scientists, later celebrated its boldness and Hipparchus made it the basis of his *Geography*. At the same time, as Eratosthenes seems to have done himself, he added 2,000 stadia, so as to have a number—252,000—divisible by 360.

We may wonder how the ancients could have done better with the rudimentary procedures of the day—Eratosthenes employed a gnomon to estimate the zenith distance of the Sun. Yet a Syrian geographer born c. 135 B.C., by name Posidonius, believed he could improve on Eratosthenes. He taught at Rhodes, where his students included Cicero and Pompey, and he had the curious idea of applying Eratosthenes's method to the measurement of the meridian arc between this island and Alexandria. It was a curious idea, because sea lay between the two extremities of the arc, and Posidonius could not drag his surveyor's chain through the water. . . . Instead of observing the position of the Sun, he observed that of the star Canopus, which stands just on the horizon of Rhodes, whereas, because of the lower latitude, it rises to 7° 30' above that of Alexandria. He arrived at 240,000 stadia for the circumference of the Earth, which is only 23,600 miles.

This figure gradually supplanted the one advanced by Eratosthenes and Hipparchus. The geographer Marinus of Tyre (first century A.D.) adopted it, and Ptolemy assured it rocklike security for six centuries.

Hipparchus makes the epicycles revolve round the Earth

Hipparchus was younger than Eratosthenes by about eighty-five years. He was therefore in possession of the results obtained by the latter and there can be no doubt that, if he supported them, it was only after serious examination. Hence it is significant that when he set about erecting a theory of the cosmos in his turn a man of such a realistic and precise mind should have rejected Aristarchus's system and given his support to Apollonius's. Fundamentally, the first was the correct one, but, as it admitted only circular and uniform movements, it accorded less well than the second with reality.

The mechanism of eccentric orbits forged by the author of *Conics* was by no means faultless, and Hipparchus quickly realized that it must be recast in the light of his own observations.

The Sun continued to describe the eccentric circle ascribed to it by Apollonius, but Hipparchus determined for himself the eccentricity and the nearest point to the Earth (the *perigee*). Once he knew this orbit exactly, he was able to draw up numerical tables in which the position of the Sun was calculated for the next six hundred years and eclipses foretold to within one or two hours. 'They included the astronomical tables appropriate to each nation,' explains Pliny, 'the days, the hours, the position in respect to each region and the various aspects of the heavens relative to various peoples. . . .'

The eccentric closest to the Earth is described by the Moon. Unfortunately for Hipparchus, however, the movement of the Moon is affected by numerous small irregularities which make the long-term prediction of this luminary's course extremely problematic. Hence his theory of the Moon was not crowned with the same success as his theory of the Sun. But at least we may place to the great astronomer's credit his discovery of one of these irregularities, the *equation of the centre*.

By contrast, he had every reason to congratulate himself on his theory of the planets. In this instance, the three main phenomena to be explained were the variations in brightness (especially in the case of Venus and Mars), the halts and retrogressions, and the fact that a planet does not take the same time to travel round the zodiac as it does to return into opposition or conjunction, that is to say into alignment with the Earth and Sun. Now, the first and third of these phenomena were adequately accounted for by the theory of the eccentrics. To describe the second, Hipparchus imagined that, while each planet described its eccentric (its *epicycle*), the centre of the latter itself described round the Earth a path called the *deferent*. Thus the planet was involved in two forward movements in an anti-clockwise direction, first its revolution on the epicycle, then the translation of this epicycle along the deferent.

Ptolemy's luck

Hipparchus died towards the end of the second century B.C.; Ptolemy was born around the beginning of the second century A.D. That is to say, more than two centuries lay between them. Two centuries which saw the school of Alexandria reach the apogee of its brilliance and then begin slowly to decline.

The first kings of Egypt gathered together illustrious courts in which men shone not by virtue of wealth or power, but by knowledge and intelligence. Imagine the scientists immersed in their researches at the Museum, the scholars at the Library, the royal receptions at which Euclid could converse with Aristarchus or Eratosthenes with Apollonius. This brilliance was not manifested only in science, but

74

also illumined technology (remember the names of Ctesibius and Hero) and as it was spread by the most active commerce in the world it turned the latter into a vast hive permeated by Hellenism.

Imperceptibly corrupted by whiffs of the old Egyptian esotericism, by over-indulgence in argument in which verbal brilliance more and more frequently bested depth of thought, by the disdain of the Roman soldiers who had just trampled the country underfoot, the school started to decline long before the birth of Christ. Moreover, a new act was beginning on the stage of history. The Roman Empire was born. The turbulent, independent, chaotic, colourful cities were succeeded by the *Pax Romana* and the rule of the sword, which brought order, discipline, glory, but also extinguished the last sparks of the antique scientific spirit of Greece. The troopers of the legions were not bothered about astronomy or rationalism. What they wanted in the way of intellectual culture were treatises on the military art, architecture, agriculture and geography. While they themselves amassed booty, they charged poets like Virgil with the task of celebrating the charm of rustic labour and preaching a return to the land. Original investigations, like those of Eratosthenes or Hipparchus, were far less prized by them than practical writings that were easy to consult and provided them with an immediate answer to questions relating to military technique, medicine or civil engineering.

In a word, the Roman period introduced the epoch of those *Summae* or epitomes whose multiplicity and reputation for infallibility were to block every avenue of knowledge during the Middle Ages. Epitomes of architecture and mechanics by Vitruvius, of geography by Strabo, of natural history by Pliny, of medicine (and many other things) by Celsus and Galen—these were huge compilations in which the observations of the ancients were jumbled together with stories of sorcerers, empirical prescriptions and more or less apocryphal anecdotes. Strabo's encyclopaedia filled seventeen books, Galen's twenty, Pliny's *Natural History* thirty-seven. It would have been surprising if astronomy, which had been one of the most keenly pursued of the sciences and to which astrology, now coming into fashion again, owed so much, had been left out. Claudius Ptolemaeus addressed himself to the task of writing its epitome, in thirteen volumes.

We must at once rectify the false impression the reader may have gained by seeing Ptolemy placed on the same level as Pliny. If he was not a brilliant thinker like Hipparchus, Ptolemy was at least a true scientist. One proof of this is his modesty, which has left us in total ignorance of any details about his life. We know only that he lived during the second century A.D., in the reign of the emperors Hadrian and Antoninus, that his first astronomical observation dates from A.D. 127 and the last from 151, and that he lived, if not in Alexandria itself, at least in its immediate vicinity.

On the other hand, unlike so many illustrious works that have vanished for ever—those of Thales, Eratosthenes, Hipparchus—his major work has come down to us in its entirety. This is the *Mathematical Syntax*, called the *Almagest*, which dates from A.D. 142–146 and became, by an extraordinary stroke of fortune, the astronomer's Bible for fifteen hundred years. The *Almagest* is a complete treatise of astronomy built up out of the works of the Greek scientists, particularly Hipparchus, to which the author occasionally adds his own investigations. We thus find in it an exposition of Hipparchus's geocentric system, the theory of the orbits of the Sun and Moon, the calculation of eclipses and of parallaxes, and a catalogue of stars. In a word, it was a complete summing-up, an excellent restatement; we can understand its having been received with favour by Ptolemy's contemporaries and with interest by his successors; but it is not so easy to explain why it should have inspired such transports of enthusiasm and admiration during the whole of the Middle Ages and Renaissance. For, after being annotated by the last astronomers of the school of Alexandria—of whom Theo (fourth century) was the final representative—after being translated into Latin by Boethius (fifth century), the *Mathematical Syntax* saw its fame survive the grandeur of Rome and persist after the great invasions and the Muslim conquest. It was translated into Arabic in A.D. 827, and it was the Arab astronomers who honoured it with the Greek superlative $\mu\epsilon\gamma\acute{\iota}\sigma\tau\eta$—*Al Meghistê*, of which we have made *Almagest*, the Very Great.

After the shipwreck of ancient civilization in the murky waters of the high Middle Ages, Ptolemy's book was one of the few left floating on the surface, along with Galen's and fragments of Aristotle's. It aroused all the more admiration among the learned because it was all that remained of the famous Greek science. Until Galileo's day, astronomers argued by Ptolemy, as physicians argued by Galen and everyone by Aristotle.

In our own day, obviously, this book appears in quite a different light. It no longer seems in the least worthy of its Arabic title, any more than it deserves the contempt heaped upon it after the triumph of the heliocentric theory. For the *Almagest*, based largely on the works of Hipparchus, is the sole path by which these have reached us. It possesses no small merit. Thus, for some dozen centuries, it was the only coherent synthesis of celestial phenomena, the sole system capable of co-ordinating observations, of rendering them effective and imposing order upon the heavens—and a faulty order is better than no order at all.

For the rest, let us not accord the Alexandrian astronomer more praise than is his due. Everything valid that he wrote was borrowed from Hipparchus, whom he sometimes shamelessly copied. Is it not significant that his catalogue of stars was the same as his illustrious predecessor's and contains only those luminaries visible from Rhodes— where Hipparchus observed—although the sky over Alexandria should have furnished additional ones? Canon A. Rome, writing in *Ciel et Terre*, has compared the errors of Hipparchus and Ptolemy in calculating the equinoxes and solstices. With the former they vary from two to twelve hours; with the latter, from eighteen to thirty-two hours. This is sufficient to show how much he is worth as an observer.

On two points only, Ptolemy's reputation does not seem spurious. First, in respect of the distance and diameter of the Moon, which he estimated at 29 and 0·29 terrestrial diameters respectively, figures that are much closer to reality than Hipparchus's. Second, as regards the extent to which he perfected the geocentric mechanism. He, too, denied that the Earth moved: how could it revolve round the Sun since the stars did not appear to shift in relation one to the other? And how could it rotate upon itself when, if it did so, everything not bedded in the ground—clouds, projectiles, birds—would fly westward? How much easier it was, in Ptolemy's eyes, to make everything revolve around the Earth, the Sun, Moon, planets and epicycles—even when he had to add supplementary epicycles to account for newly discovered irregularities, such as *evection*, which he himself discerned in the movement of the Moon!

A counter-blow to the conquest of the skies

Just as the name of Copernicus is now attached to the heliocentric system invented by Aristarchus, so Ptolemy's name has remained coupled with the geocentric system originated by Hipparchus. In both instances, the memory of the propagator has eclipsed that of the original scientist; the uproar of publicity has drowned the still, small voice of discovery. A phenomenon that is perhaps explained in Ptolemy's case by the mystical resonance of his work, which was so much in harmony with the deterioration of the critical sense and the renascent esotericism of these early centuries of the Christian era. We must remember that the epoch of Ptolemy was also that of the multiple heresies which rent the Christian Church at its outset—Montanism, gnosticism, Marcionism—as well as of a universal belief in astrology and the introduction of religions of Oriental origin with magical tendencies, such as Mithraism. To these were added the doctrine of the last Alexandrian philosophers, Plotinus's neo-Platonism, not to mention the syncretism that amalgamated certain of these diverse tendencies—all of them affronts to rational thought.

Let us remember, too, that the great Roman peace of the early days of the Empire gradually gave place to a muffled turmoil, in which the cries of the plebeians, thirsting for the bloody entertainment of the circus, and of the patricians, as they plunged deeper and deeper into disorder and depravity of every kind, mingled with the distant and confused mutter of the encamped barbarians.

The *Almagest* appeared at just about the same time as St. Justin's *Apologia* (A.D. 150), the period of the first persecutions of the Christians. The last manifestation of ancient astronomy, it was a counter-blow to the conquest of the skies that had gone forward since Thales. The school of Alexandria dragged lethargically on for a few more centuries, torn by sectarian conflicts, its venerable past slowly sinking beneath the dust of oblivion and the ashes of destruction. In A.D. 415

the beautiful mathematician Hypatia, daughter of Theon and author of the Commentary on the *Almagest*, fell victim to the vengeance of fanatics. In an Alexandria turned Christian she had remained a pagan, which the uncultivated populace considered an intolerable scandal. The day on which the mob dragged her from her chariot, stoned her and tore her body in pieces, rang the final knell of Hellenic science. The incomparable Library counted 400,000 papyrus scrolls in the reign of Ptolemy Philadelphus and 900,000 in Caesar's time. There was nothing left of them in A.D. 640, when the city was taken by the Arabs. But was anyone still capable of feeling horrified by this catastrophe, which deprived us for ever of the treasures of ancient knowledge?

3

At the school of barbarian science

The shipwreck of science in the Middle Ages—Civilization is
saved by the barbarians—The Arabs carry on the conquest of the
skies—Mongols and Turks erect observatories—Astronomy and
navigation: Europe's upsurge during the sixteenth century—
Ptolemy is subjected to cautious criticism—Copernicus, or the
lost battle

THE work of astronomical research is like a great patch of light
thrown by a projector upon the clouds and moving hither and
thither in the sky. At the beginning of historical times several of these
patches of light were cast upon the globe, one on China, another on
India, a third on Mesopotamia and a fourth on Egypt. Then they all
paled, while another patch blazed out over Greece.

After this the light shifted and at the same time grew dim. Rome
inherited astronomical knowledge from Alexandria, but, being
exclusively occupied with her terrestrial conquests, had no use for this
science and allowed it to lapse into oblivion. The emperors took no
interest in the heavens. It is true that Claudius is said to have predicted
the solar eclipse of A.D. 45, which took place on his birthday; and
certain Latin writers—Censorinus, Firmicus Maternus, Ausonius,
Synesius, Martianus Capella, Boethius and others—and even a few
Christian priests such as Anatolius, Victorius and Isidore of Seville,
are said to have occupied themselves half-heartedly with astronomy;
but how can we forget the utter futility of all their astrological divaga-
tions? The primary aim of the pagans was to bring the legions and
their leader the comfort of favourable predictions. That of the
Christians, to serve the cause of dogma and morality.

Bishop Achilles Tatius compared the globe to a grain of millet
held in suspension in a bladder because someone is blowing on it;
Macrobius revived the music of the spheres thought to have been dead

and buried since Pythagoras, ascribing high-pitched notes to the most distant planets and the deepest tone to the Moon; Alban gave the Earth the shape of a horse-shoe, Cosmas that of a parallelepipedic chest; a doctor of the Church, Isidore of Seville, and the Venerable Bede, priest of the monastery at Jarrow, vied with one another in grotesque notions worthy only of the Sumerian astrologers, just as though Aristarchus, Hipparchus and Ptolemy had never existed. The difference between the latter and any of these pseudo-astronomers is as great as that between Einstein and a Burmese fakir. . . .

The scientific spirit began to decay when Roman arms imposed themselves upon the world. Nothing was more opposed to disinterested research and meditation than the frenzied lust for pillage of the legionaries, who inaugurated their rise to power by murdering Archimedes. The process of disintegration was hastened by the decline of the Roman Empire. Its population was rotten with vice, no longer believed in anything except astrology and magical mumbo-jumbo, and remained unstirring in its brutish lethargy as threats piled up around its frontiers. In A.D. 395 this vast domain, which stretched from Scotland to Mauretania and from Gibraltar to the Euphrates and was now undermined and corrupted everywhere, split in two. One half, the Eastern Empire, with its capital at Byzantium, had another thousand years to live. The other, the Western Empire, with Rome still at its head, disappeared for good in A.D. 476.

The shipwreck of science in the Middle Ages

The story of celestial discovery, which it is our task to relate, could be summarized at this point, the dawn of the Middle Ages, by a blank page—a page representing ten centuries. This refers, of course, to what had been the western half of the Roman Empire and was to become Europe. What pitiable use this Western Empire, the heir of Babylon, Miletus, Athens and Alexandria, had made of its prodigious heritage! It was nothing now but a great lifeless corpse, upon which the watchful barbarians flung themselves from the heart of Asia. Famines, epidemics, invasions—it suffered them all. The *Pax Romana* was only a memory, along with the crumbling bridges, disintegrating roadways and drying aqueducts. We will not paint yet again the picture of this shipwreck in which ended fifteen centuries of Greek civilization, but shall confine ourselves to stating that civilization sank back to the level of the Neolithic age. When every individual's most pressing concern was to find food, who could take heed for the things of the spirit? When everyone's sole aim was survival, who could trouble about the conquest of the skies or the continuation of the work of Hipparchus and Ptolemy?

Hipparchus and Ptolemy, like Archimedes, Aristotle and Plato, were dead and buried. Their books had vanished in the burning of the libraries, their memories in the smoke of invasions, their traditions in the blood of massacres. There was no one left who could read and write save a few Benedictines, whose labour of piety it was to recopy the few ancient manuscripts that had withstood the ravages of the centuries. We have to be grateful for the occasions when these monks, well-intentioned but short of parchment, did not take it upon themselves to erase a text which they considered devoid of interest and replace it by some homily by a Father of the Church. In 1906, for example, major works by Archimedes were found under a collection of mediaeval prayers. . . .[1]

We will say no more about these abysmal ages. To show the depths to which astronomy had sunk, suffice it to note that the Church just about tolerated the supposition that the Earth was spherical, that Rabanus Maurus claimed it was square, that St. Augustine did not believe in the Antipodes and that Gerbert, who became Pope in 999 under the name of Sylvester II, was regarded as a fount of wisdom because he knew geometry, astronomy and mechanics. We can gain some idea of the latter's scientific status by recalling that his chief claim to fame lay in the fact that he improved the abacus then used for counting—by the introduction of Arabic numerals. As may be seen, there was no longer any question of studying the precession of the equinoxes, as Hipparchus had done, or the inequalities in the motion of the Moon, like Ptolemy. . . .

The western half of what had been the Roman Empire sank into darkness, rent by invasions and delivered into the hands of the robber

[1] G. Sarton, *Revue d'Histoire des Sciences*, January-April 1949, p. 104.

chiefs, some of whom, like Chlodwig, called Clovis, strove to establish a lasting dynasty. Was the eastern half any better off? Yes, commercial prosperity and the energy of certain emperors had enabled its riches to be protected from outside cupidity. It also profited from the inestimable advantage of having alone remained in contact with the Greek world. Thus the works of the ancients had a chance to spread in the eastern half, where Archimedes and Ptolemy were still read, while the westerners did not even know the names of these scientists. An iron curtain cut the world into two parts, one of them possessed of the whole heritage of antiquity, the other totally destitute.

However, it seems that even association with the great men of Greece was powerless to bring about a rebirth of the scientific spirit, for we shall search in vain, throughout the whole history of Byzantium, for the name of an astronomer of any worth. Instead of scientific works we find interminable theological disputations, oratorical jousts that have caused the adjective 'Byzantine' to become descriptive of just such controversies. It is difficult to understand how Hipparchus and Ptolemy could be read without one single individual feeling the urge to continue their work; the most likely explanation is to be found in the stagnation of technical progress and the contempt felt for craftsmen. The observations of the last Alexandrian astronomers had reached such a pitch of perfection that it was impossible to surpass them, except by using more highly developed instruments. But the construction of such instruments involved problems—the fineness and regularity of graduations, for example—that could be solved only by a technology that was well informed, vigorous and provided with powerful resources. But an interest in technology and the desire to foster its progress were the last things that entered the heads of Byzantine businessmen who made their fortunes by financial speculation.

Thus, throughout the whole area of the globe that had previously striven to conquer the heavens at the same time as it created civilization, this dual advance came to a halt. The disappearance of the nascent technology and industry of Alexandria and Rome put an end both to economic activity and to all interest in the study of the firmament.

Why bother to observe the heavens with the aid of costly and laboriously manufactured instruments, if the same results could be achieved by divination? Why spend uncomfortable nights measuring the movements of the Moon and planets if these measurements were never put to any use—if, for example, there were no longer any mariners to employ them in taking reckonings?

The civilization of antiquity was gradually plunged in darkness, debased, split by schisms, stripped of everything that had made it great. To bring it back to life it needed a transfusion of new blood, a violent jolt that would shake out its rottenness, the irruption of all sorts of technical inventions that would reanimate its bloodless economy and its intellectual appetite.

It needed all the things the barbarians were about to bring it.

Civilization is saved by the barbarians

To justify the view that the barbarians brought the West what it lacked in order to accomplish its destiny, we need only ask ourselves what would have happened to the West if it had been left to its own resources, in its ignorance and decrepitude. It might eventually have discovered Archimedes and Hipparchus, have invented printing and the scientific method; but after how many centuries' delay?

The fact, in any case, is this: the great area of light which the conquest of the skies once cast upon Alexandria went out with the Roman Empire, turning Europe into a zone of darkness. At the same instant, another patch of light expanded on Asia—that Asia which the Romans portrayed as a vast and confused agglomeration of what they called 'barbarians'.

We are accustomed to imagine these barbarians as savage nomads living by raiding, who poured over Europe in successive waves throughout the Middle Ages, leaving her littered with ruins as each wave receded. But recent investigations by historians of science lead us to ask which were the barbarians, the Europeans or these Asiatics? Were Theodoric or Attila more brutal than Fredegond or Dagobert? Did not Alaric read Greek, which scarcely any European 'scholar' now knew? Is it not to the Huns that we owe the saddle and stirrups? To the Mongols, the harness-collar and breast-harness? To the Turks, the windmill? To the Norsemen, advances in navigation and possibly the compass? Was it not the reputedly uncultivated and savage hordes of the Arabs and Saracens who transmitted to the West the Hindu system of numeration, which was to become our own, and those cardinal inventions of the Chinese, silk, china, gunpowder, paper and printing? And was not one of the greatest astronomers of the Middle Ages Tamerlane's grandson?

The barbarism was on the Western side. The salvage of Greek thought, which Europe had already allowed to disappear and which was crumbling away a little more each day in the feeble hands of the Byzantines, was left to the East. Asia resumed the conquest of the skies, thereby engaging humanity on the road of progress.

The Arabs carry on the conquest of the skies

This new stage began with the founding of a new religion; it continued with the crusade upon which its adepts embarked in order to propagate it. When Mahomet died, in 632, Islamism had already launched its assault upon the moribund societies. The apostles of Christ had converted by the word; those of the Prophet converted by fire and sword. Pillage, sacking, massacre, the destruction and burning down of forests and libraries—among them the library of Eratosthenes at Alexandria—the devastation of cultivated lands, towns, places of work, this was the contribution of Mahomet's Bedouins, whose level of civilization was no higher than that of the Huns or Norsemen.

When Charles Martel defeated them at Poitiers in 732 they had extended their dominion over North Africa, the Middle East, half Asia and, in Europe, Spain. Their supreme head, the Caliph Al Mansur, then established his capital in Persia, at Bagdad, and the founding of this city marked a turning-point in their history. Arab vitality made of Bagdad an increasingly active centre of commerce, to which merchandise flowed from every corner of the empire. Along with this merchandise the conquerors came into possession of inventions which, in their turn, they passed on to the West in the course of their raids—the game of chess invented in India, lacquer imported from China, honey, sugar, a multitude of objects and practices.

As almost always happens, it was the victims who colonized their conquerors. When they came in contact with the ancient Persian civilization, permeated by the Greek tradition, the Arabs' minds opened up, their curiosity was aroused. Mesopotamian monks translated Aristotle for them in the eighth century and, in 827, Ptolemy, whose work excited such admiration that it received the now immortal surname of *Almagest*. These were followed by Hipparchus, Archimedes, Euclid and Apollonius. Acquaintance with the great scientists of antiquity inculcated a desire for culture. A university was created at Bagdad, modelled on that of Alexandria, in which the scientific heritage of Greece was combined with the patrimony of the Hindus (decimal numeration and the figure nought) and Mesopotamia (algebra and Babylonian astronomy) and the traditions of Egypt and China. By the end of the first millennium, when what had been the Roman Empire was nothing but a nameless chaos, the university of Bagdad had become the intellectual centre of the world. In 807 Charlemagne, himself almost totally illiterate, received as a gift from a highly civilized Caliph, Harun-al-Rashid, an extraordinary clock that indicated and sounded the twenty-four hours and was embellished with automata and chimes.

Of the Greek works translated into Arabic, those on astronomy, and particularly the *Almagest*, rapidly acquired the greatest importance: partly because a knowledge of the movements of the heavenly bodies was useful for regulating the agricultural calendar, but above all because it proved indispensable in fixing the hour for religious duties. Moslem rites prescribed certain prayers for certain well-defined times of day, and it was in keeping with Arab attention to detail to strive to determine these times with the greatest possible care. To these must be added magic and astrology, whose credit had not diminished since the days of Babylon.

It was for these various reasons that Caliph Al-Mamun (786–833), son of Harun-al-Rashid, had observatories built at Bagdad and Damascus. Unfortunately we do not know much about these establishments and can only guess that their instruments resembled those of Hipparchus and Ptolemy. In addition to these, however, it seems that frequent use was made of the *astrolabe*. This was a disc graduated in 360 degrees and suspended vertically in a ring. When trained on the Sun, it served to measure the latter's angular height above the horizon and so to calculate the time of day. When placed horizontally, two further discs could be added: a fixed one showing the principal circles of the celestial sphere projected on to a plane (the meridian and the horizon, for example[1]), and a movable one showing the ecliptic and the chief stars. By rotating the latter on the former, the position and co-ordinates of the heavenly bodies could be determined.

The astrolabe, the armillary sphere and the wall quadrant derived from the Alexandrian *plinth* were all instruments intended for measuring angles. It is clear from what has been said already that, in order to carry forward the work of Hipparchus and Ptolemy, the Arab astronomers had to increase its precision. Thus in 988 Caliph Sharaf-al-Daulah installed at Bagdad a wall quadrant some twenty-five feet in radius, and even a *sextant*—that is to say, a limb graduated in 60 degrees—sixty-six feet in radius, which gave not only the minute of arc, but sometimes the second. This effort received its just reward. In about 868 an estimate of the obliquity of the ecliptic gave 23° 33′, an error of only six minutes; and a terrestrial degree was calculated by Eratosthenes's method at 130,000 yards, an error of five miles.

As the purpose of observations was always to predict the motions of the heavenly bodies—for example, to draw up tables giving the position of the Sun, Moon and planets for the years to come—it was necessary to possess not merely these angular data, but also a mathematical method enabling them to be utilized. As we know, such a method, trigonometry, was created by Hipparchus. In this method every angle, supposed at the centre of a circle with radius equal to one, was represented by the chord subtended by its arc. The Arab scholar Al-Battani (*c.* 850–929) had the idea of using, instead of the chord, the semi-chord of the double arc. This semi-chord was the *sine*, to which Al-Battani added the *cosine*. The director of the Bagdad observatory, Abul-Wefa (939–98), added the *tangent* and *secant*, thus

[1] In stereographic projection on the plane of the equator.

laying the foundations of modern trigonometry. Abul-Wefa's value as an observer was no whit less than his qualities as a mathematician, for he discovered that, besides the two irregularities in the motion of the Moon noted by Hipparchus and Ptolemy, there is a third, known today as the *variation*.

Thus possessed of observational instruments and mathematical tools of equal perfection, Arab astronomers set enthusiastically to work to continue the *Almagest*. In about 964, Al-Sufi (903–86) published a catalogue of stars that was a considerable improvement on Ptolemy's. The brightness, or, as it was called, the 'magnitude' of each star was so accurately estimated that it agrees almost exactly with the measurements made nine centuries later by the German astronomer Argelander. Where Greek names were lacking, the author designated the stars by their Arabic names, thus making identification easier. The names ascribed to the stars by Al-Sufi survived the centuries, and many of them are still in use today. Examples are Aldebaran, Mizar, Altair, Denebola, Achernar and others; a total of one hundred and six Arab names are employed out of one hundred and fifty named stars.

At the moment when Al-Sufi published his catalogue, the huge Arab empire was beginning to fall apart. Africa had already broken away, and the city of Cairo, founded in 970, was the capital of an independent state. King Hakem, a cruel sovereign, but a friend of science, had an observatory erected there in 996. It was here that an astronomer named Ibn Yunis (died 1009), a former pupil of Abul-Wefa, drew up astronomical tables. Hakem's motives in encouraging such an abstract undertaking were simple and by no means disinterested: his sole purpose was to determine the hour for prayers and the days for fasting and other religious practices, matters which, in Hakem's eyes, surpassed in importance anything else in the world.

A third piece of the empire had remained intact in Spain. Here again, at Cordova and Toledo, there functioned universities whose brilliance attracted men of letters from all over the globe. It is significant that at the time when scholars like Arzachel (1029–89) and Averrhoes (1120–98) were observing and calculating there, the rest of Europe was still submerged in fire and blood, ravaged by the Norsemen and the feudal lords, and then dragged into the vast turmoil of the crusades. How discreet, by comparison with this flood that carried with it a seething torrent of fighting men and unfortunate civilians, appears the flow that drained towards Toledo or Cordova all those, whether Christians or Jews, who felt the thirst for knowledge! Nevertheless, it was from this almost imperceptible current that there emerged the first Western European name worthy of mention in this book, that of the Catholic King Alfonso X of Castille (1223–84). This enlightened prince appointed a commission of Arab and Jewish astronomers to draw up the *Alphonsine Tables*, which remained for several centuries the basis of all observational astronomy.

Mongols and Turks erect observatories

It must be confessed that this list of names and achievements strikes us at first sight as insignificant. And it is perfectly true that Abul-Wefa and Alfonso X are very small beer by comparison with Aristarchus and Hipparchus. . . . The Arab scholars never made any original discoveries, and we cannot expect from them any extension of the celestial territory conquered by the ancients. But we nevertheless owe them a debt of gratitude. When the thought of antiquity, scorned and degraded by the West, was on the point of going under, it was these scholars who caught it by the hand. Not only did they preserve the actual heritage, the great works of Archimedes, Hipparchus and Ptolemy, but they gave it new life by their own efforts and, as far as they were able, improved upon it.

Unfortunately, when their power began to collapse and their dominion to crumble towards the end of the first millennium, Europe was still far from ready to take over the relay. Lothair, Charlemagne's grandson, had a silver planisphere broken in pieces to pay his soldiers, which gives us some idea of his degree of civilization. And the case of Alfonso X peacefully presiding over a scientific commission among the 'barbarians' must not cause us to forget the *autos-da-fé* of books, the brigandage of the feudal overlords, the ferocious slaughter of the Albigenses, the establishment of the Inquisition and torture, which were taking place at the same time in the Christian West. The legacy of antiquity would have vanished with the conquest of the Arab world, if other barbarians had not been there to take it over.

These were the Mongols. After razing Bagdad in 1258, their leader, a nomad surnamed Genghis Khan, uncultured but athirst for order and civilization, savage but with gifts of organization and statesmanship, had created in Asia the greatest empire in the world. A family of Europeans, the Polos, spent thirty-five years, from 1260 to 1295, travelling all over this empire from the Crimea to Peking. They were amazed by the order that reigned there, by the well-kept roads and canals, the commercial traffic, the postal service, the wealth of its warehouses, its social organization with its state granaries and food distributions, and above all by its tolerance, so striking to travellers who remembered the fanaticism of the Moslems and the bloody fury of the Inquisition.

Once again civilization had vanquished its conquerors. In succession to the Chinese, the Persians and the Arabs, the Mongols had been initiated into the labours of the mind. They, too, had made the acquaintance of Aristotle, Archimedes, Hipparchus and Ptolemy. This was why, only one year after the sacking of Bagdad, Genghis Khan's grandson Hulagu (1217–65) had a magnificent observatory built at Maragha, near Tabriz in Azerbaijan. Lavishly-paid astronomers were appointed to work there under the direction of the royal astronomer Nassir ed-Din (1201–74). Their task was to draw up astronomical almanacs modelled on those of Ibn-Yunis; these almanacs were completed in 1269 and remained in use for over a century.

The same concern for science (especially when it was directed towards astrology) subsequently guided the Sino-Mongol Emperor Kubilai (1214–94), to whom Peking owes its observatory (built in 1270 or 1279). And again it inspired the conqueror of the Mongols when they, in their turn, grew soft and exhausted and were invaded and subjugated by fresh barbarians.

This time it was the Turks who appeared on the stage, led by Tamerlane. Between 1371 and 1405 this ferocious conqueror had put the greater part of Asia at his feet. He raised pyramids of severed heads at the gates of cities, and in between times took pleasure in embellishing his capital, Samarkand, encouraging sciences and arts and chatting with the Persian poet Hafiz. His son Shah Rokh and his grandson Ulugh Beigh each inherited only one part of his tastes, since the one confined himself to mastering manuscripts and the second to extending the conquest of the skies.

In fact by the beginning of the fourteenth century, while, in Europe, France and England were exhausting themselves in the Hundred Years War and the Church, once a civilizing and unifying factor, was more divided than ever, Samarkand had become a splendid capital in which painting and letters flourished. Tamerlane's successor, Ulugh Beigh (1394–1449), was a learned astronomer who erected there an extraordinary observatory. It was a three-storey building, the chief instrument in which is said to have been a wall quadrant of 200 feet radius! Each degree occupied no less than a yard. More than a hundred specialists were employed in this observatory to draw up a celestial almanac and a catalogue of the stars.

Ulugh Beigh's catalogue was the only one worthy to replace Hipparchus's. That is to say, it far surpassed in accuracy the similar works of Ptolemy and Al-Sufi. It covered 1,018 stars, whose co-ordinates and 'magnitude' had been measured with the greatest care. Its author published it in 1437. Sixteen years later these Turks, the only people in the world to possess an observatory and to cultivate astronomy in the spirit of Hipparchus, took possession of Byzantium, populated by fanatical and backward proponents of religious orthodoxy.

Astronomy and navigation: Europe's upsurge during the sixteenth century

The West learnt with horror of the fall of Constantinople. It had a sense of solidarity with these Greeks of the East, and the futility of the metaphysical disputes carried on in Europe between Nominalists, Occamists, Realists and other scholastics fell no way short of the disputations of the Byzantines themselves. Shut up in their schools, the Western scholars were serving a laborious apprenticeship in science. Several centuries before, the Arab universities had brought them the revelation of the great Hellenic authors, headed by Aristotle and Ptolemy, and by this revelation they were thunderstruck. The Arabic language, the medium through which they made this discovery, seemed to them the very language of knowledge and they set about learning it. In 1231 the University of Paris created chairs of Arabic and Tartar and a start was made in translating the Arabic versions of the Greek classics into Latin. The first Latin translation of the *Almagest* was produced by the Lombard physician Gerald of Cremona (1114–87) in 1175.

The invention of printing, in 1447, greatly increased the diffusion of these works. In 1472 the first printed book on Astronomy came off the press, a totally valueless poem entitled *Astronomicon*, written during the century of Augustus by Manilus.

The vogue for Aristotle and Ptolemy and the spread of the intellectual patrimony of the Arabs, Mongols and Turks indicates the trend of science in Western universities. It was a matter of endless glosses drawn out into a sequence of syllogisms, which nobody thought of replacing by the direct study of nature. Only among the 'barbarians', at Bagdad or Samarkand, was an actual observatory to be seen! Among the civilized peoples astronomy consisted in hunting for faults in Ptolemy by comparing him with Aristotle and the Fathers of the Church—without forgetting, of course, the most fuliginous superstitions of sorcery and astrology. Most of the kings had their official astrologers. Even Pope Paul III, to whom Copernicus dedicated his book, took no important step without first ascertaining the celestial influences. In short, the West was not yet ripe for drawing any profit from Archimedes, Aristarchus, Hipparchus or Ptolemy himself.

It is true that, in addition to this purely bookish revelation, the East had transmitted a more immediately fertile ssed—all those technical and practical inventions born somewhere in Asia, several of which have been listed on page 87. From these—especially from animal, hydraulic and wind power, metallurgy and navigation—there sprang increasingly rapid industrial progress as well as a growing extension and speeding-up of commercial travel. In 1453 the Hundred Years War came to an end, the nations of Europe settled down and an era of peace opened, which encouraged merchants to send out ships and caravans in search of the riches of the globe.

These riches, which caused the sceptre of the world to pass from Asia to Europe, were gold, precious stones, perfumes, spices, silk, amber and ivory, all of them products that had to be fetched from overseas, from India or as far afield as China. Trade brought Spain its fortune, the basis of its political supremacy during the sixteenth century, and this fortune was gained on the seas—thanks to astronomers.

The Turks, after moving down from Constantinople, spread little by little over the whole eastern seaboard of the Mediterranean. They cut Europe's lines of communication with Asia and, in particular, the silk road. Venice succumbed to progressive asphyxiation. To escape from it, Spain and Portugal looked for other routes to the Far East, either by rounding Africa to the south, or by sailing due west into the Atlantic in the hope of striking the coast of Asia.

Everybody knows the outcome of this adventure, how Bartholomew Diaz sailed round the Cape of Good Hope in 1488 and Vasco da Gama reached India in 1498, while, in the opposite direction, Christopher Columbus discovered America in 1492. Henceforth all the treasures of the East were poured out on the counters of Europe. Gold gave the West dominion over the world. The reign of Europe had begun.

This historical upheaval was possible only because the Spaniards and Portuguese possessed mastery of the seas. If their vessels held course with such assurance thousands of miles from the coast, it was because they were equipped both with improved methods of navigation and new means of steering. The galley had given place to the true sailing ship, higher and more stable, fitted with a keel, rigged with square sails and responding to a fixed axial rudder. Coasting had been replaced, under the initial impulsion of the Portuguese Prince Henry the Navigator (1394–1460), by long-distance sailing. The simple magnetic needle had turned into the compass. In 1492 Christopher Columbus even made use of the *magnetic variation*, the angular difference between the magnetic and the geographic north.

Between 1492 and 1522, between Columbus and Magellan, the length of the known coasts doubled. A correct picture was formed of the distribution of continents and oceans over the surface of the Earth and accurate maps and charts were drawn. The latter were originally *portulans*, that is to say simple plans of coast lines. They took only very rough account of latitude and longitude, so that when, at the beginning of the sixteenth century, ships lost sight of land and were therefore compelled to turn to less empirical methods of navigation, these portulans had to be replaced by really scientific charts drawn according to the principles laid down by Ptolemy in his *Geography*.

The Earth was supposed covered by a rectangular network of meridians and parallels, and position at sea was determined by the parallel and meridian on which the ship lay, that is to say by its latitude and longitude. The problem of latitude had been solved long ago. The latitude is equal to the angular altitude of the celestial pole above the horizon; hence all that is required in order to obtain it is to measure the altitude of the pole star, taking into account the fact that it is not exactly at the celestial pole. Mariners worked out this altitude by means of a *marine astrolabe* or an *arbalest*. The first, derived from the instrument described on page 87, was a graduated disc with an alidade pivoted on the centre; the second, a graduated rod on which slid a runner; observation was carried out by adjusting the latter so that one end pointed at the star and the other at the horizon.

Determination of latitude became more complicated when, from 1474 onwards, ships ventured south of the equator: the polar star was no longer visible. The sight of the familiar constellations disappearing beneath the northern horizon and the Sun describing its orbit in the north must have come as something of a shock! To solve this unwonted problem, King John II called together, in 1481, a *junta* of cosmographers, the most celebrated of whom was a Nuremberg cloth merchant named Martin Behaim (1450–1507). This *junta* got over the difficulty by establishing precise rules for working out the latitude from the altitude of the Sun at midday.

It is true that knowledge of the latitude was not enough, and that the problem of ascertaining longitude was a great deal more difficult. The question could be posed thus: the zero meridian being at that time the one that passes through Cape Verde, near Dakar, what time was it at this zero meridian when the Sun passed over the meridian of the ship? It could not be answered unless the time at the zero meridian was known aboard the ship . . . and needless to say, around 1500, to keep the exact time for days, weeks and months was absolutely impossible. The hour-glass was unknown; even the great clocks on cathedrals were liable to errors of up to one hour. John II's *junta* rightly advocated observation of phenomena such as the movement of the Moon, the occultation of stars, and eclipses, phenomena whose timing was perfectly established at the zero meridian and of which the astronomer Regiomontanus had drawn up tables; but navigators nevertheless continued to make monumental mistakes in their calculations—one of them who imagined he was making landfall at Mauritius sailed into Dieppe,[1] and errors of several degrees, that is to say hundreds of miles, were quite common.

Ptolemy is subjected to cautious criticism

These anomalies became more and more glaring in proportion as sea voyages increased, making it possible to rectify and perfect maps. It soon became inescapably evident to cartographers that the maps they were now drawing differed more and more from those in Ptolemy's *Geography*. The latter confined the globe between the Canary Isles and India, lengthened the Mediterranean, placed the equator in the middle of Ethiopia, north of the Gulf of Guinea, and asserted that south of the tropics the oceans boiled and men turned quite black. When mariners realized that the writings of the famous Alexandrian astronomer were shot through with fables of this sort, Ptolemy lost much of his credit. It struck people that if he was wrong over such and such a point he might well be wrong over others, and they began to examine with a critical eye the *Geography* and the *Almagest* which had hitherto been accepted implicity.

The Renaissance was at its height. Men of letters were consumed with a tremendous curiosity regarding books. The invention of printing satisfied this curiosity by a plentiful dissemination of such major works as the Bible, Aristotle, the *Almagest* and Galen. We know what followed from these books, upon which the civilization of the

[1] Quoted in *Histoire générale des Civilisations* (Presses Universitaires), Vol. IV, p. 361. The author of this work, M. Roland Mousnier, was good enough to confirm the accuracy of his quotation and to give his references (Georges Fournier, S.J., *Hydrographie*, Paris, 1643, Book 12, Chapter XXXV, p. 611).

day may be said to have been founded, becoming accessible to all and open to unfettered examination by anyone. Free interpretation of the Bible gave rise to the Reformation and the Protestant Churches; that of Aristotle set up a vigorous reaction which, fed by Robert Grosseteste, Roger Bacon, William of Occam and Theodoric of Freiburg, led to experimental science; finally, criticism of Ptolemy caused an increasing number of independent minds seriously to revise his basic notions, to pick out their weak points, and eventually to jettison his whole conception of the world.

When the sixteenth century dawned, the Ptolemaic system had ruled the roost for 1,350 years. It was considered beyond discussion and revered as one of the pillars of society. Every philosophical theory and every practical undertaking—in the field of navigation, for example—was based upon it. The commentaries to which it had given rise were beyond counting. The most popular was a paraphrase of the *Almagest* by the English mathematician and astronomer John Holywood of Halifax, also known as Johannes de Sacrobosco (died 1230). This work, *De Sphaerâ Mundi*, written during the first half of the thirteenth century and printed in 1472, re-taught cosmography to the West. It became a classic and had appeared in sixty-five successive editions by the seventeenth century.

However, there have always been nonconformist spirits to dispute generally accepted views. Thus, in proportion as the reports of navigators contradicted the didactic statements of the *Geography*, in proportion as the most sagacious minds grew more impatient of argument from authority and more sensitive to the observation of nature, the *Almagest* came up against bolder and bolder contradictors.

First there were the two bishops—a Frenchman, Nicolas Oresme, in 1377, and a German, Nicolas of Cusa, three-quarters of a century later. Oresme (1323–82), bishop of Lisieux, was a highly gifted mathematician who, while lavishing tokens of respect on Ptolemy, insinuated that one might well suppose 'that the Earth is moved by the daily (diurnal) revolution, and not the sky', the Sun remaining motionless at the centre of the universe and our globe revolving round it. Cusa (1401–64) was a no less independent mind, as may be seen from the fact that he proposed to reform the calendar and was imprisoned for his religious opinions. He, too, considered that Ptolemy's teaching was by no means an article of faith, and he even went so far as to write: 'It is already evident that our Earth moves, even if we do not see it, but this is not manifest except by comparison with that which is fixed.'

At the University of Vienna, where he taught, Nicolas of Cusa came into contact with a student possessed of a great enthusiasm for astronomy, Georg Aunpekh, called Peurbach (1423–61). No doubt he told him of his ideas, for, after this young man had become a celebrated astronomer sponsored by the Emperor Frederick III and the Archduke of Austria, he undertook a whole series of observations designed to check Ptolemy's statements. To this end he constructed or perfected a large number of astrolabes, quadrants and celestial globes.

An early death at the age of thirty-eight prevented him from carrying his plan to a conclusion, but left him time to communicate it to one of his pupils from Vienna, Johann Müller (1436–76). The latter, a miller's son, was only fourteen, but he had studied at the University of Leipzig since he was eleven and composed an astronomical almanac at the age of twelve. Born at Königsberg (the town in Bavaria, not the present Kaliningrad, the birthplace of Kant), he adopted the name Müller of Regio Monte (*Königsberg* means in German 'royal mountain'), an appellation that was Latinized after his death into Regiomontanus.

Regiomontanus's fame began when he published an extract from the *Almagest* and astronomical tables that proved of the greatest service to mariners. It spread when, thanks to a Maecenas, Bernhard Walther, he was able to erect at Nuremberg a model observatory combined with a printing press and to send tables and calendars out into the world. It became positive glory when Pope Sixtus IV called him to Rome, as the greatest astronomer of his day, to reform the calendar that had been in use since Julius Caesar. This glory was not beneficial to him: like his master, Peurbach, Regiomontanus died young, leaving his major task scarcely begun, and was buried in the Pantheon at Rome a year after arriving in that city.

This major task was the detailed verification of all Ptolemy's ideas by means of systematic observation of the planets. It was to this end that Regiomontanus employed his Nuremberg observatory and the fortune placed at his disposal by the generous Walther. What would have emerged from this undertaking, had it not been cut short by death? It would undoubtedly have shown that the Ptolemaic system was incapable of explaining the planetary motions once they included the details brought to light by his perfected instruments. He would have been obliged to abandon it and give his support to the heliocentric system, and Copernicus would have been forestalled by a good half century.

There is no object in speculating on what did not take place, but it cannot be doubted that confidence in the *Almagest* was by now seriously shaken. Oresme, Nicolas of Cusa, Peurbach and Regiomontanus were all scientists whom the blinkers of scholasticism did not blind to the imperfections of Ptolemy's notions. To this list we may add a number of Italian astronomers of the second rank who were no less convinced that all was not well with the geocentric theory: Calcagnini (1479–1541), Fracastor (1483–1553) and Amici (1502–38)—not to mention another Italian, this time of the first magnitude, who seems to have adopted the heliocentric theory in 1510, at least as a convenient hypothesis: no other than Leonardo da Vinci.

Not one of the astronomers just referred to reached a definite conclusion, however; the greater the accuracy of their instruments, the less the movements of the planets seemed to agree with Ptolemy, and from this they did, indeed, deduce that a theory according to which the Earth revolved round the Sun would better account for the facts; but none of them obtained irrefutable mathematical proof. This proof could only be obtained by tracing the movements of the planets for years on end and comparing the results with the astronomical tables: the discrepancy would have stood out a mile. Two men only were capable of carrying such a task through to a successful conclusion, Peurbach and Regiomontanus. Death clipped their wings. Who would arise to take their place and furnish the proof for which many were secretly waiting?

Towards the end of the first half of the sixteenth century—the period of Luther, Magellan, Cortez, the creation of the College of France, the battle of Pavia, Ignatius Loyola, the coronation of Charles V of Germany, Erasmus, Albrecht Dürer, Raphael and Rabelais—there circulated among people interested in astronomy a book written by Rheticus (1514–78), a young professor of mathematics at the University of Wittenberg. This book was in the nature of an interview with an old Polish monk named Koppernigk. According to Rheticus's enthusiastic account, this Pole had evolved a cosmological system whose great novelty lay in placing the Sun motionless at the centre of the universe. No doubt men of science looked at one another as they read this monograph. Who was this Koppernigk? For though they knew of a prelate, the bishop-prince of Ermland, bearing this name, no one suspected that he had left a nephew and still less that the latter would one day be far more celebrated than his uncle.

Nicolaus Koppernigk, who Latinized his name to Copernicus (1473–1543), was appointed canon of the cathedral at Frauenburg (now Frombork in Poland), through his uncle's influence, at the age of twenty-seven. Let there be no illusions about this title of canon: rather than the conduct of divine services, Copernicus's duties consisted in governing part of the diocese and collecting the taxes. As a large-scale landowner, he lived 'from his twenty-fourth year,' writes his most recent biographer, 'on prebends, sinecures, on the sweat of toiling peasants'.[1] Those who are inclined to regard astronomers as ethereal spirits soaring above base material considerations might note that this one was a financial expert and one of the most eminent economists of his day. In fact it was he who, at the request of the king of Poland, dealt with the currency crisis of 1521.

Leonardo da Vinci the painter has eclipsed Leonardo da Vinci the engineer, just as Galileo the scientist has eclipsed Galileo the painter. Who knows whether Copernicus's reputation as an economist might not have stood higher than his reputation as an astronomer? For it was

[1] H. Kesten, *Copernicus and His World* (trans. E. B. Ashton and N. Gutermann, New York, 1945).

between these two activities that the quiet life of the canon of Frauenburg was divided. During the period of his studies at Bologna he became friendly with a former pupil of Regiomontanus, Giovanni Domenico of Novara (1454–1504). The latter probably communicated to him his teacher's doubts regarding the Ptolemaic system, for from this time on Copernicus began to devote himself to astronomy, while nevertheless obtaining his doctorate in both canon law and medicine.

The only way to test the geocentric theory was the one proposed by Peurbach and Regiomontanus: to obtain and compare more accurate observations than Ptolemy's. We know the instruments Copernicus employed for this purpose—a quadrant, an armillary sphere and a *triquetrum* made up of three rings arranged in an adjustable triangle, used to measure the altitude of heavenly bodies above the horizon. These appliances, made of wood and graduated in ink, were very small and very crude by comparison with those of Abul-Wefa and Ulugh Beigh. The Polish astronomer added to his own observations those of some of his predecessors, notably Bernhard Walther, who carried on the work of Regiomontanus. The total result was really of little value, and the proof of the immobility of the Sun and the circular motion of the planets, which the author deduced from it, was not very convincing.

Copernicus reached this conclusion in 1507, but he waited till 1543 before publishing the work in which he expounded it, *De Revolutionibus Orbium Coelestium*, 'On the Revolutions of the Heavenly Spheres'. Indeed, he was on his death-bed when he opened the first copy. Why did he keep the manuscript so long before sending it to the printer? Why should a scientist who had discovered a truth at the age of thirty-four have waited till he was sixty-six before revealing it? His attitude becomes understandable when we remember that the geocentric system was then considered an integral part of the philosophy of Aristotle, which had become the foundation of Christian doctrine. To attack this system meant to come into head-on collision with the all-powerful Church and the formidable Inquisition. Since Savonarola, a number of heretical spirits, not to mention the Jews, the Protestants and wizards, and without waiting for Servetus, Vesalius, Giordano Bruno, Campanella and Galileo, had learnt the cost of being innovators.

Copernicus felt no urge to become a martyr. He lived a peaceful and happy life and was anxious to do nothing to disturb it. Unlike the great discoverers with fervent convictions—Socrates condemned to the hemlock, Christopher Columbus brought back from America in irons, Giordano Bruno burnt at the stake—Copernicus valued his tranquillity above everything, an all the more faint-hearted attitude because Poland at that time lay outside the power of the Church. The best proof that he would have run no risk may be seen in the fact that Pope Paul III, on reading the manuscript of *De Revolutionibus*, congratulated its author, and that the book was not placed on the Index till 1764, 220 years later. . . . [1]

Nevertheless, it was only when sheltered by his advanced age and ravaged by disease that Copernicus consented to 'pass his book for press'.

This famous document presented heliocentrism only as a hypothesis, considering it 'more probable' that the Earth was in motion than that it was at rest. As we know, there was nothing original about this hypothesis, since it had been maintained by Philolaeus, Heracleides Ponticus, the Pythagorean Ecphante and above all by Aristarchus of Samos, who almost paid for it with his life. Copernicus even carried his determination to copy the Greeks to the point of adopting their notion of necessarily circular and uniform movements. The most curious fact is that, in order to explain certain phenomena, he had to resign himself to the introduction of epicycles, and the only element in his system really his own was an annual rotation of the Earth round the pole of the ecliptic, a rotation that does not take place. . . .

Contrary to the ideas of the age, particularly to those of the Protestant exegetists, and more complicated than the Ptolemaic system, the Copernican system had the misfortune to account for phenomena less effectively than the latter. We can understand that it was unfavourably received, not only by scholars and philosophers, but also by astronomers and mariners. Only one man of science rallied to its support, the German astronomer Reinhold (1511–53).

[1] It was not until 1953 that Czecho-Slovakia restored to Poland the original manuscript of Copernicus's book.

When the latter drew up a new celestial almanac, the *Prutenic Tables* (1551), intended to replace the Alphonsine Tables, he took the original step of basing them on Copernican principles.

Only two scientists dared to accept these principles openly—the English physician William Gilbert (1540–1603), a pioneer in the field of terrestrial magnetism and electricity (and inventor of the terms 'electric force' and 'electricity'), who did so in 1600, and the Belgian Simon Stevin (1548–1620), a pioneer in mechanics, who did so in 1605.

Today, looking at them from a distance of four centuries, we can see the long chain of astronomers who, as they emerged from the Middle Ages, worked for the victory of the revolutionary theory of heliocentrism over the official geocentrism—a chain that had been broken since Aristarchus, was joined up again by Martianus Capella (fifth century A.D.) and led, despite the persistent prohibition of the Church, to the universal adoption of the modern view in the seventeenth century. In this chain, Copernicus was one link. But it was not he who delivered the death blow to Ptolemy. His own observations were too crude; he did not sufficiently check those he borrowed from the ancients; he had neither the clear-sightedness to reject the sempiternal circular and uniform movements, nor the talent and courage to impose his opinions. His caution, incidentally, did not prevent his book from being attacked the moment it was published by the Protestants, those frowning guardians of the biblical text. Luther condemned it before he died, supported by Melanchthon. This condemnation was benign by comparison with the one pronounced by the Catholics when a monk of that denomination, the Dominican Giordano Bruno, began to preach Copernicus with heretical fervour. His condemnation to the stake, in 1600, preceded the condemnation of the heliocentric theory itself in 1616.

This was the period during which Spain, having monopolized the discovery of America, exploited her conquest by bleeding it white. In 150 years she had torn from it 180 tons of gold and 16,000 tons of silver. Having become the richest country in Europe, she was also the most powerful and under the sceptre of Charles V her presence was felt in Italy, the Netherlands and Austria. Her victory was the victory of the Church, whose doctrine the Council of Trent, called in 1545, was in the process of codifying. Scientific curiosity was there condemned as partaking of original sin and the old notion of man as the centre of nature and the measure of all things, momentarily compromised by Copernicus, was restored. The human being, more powerful than ever, became once more the ultimate purpose of creation. The skies and all heavenly bodies were nothing but a backcloth to his activities. Since his sole aim in this world was to attain salvation, what did the magnitude or size of the heavenly bodies matter to him? As the pivot of the universe, round which the Sun, Moon, planets and stars revolved, man had no right to direct towards these objects anything but a condescending and self-seeking curiosity.

Thanks, therefore, to the opposition of the Church, exploration of the skies had to be confined to the mere description of phenomena. Any interpretation, any conclusion became dangerous and might lead to the stake. Consequently, astronomical observation was left either to wealthy burghers who owned instruments or to physicians accustomed to the objective study of phenomena. Only prosperous countries possessing an advanced technology could possibly undertake it. These conditions ruled out Asia, which had remained since the days of Alexandria the repository of the study of the heavens. Europe henceforth showed herself capable of carrying on the enterprise begun by the Mesopotamians, continued by the Greeks and honourably maintained by the Arabs, Mongols and Turks.

With Copernicus, Europe had fought its first battle in this campaign of conquest.

The battle was lost.

4

The four great names in the conquest of the skies

Tycho Brahe, the lord of the skies—Pious Kepler establishes the plan of the solar system—A free mind: Galileo—The first harvest of the telescope—Galileo's condemnation is his victory—France, England and the Low Countries provide arms for the conquest of the skies—Newton, or unadulterated genius—How Newton discovered universal gravitation—The heavenly bodies subject to scientific law

THE Church had fired a warning shot that reverberated over the whole of scientific research and astronomy in particular. All those who were tempted to philosophize knew the risks they were running, and outside the countries in which the Reformation had emerged victorious they confined themselves strictly to observation.

Observation of nature was precisely the task of physicians, and it is to their credit that, at this perilous epoch, they did not limit themselves to the domain of biology, but extended their curiosity to phenomena far removed from it. The French physician Jean Fernel (1497–1558), for example, measured a degree of the terrestrial meridian, an operation that had not been repeated since 988 in Bagdad; the Flemish physician Gemma Frisius (1508–55) expounded the method of calculating longitudes by transfer of the time of day; the Calabrian physician Aloysius Lilius (d. 1576) worked to reform the calendar; the Czech physician Tadeas Hâjek (1525–1600) taught the determination of the position of a heavenly body by the time at which it passed the meridian; and we must mention again the English physician William Gilbert, already referred to on p. 102, the Saxon physician Gaspar Peucer (1525–1602) and many others. Besides these practitioners, mention should also be made of geographers like the Portuguese Nonius (1492–1577), originator of the *Loxodromic curve* or *rhumb-line*,[1] the German Reinhold, author of the Prutenic Tables, the Englishman Thomas Digges (d. 1595), who first introduced the measurement of parallaxes, the Dutchman Snellius (1591–1626), one of the fathers of geodesy, and even that noted astronomer, the Landgrave William IV of Hesse (1532–92), whose observations extended over thirty years.

All these seem today, however, to be overshadowed by a German pastor and jurist named Johann Bayer (1572–1625). In 1603 this amateur astronomer published his *Uranometria* or chart of the heavens. He listed sixty constellations, each of them finely mapped out and represented, according to the custom of the day, by allegorical figures. These sixty constellations comprised the forty-eight asterisms universally recognized since Ptolemy, and the twelve new ones that had emerged from navigators' descriptions of the southern sky. But the great advance introduced by the *Uranometria* was the designation of each star by a letter, and no longer, as was previously done, by a periphrase such as 'the star that is at the tip of the tail of the Great Bear', or 'that which is beneath the right elbow of Hercules'. Bayer attached the Greek letter α to the brightest star of each constellation, the letter β to the next in brightness, γ to the next, and so on. In this way, the most beautiful stars of the Bull, for example—in order of decreasing brightness 'the southern eye', 'the tip of the left horn', 'the nostrils', and so on—became more simply α Tauri, β Tauri, γ Tauri, etc. Although a minor reform which was in no way comparable to the great innovations of Hipparchus, and yet it was of capital importance, since by simplifying charts of the heavens and making observation easier it clarified the celestial array and facilitated its scientific study.

It must be added that, even in the case of the most objective scientists among those quoted, astronomical observation was by no means untainted by astrology. In fact, as Boquet writes, 'astrology and astronomy were one and the same science'. The Church, which proved so touchy when doubt was cast on Aristotle or Ptolemy, gave every encouragement to the vagaries of those who sought to tell the

[1] The loxodromic curve is one which cuts all the meridians at the same angle. It is much used in navigation.

future by the skies. This was the case, to give only one example, with the Neapolitan Bishop Gauricus (1476–1558), whose prophecies won the favour of four successive Popes. Among the devotees of astrology were to be found physicians, such as the Frenchman Jean-Baptiste Morin (1585–1656), who predicted the birth of Antichrist, and even true scientists, who could not offer as an excuse for their subservience to this miserable nonsense the need to earn a living. Who, on reading these fervent lines, 'By what bizarre injustice does this so noble and useful science (astrology) find so many unbelievers, when arithmetic and geometry have never met a single one?' would guess that they were written by Tycho Brahe, an astronomer of severely critical mind, who never recorded an observation without having scrutinized it from every angle?

Tycho Brahe, the lord of the skies

Such was the man who now takes his place in this story, a complex character, a rich and powerful nobleman whose proud nature forbade blind obedience to the rules of his caste; a scrupulous scientist, who nevertheless firmly believed in the influence of the heavenly bodies on human destiny; a scientific genius who, without knowing it, and even without wishing it, finally tilted the balance in favour of the heliocentric theory, and whose work outweighs on its own that of all the astronomers who filled the years between Hipparchus and himself.

The foregoing chapters have shown the burning interest men have always felt in the problem of the universe. Since the most remote times and in spite of the rigours of their everyday existence, men have speculated about the nature of the celestial vault, the luminaries suspended from it and the various phenomena that occur upon it. Deep thinkers of ancient Greece came within a hair's breadth of the solution. Aristarchus had an inkling of the vast organism that constitutes the solar system, with its circle of planets revolving round the Sun against the motionless background of the stars. But apprenticeship in the school of reason had already taught men not to rest content with intuition, but to demand proof for every explanation. This proof—

the proper motion of the planets round the Sun—could be gained only by assiduous observation of these planets, by locating their changing places on the background of fixed stars. We know how Peurbach, Regiomontanus and Copernicus strove after it, and we also know why they failed: the real movement of the planets is so slow, so slight, so gradual that to attempt to show it with the instruments of the day was like trying to dissect a flea with a butcher's knife. Before tackling the problem, it was essential to improve the instruments.

Improvements of the instruments, of sights and divided circles, was a thankless task that in no way stirred the imagination. How much more exciting to forge a grandiose theory of the cosmos than to slave over graduations or try to gain one place of decimals! Yet the latter is a *sine qua non* of the former; unless supported upon impeccable observation, any theory is only a shaky scaffold unattached to reality. Copernicus's idea was correct in broad outline; nevertheless it collapsed because it was not founded on the rock of irrefutable observations. The final victory of the heliocentric theory had, therefore, to wait until it was buttressed by firmly established observations, which could not be obtained until considerable improvement had been made in the instruments employed.

This was a logical development, illustrated by the case of Tycho Brahe himself.

On 21 August, 1560, a partial eclipse of the Sun was visible at Copenhagen. It made a deep impression on a boy of fourteen, Tycho Brahe, the son of a noble family of Knudstrup, a village near Malmo in Southern Sweden which at that time belonged to Denmark. Young Tycho, who was born on 4 December, 1546, was particularly amazed that astronomers should have been able to foretell the eclipse and give its date in calendars. He was so struck by the accuracy of this forecast that he watched out for other celestial phenomena, curious to see whether they accorded equally well with the predictions. Thus, to the great displeasure of his family, began his study of astronomy.

The young man was now in possession of two astronomical almanacs giving details of the position of the planets: the Alphonsine Tables, based on the Ptolemaic system and more than three hundred years old, and the Prutenic Tables, based on the Copernican system and only a few years old. With a simple compass he measured the angular distance from each planet to the neighbouring stars, and checked this measurement against the figure in the tables. As a rule the figures did not agree. On 24 August, 1563, for instance, there occurred a conjunction of Jupiter and Saturn which the Prutenic Tables forecast with an error of several days, and the Alphonsine Tables with an error of one month! We are not surprised by this discrepancy, since we now know that the latter was several degrees out, while Copernicus and Reinhold strove to keep within ten minutes of the correct figure. Brahe quickly realized that in order to make valid predictions the first task must be to calculate the position of the stars in the sky with the greatest possible accuracy, so as to have immovable points of reference; then to determine the course of each planet in relation to these reference points with equal strictness. These two aims called for the use of large and perfectly constructed instruments.

The liberality of an intelligent and generous ruler, King Frederick II of Denmark, enabled him to put his plans into execution. This Maecenas presented him with an island, a grant of money with which to erect an observatory on it and a pension with which to maintain the staff, buildings and instruments. The island was Hven, some fourteen miles north of Copenhagen. Conscious of his talents, dealing with the sovereign on equal terms, ruling with a rod of iron the peasants who were there to do his bidding, and overflowing with money from taxation (he was also governor of Kullagaard, canon of Roskilde, and so on), Tycho embarked upon the extraordinary life of a wealthy nobleman and a scientist to whom nothing was barred.

In the centre of the island rose Uraniborg. This was a red-brick palace in the Renaissance style bristling with pointed turrets—the revolving towers from which observations were made. The bedrooms, libraries and laboratories housed a multitude of assistants and pupils, not to mention the family and servants. Farther south lay Stjerneborg —Star Burg—a subterranean observatory that protected the instruments from the action of the wind and whose domes alone rose above the ground.

A mass of evidence tells us of Tycho Brahe's life at the head of this little state. Spending money like water, terrorizing the rustics, so proudly anti-conformist that he broke with his family in order to devote himself to science, married a simple peasant girl, defied Aristotle when occasion arose and regarded religion with supreme indifference, he was by no means the lachrymose and grandiloquent visionary portrayed by Max Brod in *The Redemption of Tycho Brahe*. His methods and achievements show him to us rather as an exceptionally clear-thinking, level-headed man, who forced the most venerable traditions to bow to the facts and for whom the most ingenious hypotheses were untenable when they contradicted straightforward observation.

What instruments were sheltered beneath the pointed towers of Uraniborg and the domes of Stjerneborg? As always since Hipparchus and Ptolemy, there were quadrants, armillas and movable sextants. The latter were graduated bars along which slid alidades with sights, by means of which bearings could be taken on the stars. This enabled their co-ordinates to be found—either the azimuth and the altitude above the horizon, or the right ascension and the declination. The largest quadrant measured seven feet in radius and rotated on a vertical axis in such a way as to sweep across all azimuths. Another, of six feet, was permanently attached to a wall in the meridian. An armilla was constructed on the same principle as our present-day equatorial telescopes: a divided circle of four feet six inches radius pivoted on one of its diameters fixed parallel to the axis of the Earth. The declination could be read directly from this first circle, while the right ascensions were given by a second circle welded in the equatorial plane of the first.

The majority of these instruments were of metal, not wood. The divisions were engraved on copper. The *vernier* had not yet been invented, but to increase accuracy Tycho employed a supplementary graduation in *transversals*, which enabled him, in some cases, to read down to ten seconds of arc. How different from Copernicus's crude triquetrum, with degrees drawn in ink on pieces of wood! To appreciate the accuracy of Tycho's observations we must recall that the most exact of modern appliances, such as the transit instrument, are provided with circles two to four feet in diameter, divided every, say, two minutes of arc, and that it is only after repeated readings with the aid of micrometric microscopes that they give the second. The astronomer of Uraniborg was acquainted neither with the telescope, nor the microscope, nor the method of repetition, and his timing apparatus was not a quartz clock capable of running to the second for a year, but a mercury clepsydra. This did not prevent him from calculating the co-ordinates of a star, α Arietis, taken as a reference point, to within fifteen seconds; deducing from this, by proceeding step by step, the co-ordinates of eight other basic stars to within twenty-five seconds; and then completing a catalogue of 977 stars with a precision about ten times as great as Ptolemy's catalogue. It is not surprising that with such emphasis on accuracy Tycho discerned in all his observations a discrepancy of four minutes and spotted the effect of atmospheric refraction already discovered by Roger Bacon; nor that he noted new inequalities in the movement of the Moon; nor, especially, that in the course of twenty years devoted to following the movements of the planets he finally described them to within one minute.

This we may recall, was the aim of all his labours, as it had been of Regiomontanus and Copernicus. Like his two forerunners, the lord of Hven intended to extract from his findings an astronomical almanac that would replace the Alphonsine and Prutenic Tables. These new tables, the criterion of the reliability and permanence of his work, were to be its true crown, the justification of all the toil effected at Hven and the proof that Frederick II's generosity had not been in vain.

But Fate crossed Tycho's path. His intelligent sovereign died, his other patrons disappeared. The hostility and jealousy excited by his exceptional situation now broke their bonds. Forced to leave his island, the astronomer took refuge in Bohemia at the head of a vast train of staff, furniture and astronomical equipment whose passage terrified the population.

All that Fate left him time to extract from the material he had amassed was a cosmological theory—a hybrid theory in which Tycho, too well informed to remain a Ptolemist, could nevertheless not make up his mind to become a Copernican. In Tycho Brahe's system the planets moved round the Sun, and the Sun, Moon and planets round the Earth, which was motionless in the centre of the universe.

Tycho Brahe was the greatest astronomer we have met in the course of this story since Hipparchus. He was also a man of haughty character, despotic, harsh towards his inferiors and exacting towards others, a man in whom the love of science took precedence over every other consideration. An individual of this stamp is respected and flattered as long as he is felt to be supported by the favour of the great, but as soon as this support is withdrawn he becomes the object of all the dammed-up hatred and envy inspired by his position. Tycho never recovered from his expulsion from Hven. He died at Prague on 24 October, 1601. His tomb may still be seen in the Teyn church, covered with a bas-relief in pink marble. Only four years had passed since his departure from Hven, yet Uraniborg and Stjerneborg were already in ruins. Through the greed of the prebendaries and the vengeance of his enemies they had been pillaged, laid waste and razed to the ground. A few years later, evidence that the palatial dwelling really existed was sought in vain. Not until 1951 did excavation uncover a few traces.... Even Tycho's magnificent instruments were destroyed during the Thirty Years War, when the scientist's widow had already died in poverty and want. Nothing was left of Tycho Brahe, nothing but a few bundles of paper which he passed to one of his assistants, with a nerveless hand, a few hours before he died. This heritage, his observations of the planets, he bequeathed with the request that they should be used to produce an astronomical almanac, to be called the *Rudolphine Tables* in honour of the Emperor Rudolf II.

Among his innumerable assistants, a few had occupied a particular place in his life. Tengnagel became his son-in-law; Longomontanus stayed at his side through hard times as well as good; and there was the absent-minded young mathematician who had come to join the team, then exiled in Bohemia, one misty morning in February 1600.

It was to this man that Tycho left his records. His name was Johann Kepler.

Tycho Brahe was a man of genius not only because his observations were superior to anything that could be expected at that period, but also because he was able to recognize and call to his side the only man in the world capable of turning them to account. Brahe's perspicacity and the consequent meeting of two brains made to complement one another strikes us as one of the most fortunate events for astronomy that occurred throughout the ages. It was totally unexpected, and in fact Brahe and Kepler seemed poles apart.

The former reigned in his princely abode at Prague, a celebrated scientist surrounded by the perpetual coming and going of admirers and the benevolence of the Emperor. Kepler was nothing but a poor professor at the University of Graz—an Austrian town 220 miles to the south—living on the verge of penury. Born at Weil, in Würtemberg, on 16 May, 1571, this sickly young man had been successively waiter, farmer and seminarist. A Protestant by religion, he studied at the University of Tübingen. Here, far more than theology, he was interested in mathematics and astronomy, which were taught by Michael Maestlin (1550–1631). The latter also deserves the gratitude of mankind; it was he who, in defiance of official injunctions, taught his pupil Kepler the heliocentric system. He is said also to have taught it to Galileo himself in the course of a trip to Italy.

Young Kepler was appointed professor of mathematics at Graz in 1596, and he had just published his first book. Like every eminent scientist, Tycho Brahe received a copy. He realized at once what promise the unknown author showed and wished to have his collaboration. How could Kepler refuse to work with the great astronomer of Hven? Burdened by a family of five children, he could 'make ends meet' only by casting horoscopes in which he may not have believed. Thus, in 1600, he arrived in Prague to collaborate in the project of the *Rudolphine Tables*.

Apart from his genius, which Tycho alone recognized, Kepler had nothing in common with the latter. He was ignorant of the ways of society and disdained good manners, which did not matter. His intelligence was as abstract and mystical as Tycho's was clear and practical, which was a more serious source of conflict. The ambition of the former lord of the island was to construct instruments graduated with such exactitude that their accuracy was beyond dispute. Kepler's tastes carried him towards Pythagorianism, religious exaltation, grandiose and baroque flights of the imagination. His first 'scientific' achievement was to demonstrate the harmony of the universe by comparing the number and arrangement of the planets with the five inscribable regular polyhedrons. His geometrical proofs were interspersed with lyrical apostrophes to the Creator, and he was firmly convinced that God had made the stars to help man take his bearings at night and that man was the centre of the universe.

This naïve finalism did not prevent him from giving wholehearted support to the heliocentric theory of Copernicus—another point of conflict with Tycho. Kepler knew his scientific superiority and he was a dreamer with a liking for vague theories; his host was a man filled with pride of birth and a meticulous investigator who could not imagine science otherwise than as the accumulation of carefully checked facts. Nevertheless, it was to this exasperating assistant, who stirred him to alternate admiration and annoyance, that he left his treasure of twenty years' observation.

His patron dead, Kepler became once more a wanderer, seeking a position with the Emperor, a post at the University or employment as astrologer with a military leader. He was now escorted by twelve children and showered with securities by the great, who forgot to pay him. But his wealth lay in this inheritance from Tycho, which it was his task to bring to fruition.

To bring Tycho's heritage to fruition meant to see whether the positions given for each planet really lay on the eccentric circular orbit ascribed to it by Ptolemy. Kepler considered the case of Mars, collated the observations and noted that they differed by eight minutes of arc from the predictions in the tables. The discrepancy could not arise from systematic errors, since Tycho's inaccuracies did not exceed one minute. Hence it must be the theory that was wrong, and the orbit could not be circular.

Kepler immediately adopted the Copernican hypothesis. He then saw that calculation agreed better with observation when the orbit was assumed to be oval. Finally he arrived at the first of the three major laws which posterity has christened 'Kepler's Laws': The orbit of a planet is an ellipse with the Sun situated at a focus.

The second law followed almost at once. It runs thus: The *radius vector*, joining the Sun to a planet, sweeps equal areas in equal times.

This means, for example, that the straight line joining the Earth to the Sun does not revolve at a constant speed, like the hand of a clock. Let us represent the terrestrial orbit by the ellipse in Fig. 5 (the eccentricity of this ellipse is intentionally exaggerated; in reality the greater and lesser axes should differ in this diagram by less than a tenth of an inch). The Sun is at the focus S. The Earth follows its path in the direction indicated by the arrow. At the summer solstice it is at the *aphelion* A, and at the winter solstice at the *perihelion* P. Let us suppose that, near the aphelion, the Earth travels in one hour from E to E'; in one hour

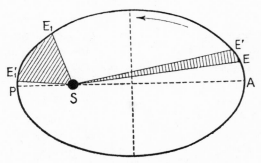

Fig. 5 KEPLER'S LAWS

Any planet E describes round the Sun S an ellipse with the Sun situated at a focus. The velocity of the planet on its orbit is such that the areas swept in equal times by the radius vector are equal—i.e., the area ESE' equals the area $E_1SE'_1$. Finally, the squares of the periodic times of any two planets are proportional to the major axes of their orbits.

the radius vector SE sweeps over the area SEE'. According to the second law, the radius vector ought to sweep over the same area in any other position of the Earth—in particular, close to the perihelion, near E_1 for example. Since the distance SE_1 is less than SE, $E_1E'_1$ must, in compensation, be longer than EE'. Consequently, the Earth travels faster at the moment of the winter solstice than at the moment of the summer solstice. This law explains the variations in the apparent speed of the Sun and planets that had so intrigued the ancient astronomers; just as the first law, regarding the eccentricity of the orbit, explains the variations in their luminosity.

These first two laws were published by Kepler in 1609 in his book

The New Astronomy, founded on the study of the motion of Mars. The third did not appear until 1619, in his *Harmony of the World*: it was more complicated and cost him seventeen years of research. The third of the great laws governing the motion of the heavenly bodies is expressed as follows: The squares of the periodic times of any two planets are proportional to the cubes of the major axes of their orbits.

We will explain this statement by an example.

One revolution of the Earth takes 365 days, the square of which is $365 \times 365 = 132,225$. That of Mars takes 687 days, the square of which is $687 \times 687 = 471,969$. The law in question states that these two numbers, 132,225 and 471,969, are proportional to the cubes of the major axes of the respective orbits of the Earth and Mars. From this it follows that the distance from Mars to the Sun and from the Earth to the Sun are to one another as the cube root of 471,969 is to the cube root of 132,225, that is to say in the proportion of 1·524 to 1.

The importance of this discovery is evident. Having found the path followed by the planets, the variable speed at which they travel along it, the distance—in relation to the duration of their revolution—they are from the Sun, Kepler had thereby established the final plan of the solar system. Henceforth there was no room for doubt. Not merely was it no longer possible to wonder whether Venus was or was not closer to the Earth than Mars: the precise dimensions of their respective orbits were determined with an exactitude hitherto known only to mathematics. Heracleides Ponticus, Aristarchus and Copernicus had formed a general idea of the organization as a whole, but this was only a qualitative interpretation, a painting sketched in without a model by brilliantly intuitive minds. For this pleasant picture, Kepler substituted a strict and accurate diagram; the circles demanded by Platonic aesthetics gave place to ellipses; uniform movements, to speeds that varied according to an inflexible formula. The planetary world ceased to be a vaguely defined aggregation obeying convenient rules; it became a coherent whole subject to inviolable natural laws, and the prediction of phenomena, instead of being a purely empirical matter, acquired the full rigour of geometry. Working with his laws, Kepler was able to state that on such and such a day, such and such a planet would be at such and such a point in the sky, on another day there would be an occultation and on yet another day an eclipse. Thus, in fulfilment of the promise he had made to the dying Tycho, he produced in 1627 the *Rudolphine Tables*.

These tables owed nothing to those of Hipparchus, nor to those of Ibn-Yunis or Ulugh Beigh, nor to the Alphonsine or Prutenic Tables, and they paid as little heed to Tycho Brahe's system as to Ptolemy's. In short, they were modern tables based on the same principles as the *Nautical Almanac* of our own day. Kepler did not omit to acknowledge his debt to Tycho. He could never have drawn up his tables without the material accumulated by the Danish astronomer.

The publication of this work heralded the triumph of the heliocentric view, and also the final burial of Kepler's hopes. Tycho's heirs demanded a share in the tables; Longomontanus added his calumnies to their claims; first the Emperor, then the Duke of Wallenstein, who employed him as an astrologer, ceased to pay him. Weighed down by too harsh a destiny, this profound genius, this sensitive and visionary mathematician, breathed his last at Ratisbon on 15 November, 1630.

A free mind: Galileo

We should be wrong in thinking that the discovery of Kepler's laws and the publication of the *Rudolphine Tables* aroused any considerable echo in Europe and immediately rallied the learned world to the heliocentric theory. Paradoxically, the opposing camp, apart from those instinctively drawn to it by their philosophical opinions and religious faith or scientific ignorance, also attracted scientists with a positivist outlook. The latter were suspicious of the extravagant hotchpotch of aesthetico-mysticism with which Kepler surrounded the enunciation of his laws. How could a pure geometer look favourably upon results which their author interlarded with statements about the music of the spheres and invocations to God? Thus, even mathematicians who maintained a personal correspondence with Kepler received his work with a reserve bordering on scepticism.

This was the case, in particular, with the professor of mathematics at the University of Padua, with whom Kepler had been exchanging letters since 1597. Although Kepler knew the professor to be a convinced Copernican, his reprimands and moving exhortations were of no avail: the professor remained icy. No doubt the esoteric impedimenta with which Kepler cluttered his proofs rendered them suspect in his eyes.

This professor of mathematics was called Galileo Galilei. Born at Pisa on 18 February, 1564, at the time when *The New Astronomy* appeared he was a man of forty-five, vigorous, with an unfettered mind and a happy disposition. There is nothing surprising about the fact that, while still young, he espoused the heliocentric theory, thus breaking with Ptolemy at the outset of his career: he was a child of the same Tuscany that gave birth to Dante, Giotto, Petrarch, Leonardo da Vinci and Michelangelo. A financial centre where huge fortunes were built up, Florence was better suited to the emancipation of intelligence than to introverted meditation. The capitalism that flourished there contributed to the development of more liberal and more realistic ideas than were current in other countries less stimulated by commerce and more tightly muzzled by the Inquisition.

What a difference there was between Galileo, a son of the new and luminous Alexandria that was Tuscany, and, say, Copernicus and Kepler, the offspring of countries that were more closed, more misty, graver and more respectful towards dogma and authority! By comparison with Copernicus, flaccidly taking the line of least resistance, determined at all costs to keep out of trouble, by comparison with Kepler, struggling in the midst of his poverty and a myriad astrological superstitions, Galileo stood out as a lucid scientist incapable of concealing the slightest particle of the truth. This truth, which horrified the partisans of scientific orthodoxy, he confessed, taught and proclaimed. Not only did he shout it from the rooftops, but he assailed its opponents, drenched them in sarcasm, turned them over and over on the grill of his irony. Not until he was seventy, and under the threat of torture and death, did he finally pretend to see reason. It is understandable that a character like his, full of pride in his possession of the truth, should not have appealed to everyone and that one authority should have written, for example: 'A curious man, whose scientific ability compels respect, but whose character is unattractive: the more we study him, the more we admire and the less we like him.' This is a matter of taste: some people prefer darkness to light and the persecutor to his victim.

We can understand the hostility Galileo aroused from the outset when we recall that, while still a young lecturer of twenty-five, he did not hesitate to repudiate the authority of Aristotle. The latter declared that the heavier a body is, the faster it falls. Galileo had only to ascend to the top of the famous leaning tower of Pisa and drop two iron balls, one weighing 1 lb., the other 10 lb., and observe that they both touched the ground at the same time. Thus began a series of studies on weight, which were irrefutable because based on experiment. This was the first time the dogmatic rules of Aristotle had been opposed by concrete reality, and it is easy to imagine the howl raised by the Peripatetics.

The republic of Venice, which appointed the great man to a chair at the University of Padua in 1592 and paid him magnificently, was the most suitable place in the world to cultivate a science so intrepidly pursued. Far from censuring his audacities, the Senate applauded them: they increased the number of students and enriched the State!

To the lustre conferred upon him by his discoveries in mechanics Galileo added the merit of practical inventions—the thermometer, the hydrostatic scales, a new fortification technique. In 1609 came the momentous discovery of the astronomical telescope.

The first harvest of the telescope

Let us make it clear at once that Galileo did not invent the telescope. It had been known for at least a year under the name 'Holland glass', and specimens could be bought from spectacle-makers in the Hague, Brussels and Paris. Roger Bacon had an inkling of the magnifying effect of lenses in 1260; in about 1590, the Italian Giovanni Battista Porta (1538–1615) produced a combination of lenses that made distant objects appear closer, and Dutch opticians—Metius, Jansen, Lippershey—began making and selling these appliances in 1608. But none of them dreamed that the 'Holland glass' could be anything but a toy. It never occurred to any of them that it might be something more than a profitable article of sale. Galileo learned of the existence of this apparatus in 1609, through a letter from a correspondent in Paris. He tried out various arrangements of concave and convex lenses and had little difficulty in reconstructing the one employed by the Dutch opticians. He at once applied it to celestial observation and he may justly be said to have invented the *astronomical* telescope.

Two of Galileo's earliest telescopes may be seen today in the Physics Museum, Florence; they are modest tubes fitted at one end with a convex lens and at the other, the eye-piece, with a concave lens. They magnified, at most, some twenty times. Faced by these relics, the layman will smile, recalling the gigantic telescope of Mount Palomar of which the mirror is seventeen feet across, inside which the observer is housed like an insect and which magnifies a thousand times. But the man of science will be moved, for he knows that the latter is only the descendant of the former, and that the humble contrivance devised by Galileo produced an even more abundant harvest than the Californian colossus, although the latter has extended the dominion of thought several thousand million light-years.

Galileo began to reap this harvest during the early April evenings of 1609, with instruments the most powerful of which had a $2\frac{1}{4}$ inch objective and magnified thirty times. He trained it on the Moon and at one glance perceived an earth almost the same as our own, with mountains, valleys, shadows that lengthened as the Sun went down, and the pale 'earthshine' that dilutes with a discreet glimmer the dense lunar night. Aristotle asserted that the Moon was smooth, because a perfect spherical shape was the only one appropriate to the heavenly bodies; Galileo shrugged his shoulders.

He shrugged his shoulders again when, on directing his tube towards the Sun, he saw spots. Spots on the Sun, which the Stagirite had declared to be incorruptible! He might not have believed his eyes, if he had not known that a similar observation had already been made by the Dutchman John Fabricius (1587–1615), who used only an ordinary 'Holland glass'. The German Jesuit Christoph Scheiner (1575–1650) made the same discovery at about the same time, but his provincial's obstinate adherence to Aristotelian views prompted him to caution. It was not until 1626 that he began to publish his work,

Rosa Ursina, in which he determined the duration of the Sun's rotation and the zones of appearance of the sunspots.

During this time Galileo was continuing his explorations at Padua. After the Moon and the Sun, the planet Venus entered the field of his object-glass. Slowly, evening after evening, its aspect changed. Since, according to Ptolemy, it revolved round the Earth and was lit from the side by the Sun, it was not surprising that it appeared as a crescent; but the crescent grew, became a circle, the circle became indented, shrank and vanished, then the crescent reappeared—a sequence of phases exactly resembling those of the Moon. There could be no doubt about it. If Venus had phases, it meant this planet must revolve round the Sun as the Moon does round the Earth. Copernicus was right.

After Venus came Jupiter. At the first viewing the disc appeared tiny, and close to it were three little stars. The next day, these stars had changed position and there were four of them. Intrigued, Galileo observed them closely several days in succession and saw them shift from one evening to the next, eclipse one another and pass in front of the disc of the planet. The astronomer realized that these were four satellites rotating around Jupiter. The same discovery was made simultaneously by the German Simon Mayer, called Marius (1570–1624), who made himself a telescope 'the length of an arm' with an object-glass 'one and a half fingers in diameter'.

Intoxicated with the discoveries that filled his telescope every time he raised it towards the skies, Galileo moved on to Saturn. But the image was far smaller than that of Jupiter, and also more confused. The disc seemed to be extended on two sides by 'ears', unless these were two satellites. The perplexed scientist hid his mortification behind an anagram meaning 'I observed the highest planet (Saturn) and found it threefold'. Forty-six years later, Huygens solved the mystery by showing that the strange object was a ring that encircles Saturn.

And there were the stars. What a harvest the objective reaped in the still virgin fields of heaven where, for every known orb, a hundred rose up out of the depths of invisibility. Constellations ceased to be an allegorical assembly of a few stars; they multiplied, became a concourse, sometimes a seething mass, of dozens, of hundreds of stars unsuspected by the eye. Instead of the six stars of the Pleiades, Galileo discerned forty; he counted eighty instead of seven in Orion's Belt and Sword, forty instead of three in the asterism of Praesepe, while in the Milky Way the eye was confronted by a mass of luminous dust.

Behind the familiar stellar world, behind the visible face of the philosophical world of Aristotle, whose motions had been traced by Ptolemy, Galileo discovered another, incomparably richer and more mysterious. In his turn, the illustrious Pisan astronomer drew up an inventory of them in his *Siderius Nuncius* or 'Sidereal Messenger', eighteen months after constructing his first telescope. What a stir this caused among the learned and even among the merely educated! And naturally the astonishing revelation of such marvels aroused people's curiosity to see them for themselves, as well as to discover fresh ones.

While Galileo was being showered with favours by the Medici, congratulated by Rome, appointed professor at Pisa University and elected to the Accademia dei Lincei, the telescope came into the hands of innumerable emulators and everywhere spread a taste for astronomy. How many troops there were now for the conquest of the skies! We can understand this sudden craze. How much more attractive the exploration of the heavens was, when practised in this fashion, with the aid of an instrument that sounded the invisible depths, than the astronomy of yesterday with its divided circles, its mensurations and its trigonometrical formulae! Armed with the telescope, Galilean astronomy was a stimulus to the imagination, a spur to thought. It was a living, stirring and popular science, just as classical astronomy, so learned and so sterile, was austere, lofty and aristocratic.

No sooner had Galileo launched his attack, no sooner had his *Siderius Nuncius* indicated the objectives to be attained, than there was an outburst of discoveries. On 15 December, 1612, Simon Marius, who had already recovered from their obscurity the four satellites of Jupiter, reported the existence, close to the constellation of Andromeda, of a strange little luminescent cloud, 'like a candle seen at night through a sheet of horn', as he described it. This was the first appearance of the great nebula of Andromeda, a sister galaxy to our own, the vast proportions of which were not known until three centuries later. As early as 1610 Peiresc (p. 127) had announced the presence of a similar cloud in the constellation of Orion: this was the nebula of Orion, studied in detail by Huygens in 1656. In 1620 the Belgian Charles Malapert discerned the phases of Mercury, which exactly resemble those of Venus. In 1630 the Italian Zucchi drew attention to the parallel belts that run across the disc of Jupiter.

Meanwhile, the primitive telescope had been improved. The first advance was due to Kepler. Galileo sent him his book; he made himself a telescope and came away dazzled by the multitude of stars it brought into view. But this telescope was incapable of great magnification and its field was very small. Kepler looked for another system of lenses that would obviate these two drawbacks. In 1611 he published the outline of an arrangement in which the concave eye-piece was replaced by a convex one, a major advance which was the starting point for the optical instruments employed in modern astronomy. Galileo's telescope remained in the form of the opera-glass and field-glass; Kepler's became the true astronomical refractor—the ancestor of the giant at the Yerkes Observatory, whose object-glass is a biconvex lens forty inches across.

Which astronomer first applied Kepler's suggestions and constructed this true 'astronomical' refractor? Perhaps, in 1613, the Jesuit Scheiner, who discovered the sunspots. Perhaps the Austrian Franciscan Schyrle of Rheita (1597–1660), whose surname, Rheita, long served as a common noun designating the telescope. In any case, it was a colleague of Scheiner's, the Italian Jesuit Nicola Zucchi (1586–1670) who, in 1616, created the reflecting telescope. In this instrument the ordinary object-glass is replaced by a concave mirror, by which the image is reflected into the eye-piece and magnified by it.

Galileo's telescope, Kepler's astronomical telescope, the reflecting telescope, celestial discoveries that echoed from one end of Europe to the other—this outburst of inventions, revelations and miracles was the cause and consequence of enthusiastic investigation of the sky, to whose new and fabulous riches the telescope provided the key.

This outburst overturned a great deal more than the existing conception of the firmament. It struck a violent blow at the teaching of Ptolemy and Aristotle and hence at the authority of the Scriptures. For, since Venus exhibited phases like the Moon, was it not evident that this planet revolved around the Sun? Did not the fact that there were four satellites circulating around Jupiter prove that not everything in the universe gravitated round the Earth? And did not the system of four globes rotating round the Jovian world illustrate what the system of planets revolving round the Sun must be like? And this illustration was all the more striking because Kepler's laws applied just as rigorously to the Jovian system as to the solar system, as was proved by the Belgian priest Godefroi Wendelen (1580–1667).

In short, the most ineluctable observations proved that the planets revolved around the Sun, not around the Earth, and therefore that Ptolemy was wrong. Galileo, who was not reticent by temperament and who liked to make truth heard, did not fail to shout it from the housetops and write it to all his friends. Naturally, the partisans of traditional astronomy were up in arms; some declared that the heavenly bodies seen by the telescope were only optical illusions created by the objective itself; others found it impossible to believe so many things that were not in Aristotle; finally, the Church refused to accept discoveries that contradicted certain passages in the Bible, for example the miracle of Joshua.

Conflict was inevitable between these two equally intransigent authorities, on the one hand the authority of observation and experiment, on the other that of faith and dogma. Seeing the world sliding farther and farther down the slope of heresy, the ecclesiastical authorities were led officially to take up a position. In 1616 they had the following two propositions examined by the Qualifiers, or experts of the Holy Office:

1. The Sun is the centre of the world and hence immovable of local motion;

2. The Earth is not the centre of the world, not immovable, but moves according to the whole of itself, also with a diurnal motion.

On 24 February the opinion of the Qualifiers was accepted by the Holy Office and the first proposition was declared 'foolish and absurd, philosophically and formally heretical', and the second was declared 'to receive the same censure in philosophy and, as regards theological truth, to be at least erroneous in faith'. Galileo was ordered to cease propaganda in favour of the heliocentric system.

It would be disregarding Galileo's impetuosity and his irresistible urge to scald his opponents with irony to imagine that he let matters rest there. In 1632 he published, in Italian, his major work, *Dialogues on the two great systems of the world, the Ptolemaic and the Copernican.* A masterpiece of ironic wit, it was nothing but a long plea for the heliocentric theory, disguised under protestations of respect for the Church. The latter ingenuously accorded the *imprimatur* and the Pope himself was not in the least shocked by the book. It took a little longer for the scandal to break. Then the supreme pontiff recognized himself in one of the characters drawn by the author, and entrusted with the task of defending Ptolemy, a picturesque individual of the type we might describe today as 'gormless'.

We know the sequel. Galileo was called to Rome, brought before the Holy Office and condemned, on 22 June, 1633, to recant the heresy that the Earth moved.

Tradition presents this grand old man to us as a pitiable victim of religious fanaticism. Let us not exaggerate: the scientist, who knew perfectly well the risk he was running, was treated as the law of the Church demanded, but with clemency. In the end it was he who emerged victorious from the debate, since his trial represented the last desperate rearguard action by the Peripatetics in flight before the rising tide of facts. Yet it took two centuries for the Vatican to admit its defeat, for Galileo's *Dialogues* were not removed from the Index until the beginning of the nineteenth century. And it was only in 1952, while receiving members of the congress of the International Astronomical Union meeting in Rome, that Pope Pius XII glorified 'the modern conception of astronomical science which was, in the past, the ideal of so many great men, Copernicus, Galileo, Kepler, Newton. . . .'

To tell the truth, though we may justly conclude that it was

Galileo who delivered the death blow to the Ptolemaic system and ensured the final triumph of heliocentrism, his victory was certainly not recognized as such at the time. It looked more like a defeat of the Copernicans. As Protestants were no less geocentrically minded than the rest, the heliocentrists nowhere ventured to present the theory as anything but a hypothesis, and dispute between them and their opponents was more active than ever.

It seems pretty clear that, among astronomers, no one was now a Ptolemist at heart. They all proclaimed their loyalty to the Scriptures, but the majority paid only lip service to geocentrism.

The Italian Jesuit Giovanni Battista Riccioli (1598–1671), for example, the author of the first map of the Moon (p. 144), accepted the Ptolemaic theory only with regret and, commenting on the decree of the Holy Office, added: 'It is not an article of faith that the Sun moves and the Earth is at rest.' Wendelen, who has been referred to above, his compatriot Canon Martin-Etienne van Velden (1664–1724) and, among the French, the Minim Friar Marin Mersenne (1588–1648) and Abbés Picard (1620–82 or 1683) and Gassendi (1592–1655) were more or less overt heliocentrists. Naturally, this dual attitude did not facilitate scientific work. Joseph Bertrand relates that in 1746, the period of the Battle of Fontenoy, Diderot's *Pensées philosophiques*, the *Esprit des Lois* and the invention of the lightning conductor, the Italian Jesuit Ruggero Boscovich (1711–87), a distinguished astronomer and a disciple of Newton, sought to calculate the orbit of a comet according to three observations, 'a completely impossible problem,' explains Joseph Bertrand, 'if the Earth is supposed motionless'. Boscovich declared at the time: 'Full of respect for the Holy Scriptures and the decree of the Holy Inquisition, I regard the Earth as immovable.' Then, having put himself in order with his conscience, he hastened to add: 'Nevertheless, for simplicity of explanation, I shall act as though it revolved; for it has been proved that appearances are the same in the two hypotheses.'

Cruelly torn between the imperatives of science, which drew them towards the heliocentric system, and obedience to the Church, which held them down to geocentrism, some scientists compromised and rallied to Tycho Brahe's thesis. But this hybrid position was highly unstable, and in spite of the angry cries of theologians and Bossuet's majestic sermons,[1] belief in the motion of the Earth spread with gathering momentum.

France, England and the Low Countries provide arms for the conquest of the skies

It must be remembered that the first years of the seventeenth century were marked by a general retreat from her possessions by Spain. The chief causes of the progressive disintegration of her empire were the Spaniards' laziness, their voracity, which led them to prefer financial juggling to commercial activity, and the omnipotence of a fabulously wealthy aristocracy and priesthood in a ruined country. The main stages in this disintegration were the proclamation of the independence of the Netherlands (1579), the rout of the invincible Armada (1588), the Treaty of Vervins and the Edict of Nantes (1598).

The downfall of Spain meant a loss to the Church and a corresponding gain to liberty of conscience and scientific research. England and the Low Countries henceforth concentrated all their efforts on economic improvement and threw themselves wide open to technical progress, while France, thanks to Henry IV, liberated herself from religious intolerance and decreed freedom of worship. Spain and Italy were thus thrown out of circuit and continued to suffocate under the iron-collar of the Inquisition; as a result the conquest of the skies withered away in Italy while becoming more and more vigorous in the Netherlands, Britain and France.

In 1633, when Galileo's recantation echoed round the world, this state of affairs was already very much in evidence. On the scientific plane, Spain had long ceased to count. Italy also abdicated, strangled by her philosophical bonds. The spirit of free investigation had crossed the frontier and was now spreading in the South of France. The astronomical telescope here enjoyed a tremendous vogue, and around

[1] 'There is no course so impetuous that divine omnipotence cannot check it when it wishes; consider the Sun, with what impetuosity it travels across the vast arena opened up to it by Providence! Yet you are not unaware that God fixed it in olden times in the centre of the sky merely at the word of a man.' (Quoted by Joseph Bertrand, *Les Fondateurs de l'Astronomie moderne*, Paris, 1865).

Aix-en-Provence a whole crop of astronomers worked enthusiastically to continue Galileo's wonderful achievements.

These stargazers were no longer men of letters or physicians; they were jurists, to whom the freedom afforded by the Edict of Nantes allowed intellectual audacities previously unthinkable. They deliberately rejected Aristotle and Ptolemy, made a point of valuing only concrete facts and logical reasoning, and set about the examination of celestial phenomena unencumbered by any prejudices. Such were Nicolas Fabri de Peiresc (1580–1637), counsellor in the parliament of Aix; Gassendi, the first to observe the passage of Mercury in front of the solar disc on 7 November, 1631; and a group of lawyers and clerics more sensitive to exact observation than to the taboos imposed by a philosopher of Stagira two thousand years earlier.

As partisans, acknowledged or otherwise, of the heliocentric system, it goes without saying that these people were simultaneously opposed to the Aristotelian conception of the cosmos. Aristotle had declared the Earth to be immovable at the centre of the universe, the stars to be moving round it with a circular and uniform motion, the planets to be imperishable and incorruptible. It was now notorious that the planetary orbits were ellipses, that the planets travelled along them at variable speeds, and that the pure countenance of the Sun might be corrupted by spots. New stars had even been observed in the reputedly unalterable skies, such as those noted in 1572 (by Tycho Brahe), in 1600 (by the Flemish astronomer Wilhelm Blaeu, 1571–1638) and in 1604.

Furthermore, and in more general terms, Aristotle had asserted that natural phenomena, since they were perceptible to us by quality rather than quantity, could not be expressed in a mathematical form. This assertion, too, was contradicted by the new discoveries. Not only had Kepler reduced planetary motions to a mathematical formula, but Galileo, in his early work, had similarly 'mathematized' the study of weight. These few mathematical relationships discerned in natural phenomena would, however, have had only limited application, if a philosopher of genius had not been led to generalize them and to interpret the universe as a whole in terms of a vast mechanism subject to strict material laws. Need we add that this was Descartes?

Galileo was thirty-two when René Descartes (1596–1650) was born. At the time of the 1633 trial, the latter was in Holland, whose liberal atmosphere, realistic mentality and commercial activity favoured a revolution in thinking. His major work appeared four years later. Applying the principles laid down in his *Discours sur la Méthode*, Descartes formulated a general theory of the world. He supposed it to be made up of an invisible substance called ether composed of very small particles in a continuous state of eddying movement, which accounted for all phenomena (the 'Vortex Theory'). He went back to the descriptions of Copernicus and Kepler, and, in addition, deduced new laws and facts in the fields of optics and mechanics.

The spiraloid shape of the galaxies restores a striking topicality to the great French thinker's views, which are for the most part now quite out of date. Outworn though they now appear to us, we cannot fail to see in them the first attempt at a truly scientific explanation of nature, the first effort to interpret nature not in purely deductive abstract terms, as the Scholastics and Aristotelians did, but on the basis of visible evidence treated according to the exigencies of reason.

The rise in the standard of living and the increased wealth of the middle classes in France, Britain and the Low Countries were largely due to technical progress. Technicians and financiers began to seem the authors of prosperity and they naturally relied upon those who, through their ability to interpret natural phenomena correctly, enabled them to improve their tools and augment profit and interest. In other words, scientists like Galileo and Descartes gradually thrust into the shadow the hair-splitting disciples of Aristotle with their contempt for concrete reality. The latter were reduced to the level of supernumeraries in the epic of civilization. It was the former who now occupied the centre of the stage. In the age of machines, whose advent they heralded, they were destined to create modern civilization.

Let us welcome this salutary interaction between the needs of economics (to be exact, of commercial navigation), which led Tycho Brahe and Kepler to improve the prediction of celestial movements; the mathematical form given to the latter by Kepler and Galileo, which induced them to state the great natural laws in the same stringent terms; and the effectiveness of these laws in enabling man to increase his power over things and so bring about the industrial revolution of the eighteenth century. Tycho Brahe's paternity in respect of this revolution is less remote than might be thought, since it was from the observations at Hven that Kepler extracted the laws of the planets, from these that Newton derived the discovery of universal gravitation and the general theorems of mechanics, and these theorems which, in turn, gave rise to the rational evolution of machines, the basis of the rapid advances in industry that took place from 1760 onwards.

At the time of the *Discours de la Méthode* (1637) Aristotelianism was no more to scientists than a dusty relic of the past. It was none the less the symbol of religious authority, and they were obliged to bow to it as the Swiss of William Tell's day had to bow to Gessler's hat. Even after Kepler's and Galileo's achievements, astronomical investigation remained permeated by an unpleasant metaphysical odour. This was because, even admitting that the planets described mathematically defined orbits, it remained to be discovered *why* they did so. What mysterious force compelled them to revolve around the Sun? Was it a 'motive virtue', sister to Molière's 'dormitive virtue'? Or was it an attraction derived from the properties of the *lodestone*, properties popularized in 1600 by William Gilbert?

Was it not possible to track down this hidden cause by the method of scientific investigation that had proved so successful in the hands of Kepler, Galileo and Descartes? This was precisely the task Galileo set himself when, after his recantation and house arrest at Arcetri, near Florence, where exploration of the firmament was forbidden him, he was able to devote himself entirely to meditation. In 1638 he published at Leyden his *Dialogues on Two New Sciences*.

This work has rightly been seen as the charter of dynamics. In it Galileo, thinking over experiments carried out during his youth at Pisa, deduced from them the basic laws of this science—the law of the falling of bodies, of the pendulum, of the inclined plane and of the rate of projectiles together with the distinction between an object's *mass* and its *weight*;[1] in it he also formulated the principle of inertia,

---

[1] We know that the *weight* of a body (measured on the dynameter) is the product of its *mass* (measured on the scales) multiplied by gravity (9·81 m /s), which is expressed in the well-known equation: F=mg.

according to which a body in motion that is free from the action of any force will continue to move indefinitely in a straight line and with constant velocity. These laws formed the basis of terrestrial mechanics. The adjective 'terrestrial' is important, because there existed another mechanics, that which governed planetary motion, whose laws had been discovered by Kepler. It is hardly necessary to state that these two types of mechanics were as dissimilar as possible and that there seemed to be no common measure between Kepler's laws and, for example, the law of the fall of bodies discovered by Galileo?[1]

Kepler died in abject poverty in 1630. Galileo, now blind, passed away in his turn on 8 January, 1642. On 4 January of the following year Newton was born.

Newton, or unadulterated genius

Everything was known and nothing was known. For if the nature of the planetary paths was now established, if it was now possible, thanks to Kepler's laws, to draw up astronomical tables incomparably more accurate than any that had gone before, the mechanism behind it all was just as much a mystery as ever. Why did the planets revolve around the Sun? What mysterious influence compelled them to describe ellipses and not circles, or, more simply, prevented them from shooting off in a straight line?

This problem was hotly discussed, especially in London. The young astronomer Halley (p. 166), who had just made himself famous by predicting the return of a great comet, the frightful gnome Robert Hooke (1653–1703), as learned as he was irascible, and the architect Christopher Wren (1632–1723), who had previously been a professor of mathematics and astronomy, pursued endless investigations, convinced they were on the brink of a solution but unable to find the ultimate 'open sesame'.

Halley knew that if the orbits had been circular it would have been possible to invoke a force of attraction coming from the Sun and varying as the inverse square of the distance. But did this law apply to elliptical orbits? Halley strongly suspected that it did. Wren declared

[1] Nowadays this law is expressed as $e = \frac{1}{2} gt^2$.

his inability to solve the problem. Hooke claimed to have solved it, but offered no proof. Perhaps he had solved it. This hunchbacked, sickly and deformed experimental philosopher appears to us now as one of the vastest brains in the history of science. Among his numerous inventions were the first screw-divided quadrant, an anemometer, a weather clock, the anchor escapement of clocks (put into practical effect later by William Clement, *see* p. 165), and a universal joint; he was the first to apply the spring balance wheel to watches. He also evolved a theory of elasticity and it seems that he divined the true doctrine of universal gravitation, but failed to demonstrate his discovery through lack of mathematical knowledge.

In any case, no convincing and acceptable solution was forthcoming. All Wren could think of was to offer a prize of £1 (worth forty shillings) to anyone who could prove, within two months, that the path of a planet subject to the law of the inverse square was necessarily an ellipse. As this bait still produced no result, Halley decided in August 1684 to consult one of his friends, a Cambridge professor called Isaac Newton.

Newton was by then already one of the great names in optics. He was born on 4 January, 1643, in the little hamlet of Woolthorpe in Lincolnshire. His career as a schoolboy and as a student at Cambridge was undistinguished except by a very great experimental ingenuity. Not till he was twenty-one did he give Barrow, his favourite professor, cause to suspect the exceptional genius slumbering within him.

In 1669 Newton succeeded Barrow as Lucasian professor of mathematics at Cambridge. By this time Newton had made a name for himself by resolving white light into its constituent colours with the aid of a prism. Perfecting Zucchi's invention, he had also constructed a metal reflecting telescope. This instrument, now one of the most precious relics of the Royal Society, excited the most lively admiration, shared and expressed by the King himself. In 1672 Newton was elected a member of this erudite company. Since then, apart from a dispute with Hooke on the fall of bodies, Newton had won fame by his famous corpuscular theory of light.

In short, when Halley came to talk to him about the controversy that had arisen between himself, Hooke and Wren, Newton was one of the most celebrated opticians of the day, but there seemed no reason why he should be able to throw light on the question at issue. We may judge the young astronomer's amazement when his friend told him he had taken an interest in the problem, and indeed, found a complete solution to it. It was typical of Newton that he attached so little importance to his proof that, in spite of Halley's insistence, he was unable to lay his hands on it and had to reconstruct it from memory.

This carelessness is more significant than might appear. It shows that Newton's scale of values was not the same as ours. He devoted no more effort to his *Principia* than to two almost valueless works of mystic erudition, *The Chronology of Ancient Kingdoms amended* and *Observations upon the Prophecies of Daniel and the Apocalypse of St. John*. It also reveals that Newton, rather than provoke argument, preferred to let his memoranda sleep forgotten at the bottom of a drawer.

This great genius was, in fact, excessively touchy. Any expression of doubt regarding one of his results put him in a state of fury. History tells us of his quarrels with poor Flamsteed and we recall his unending polemic against Leibniz, against whom Newton continued to inveigh even after his adversary's death.

Sir Harold Spencer-Jones, a man we cannot suspect of prejudice, has said of Newton: 'He was a bachelor, of retiring disposition, devoid of tact, unskilled in affairs and in the handling of men.'[1] It is difficult to believe that this description is entirely accurate, however, since he was highly successful as master of the Mint and left a pretty fortune to his heirs. As to his awkward character, it was undoubtedly of a purely pathological nature, since for two years Newton suffered from nervous depression bordering on madness.

But what does all this matter? Does its author's unsociable character prevent the law of gravity from being one of the loftiest conquests of human intelligence? And no matter how acrid his relations with his fellow men may have been, does not Newton deserve to be ranked with Einstein as the greatest scientific genius mankind has produced?

[1] *Ciel et Terre*, April-June 1947, p. 80.

For this is our first opportunity of examining a being out of the common run, an unadulterated scientific genius—not a cool, clear, balanced brain like Galileo and Descartes, but a spirit resembling Kepler, fanciful, given to mysticism, fundamentally religious and lit by brilliant flashes of inspiration.

Although Newton showed himself, in optics, an experimenter without peer, although he displayed, in his *Principia*, inflexible logic, although he rejected the use of hypothesis, even the most legitimate—the type of hypothesis whose utility was later demonstrated by Poincaré—it would be wrong to see in him an example of the modern rationalistic scientist. 'Newton was not the first scientist of the age of reason,' writes Lord Keynes. 'He was the last of the magicians, the last of the Babylonians and Sumerians, the last great mind who looked out on the visible and intellectual world with the same eyes as those who began to build our intellectual inheritance rather less than 10,000 years ago.'[1] In short he was a man of highly unusual type, whose three great discoveries were made almost simultaneously, as though at the touch of a wand.

This takes us back to the year 1665, when a great outbreak of the plague compelled Cambridge University to close down. Newton, who had just passed his first degrees there, returned to his father's house at Woolsthorpe.[2] Here—but let us rather quote Newton himself:

'In the beginning of the year 1665 I found the method of approximating series and the Rule for reducing any dignity of any Binomial[3] into such a series. The same year in May I found the method of tangents of Gregory and Slusius, and in November had the direct method of Fluxions,[4] and the next year in January had the Theory of Colours, and in May following I had entrance into the inverse method of Fluxions.[5] And the same year I began to think of gravity extending to the orb of the Moon. . . .'

[1] *Newton Tercentenary Celebrations* (Cambridge University Press, 1947).
[2] 'The house in which he was born is practically unchanged and is still owned by the family to which it was sold in Newton's lifetime.' (P. Doig, *op. cit.*).
[3] Newton's binomial, of course.
[4] Differential calculus.
[5] Integral calculus.

Thus these three months of concentrated meditation had been enough for Newton to evolve the theory of light and infinitesimal calculus and to discover universal gravitation. We can picture this young man of twenty-four roaming the countryside, immersed in thought, observing nature and applying to familiar things an incredibly acute analytical mind. We can imagine him sitting down one moonlit evening to dream beneath an apple-tree.[1] An apple detached itself and fell. Why did it fall? Why did the Moon, up there in the sky, not fall too? His Cambridge professor would have considered this question naïve—how could you compare the Moon to an apple? Was not the latter subject to weight, according to the laws of the fall of bodies and Galilean mechanics? And the former to an unknown force that kept it suspended above the Earth while it obeyed Kepler's laws?

The best proof that these two kinds of mechanics had nothing in common lay in the fact that Galileo's was governed by the principle of inertia, which did not seem to apply to Kepler's at all. Had it applied, the Moon would have travelled away in a straight line, instead of revolving around the Earth. . . .

Why, then, did the Moon not comply with this principle? What force held it to our globe? Was it not weight, whose centripetal action thus counterbalanced the planet's centrifugal tendency?

But was weight, which diminishes in proportion to the distance above the ground, still operative at the distance of the Moon? Newton knew this distance—60 terrestrial radii. At the surface of the Earth, that is to say at the distance of one radius, a falling body travels sixteen feet in the first second of its fall. If, as Newton suspected, the force of weight varies in inverse ratio to the square of the distance, the Moon, at a distance of 60 terrestrial radii ought to 'fall' 60×60 times less fast. That is to say it ought to fall only 0·00444 foot per second. Did the Moon really 'fall' at this rate?

This was easy to verify. The orbit followed by our satellite has a

[1] Newton's apple-tree died in 1814, but grafts had been taken, so that it was possible to plant its shoots in various parts of the world. In 1954, one of them was planted in Newton's Garden at Trinity College, Cambridge.

length of $2\pi \times 60$ terrestrial radii, and as its revolution takes 27 days 7 hours 43 minutes—i.e. 2,360,580 seconds—its speed comes to 0·0001597 of a terrestrial radius per second, and the distance it 'falls' in this time to 0·0000000021 of a terrestrial radius. Did this value agree with the figure of 0·00444 of a foot found above? For this we must know the number of feet in a terrestrial diameter. Now, at this period the value of the terrestrial radius was not yet known with much accuracy. The figure used by Newton was 18,437,000 feet (instead of the true figure of 21,120,000 feet). The true amount the Moon 'fell' in a second was therefore 0·00389 foot, which did not agree at all with the theoretical figure of 0·00444 foot.

When the young Newton found himself with this discrepancy at the end of his calculation he was undismayed. He was quite sure his intuition was correct. But he was less certain of his data, and particularly of the doubtful figure he had taken for the radius of the Earth. There was also a weak point in his reasoning: he had reckoned the distance from the Earth to the Moon from the centre of the Earth. This meant supposing that the force which kept the Moon revolving around our globe was situated at the very centre of the latter; in other words, that the attraction exercised by the Earth upon the Moon was the same as if the whole mass of the terrestrial sphere were concentrated at its centre. How could this be proved? While waiting to find some proof, Newton busied himself with other matters, with optics for example.

Not until sixteen years later, during the course of a meeting of the Royal Society, did he hear of the work executed by a French scientist, Abbé Jean Picard, who, in 1669–70, measured a meridian arc between Paris and Amiens. This measurement, obtained by the stringent method of geodetic triangulation, gave him 57,060 *toises* to one degree, say 3,269,297 *toises* for the radius of the Earth, or 21,250,430 feet. Newton quickly introduced this new figure into his old sum and discovered with profound emotion that it now worked out at his theoretical figure of 0·00444 foot, which, according to him, the Moon must 'fall' every second.

There remained the task of proving that the attraction exercised by a spherical mass is the same as though it were concentrated in the centre. He did not succeed in proving this until 1685, after Halley had been urging him for several months to communicate his discovery to the Royal Society. But to make his work known, to publish it, meant exposing himself to criticism and inviting discussion, something of which Newton had a horror. We must admire the devotion and generosity of Halley, a great-hearted man as well as a great scientist: having overcome his friend's objections he personally financed the printing of Newton's book, because the Royal Society had put all its capital into the publication of a *History of the Fishes*.

Newton's book, entitled *Philosophiae Naturalis Principia Mathematica*, 'Mathematical Principles of Natural Science', was published in July 1687. It has been termed the loftiest production of the human mind. There is no point in speculating on the justice of this assessment or in trying to decide what position Newton occupies in the history of science—in particular, whether he should be placed before or after Einstein. His claim to our admiration is unchallenged. No one has ever disputed the inscription engraved on the statue at Trinity College, Cambridge: 'Who surpassed the human race by the power of his thought' (Lucretius).

This unanimous esteem is explained by the fact that his *Principia* constitutes a veritable key to the universe. Whereas the greatest astronomers—Aristarchus, Hipparchus, Ptolemy, Tycho Brahe, Kepler, Galileo—had merely accumulated data and formulated incomplete theories, Newton constructed a harmonious and logical synthesis. He showed that the mover of the universe was attraction, and from this starting-point he reconsidered and explained all the facts gathered together by observation over a period of two thousand years.

Attempts have been made to find forerunners to the discoverer of this fundamental law, from Anaxagoras, Plato and Aristotle to the Italian Borelli, the Frenchman Boulliaud and above all Hooke. It is true that the idea of an attraction varying in inverse ratio to the square of the distance had been 'in the air' ever since Kepler. But a gulf separates intuition from proof, and Newton stood in about the same relation to these pioneers as the engineer who realizes a project stands to the layman who puts forward an idea in the well-known form 'all you have to do is so and so'.

In his book, the author of the *Principia* began by creating mechanics, or, more accurately, dynamics. He based it on three axioms: the law of inertia, already propounded by Galileo; the law that the rate of change of the momentum of a body measures in direction and magnitude the force acting upon it, generalized as $F = mg$ and also adumbrated by the great Florentine; and, finally, the law that to every action there is an equal and opposite reaction.

Applying Kepler's laws in the light of these three principles, Newton arrived at the law of universal attraction. He showed that the force which kept the Moon revolving round the Earth and the planets round the Sun was none other than gravity, that is to say an attraction proportional to mass and to the inverse of the square of the distance. Under the action of this force, a material point necessarily describes a *conic* (ellipse, parabola or hyperbola). Armed with this law of gravitation, Newton cast increasingly bright light on the most controversial problems, illuminating the abysses before which human intelligence had previously recoiled in terror.

The satellites of Jupiter and Saturn docilely obeyed the Newtonian principle; the rapid rotation of the Jovian globe accounted for its flattening, so clearly visible through the telescope; that the Earth was likewise flattened then appeared as a deduction from the laws of the pendulum; and in the Earth's equatorial ridge, upon which the Moon exercises a particular attraction, Newton discerned the cause of the precession of the equinoxes, which had been known but remained unexplained for 1,800 years. By means of the gravitational pull of the planets on their satellites and of the Sun on the planets, it became possible to calculate the mass of these heavenly bodies and so trace to their source the inequalities in the motion of the Moon. Even comets, whose behaviour had formerly seemed so erratic, were now seen to be governed by the strict rule of universal attraction. The comet of 1680 arrived just in time for Newton to try his power over it. He determined its parabolic orbit and showed that such objects could no more escape from the inflexible laws of the skies than the planets or any other heavenly body. He also cast light on every single aspect of the tides. He found their cause in the attraction of the Moon and, partially, of the Sun, upon the section of the ocean closest to our satellite. He even succeeded in calculating the Moon's mass by studying spring tides and neap tides.

In short, reading the *Principia* was rather like seeing the solar system, hitherto a dark agglomeration of undisciplined bodies round which blew the eerie winds of astrology, suddenly lit up, the planets bending to inviolable laws and the mystery vanishing like an insubstantial shadow before the irresistible advance of scientific knowledge.

The heavenly bodies subject to scientific law

From a distance of nearly three hundred years and living in an age when wonders of science surround us on every side, it is difficult for us to appreciate the resolution with which Newton must have dedicated his faculties to the task of erecting, storey by storey, his brilliant synthesis. His aim was to make an ordered universe, governed by a single law, out of what had been a chaos of unproductive observations and bewildering theories. He achieved it by means of perpetual concentration, his mind soaring, as it were, above his body and forcing him to ignore the most ordinary needs of everyday life. After rising in the morning, he was liable to sit for hours motionless on the edge of his bed sunk in contemplation. One day a friend of the family, Dr. William Stukeley, came to dinner. On a table a chicken awaited the beginning of the meal. Newton was nowhere to be seen. Tired of waiting and ravenously hungry, Stukeley succumbed to temptation and ate the chicken. When his host finally appeared and sat down in front of the dish, on which there was nothing left but the bones, he declared with only a hint of surprise: 'Well, well, I thought I hadn't dined, but I see I was wrong!'

Publication of the *Principia* was the zenith of this exceptional career. In 1704 he published a volume on *Optics*, but after 1687 he was already one of the glories of Britain, a celebrity who was visited with respect and curiosity and whom the King had rewarded with the post of master of the Mint. Physically, he is described by Fontenelle as 'a man of medium height, somewhat stout during his latter years, with extremely lively and piercing eyes and a face that was both pleasant and venerable, especially when he removed his wig and revealed his pure white, thick and bushy hair. He never used spectacles and lost only one tooth during the whole of his life.'

He died on 20 March, 1727, and received the highest posthumous honours. 'The pall-bearers were the Lord Chancellor,' writes Fontenelle, 'the Dukes of Montrose and Roxborough, and the Earls of Pembroke, Sussex and Macclesfield.' Westminster Abbey, the sepulchre of the heroes of English history, was the last resting-place of the man who wrote: 'I do not know what I may appear to the world, but to myself I seem to have been only like a boy, playing on the sea-shore, and diverting myself, in now and then finding a smoother pebble or a prettier shell than ordinary, whilst the great ocean of truth lay all undiscovered before me.'

The diffusion of Newton's theories through the scientific world covered a period corresponding to the reign of James II in England and Louis XIV in France. On both sides of the Channel could be seen preludes to the coming industrial revolution—increase in manu-factured goods, development of hydraulic power, expansion of trade, and strenuous commercial competition that quickly degenerated into open warfare between the two most important powers in the world.

It was naturally in Britain that the *Principia* had their initial impact, first in Edinburgh, then in Cambridge. The first edition, written in Latin, was out of print by 1691. Two more were printed between then and 1726, when the first English translation was issued. The Continent was much more difficult to conquer. It took its line from France, where Cartesianism reigned simultaneously with the Sun King. Fontenelle, Cassini, Réaumur, Huygens and Leibniz were horrified that anyone should dare to substitute for the rationalistic system of Descartes, who subjected even living beings to the mechan-istic yoke, the Newtonian hypothesis of attraction, which they held—through a mental aberration that now seems to us astonishing—to be an occult and unscientific affair. Maupertuis wrote in 1731: 'It took more than half a century to win the academies over to the theory of attraction. It remained shut up within its island, or, if it did cross the sea, it was looked upon as merely the creation of a monster that had only recently been proscribed. People so congratulated themselves on having banished occult qualities from philosophy, they were so afraid that they might find their way in again, that anything which was believed to bear the slightest resemblance to them struck terror.'

Two years later Voltaire gave a witty description of the difference of outlook between the British Isles and the Continent:

'A Frenchman arriving in London finds things very much changed, in philosophy as in everything else. He has left the world full, he finds it empty. In Paris we see the universe as composed of vortices of tenuous matter; in London they see none of that. With us, it is the pressure of the Moon that causes the flow of the sea; among the English, it is the sea which gravitates towards the Moon, so that when you believe the Moon ought to give us high tide, these gentlemen believe there ought to be low tide.... You will note, too, that the Sun, which in France has nothing to do with the matter, here contributes a quarter of the effect. ... Among your Cartesians, everything is the result of a repulsion which is scarcely understood; with Mr. Newton it springs from an attraction, the cause of which is no better known. In Paris, you picture the Earth as shaped like a melon; in London, it is flat on two sides. Light, to a Cartesian, exists in the air; to a Newtonian, it comes from the Sun in six and a half minutes. Your chemistry operates entirely with acids, alkalis and tenuous matter: in Britain, even chemistry is dominated by the theory of attraction.'[1]

But we know how the fiery polemicist took advantage of this opportunity to 'shake accepted ideas', as M. Cox puts it, and give the advocates of outworn traditions another piece of his mind. The most curious fact is that Voltaire's initiation in the Newtonian doctrine and its propagation were the work, before Maupertuis, of a woman, the Marquise Gabrielle-Emilie du Châtelet (1706–49). With her knowledge of Latin, Italian, English, Spanish and Flemish, and especially of mathematics, she was certainly of a very different stamp from the blue-stockings so cruelly castigated by Molière two-thirds of a century earlier.

We need not be too surprised to see a woman, whose position in the world might have brought her less austere successes, devoting herself to what is generally thought to be a rather forbidding science.

[1] Quoted by J. F. Cox, 'Hommage à la marquise du Châtelet', in *Ciel et Terre*, January-February 1950.

We must recall that it was good form for 'persons of quality' to discuss scientific discoveries. Remember that Fontenelle chose a marquise to act as his interlocutor in his *Entretiens sur la Pluralité des Mondes* (1686). Moreover, even without going as far back as the unfortunate Hypatia of Alexandria, Voltaire's seductive friend had predecessors—the wife of Regiomontanus, who acted as his assistant, the Duchess of Ferrara, Renée of France (1510–75), Sophie Brahe (1556–1643), who collaborated with her illustrious brother, the learned German woman Maria Cunitz (1610–64), the author of astronomical tables that were easier to use than Kepler's, and a certain Jeanne Dumée, a manuscript by whom on Copernicus's theory is said to be housed in the French National Library, Paris.

Though retarded by the obstinacy of the Cartesians, Newton's triumph was all the greater when it came. And it was France that staged its grand finale, thanks to the most brilliant constellation of mathematicians the world has ever seen, from Clairaut to Laplace. It was France that turned the solar system into a battlefield upon which science has gained splendid victories.

5

Navigators call for an inventory of the heavens

Huygens and his fantastic telescopes—Science gains prestige
under Louis XIV—Cassini, man of the world and creator of
physical astronomy—Roemer subjects light to mensuration—
Death of Cassini, eclipse of physical astronomy—The founding of
positional astronomy—Huygens, the father of precision horology
—The first inventory of the stars—Bradley establishes the position
of the stars—Resumption of planetary exploration—The Moon,
the first step in surveying the planets—Cassini stretches the
surveyor's chain from the Earth to the Sun—The transit of Venus:
adventures and misadventures

ON the evening of 15 July, 1655, three young men alighted in
Paris from the Rouen coach and took lodgings at the Ville-de-
Brissac, an inn situated at the corner of the Faubourg Saint-Germain
and the Rue de Seine. They were three foreigners, Dutchmen of good
family, who were making that pilgrimage into French society which
was then essential to a first-class education.

King Louis XIV was beginning his reign, under the guardianship
of Mazarin. In the eyes of the world, France was a bright and rising
star. A reflection of her glory fell upon Holland, who had given hos-
pitality to so many French thinkers, among them, for twenty years,
Descartes. We may imagine the avidity with which the three tourists
rushed to the sources of this brilliant civilization as they were introduced into the salons and literary and artistic circles by their country's
diplomats.

One of these young men was called Christiaan Huygens. He was
born on 14 April, 1629, the son of a highly-placed figure in the suite
of the Prince of Orange. Huygens Senior had encouraged Rembrandt
at the outset of his career, corresponded with Mersenne, read Descartes's *Dioptrique* in manuscript and lent the support of his authority

to the performance of Corneille's *Menteur*. Christiaan himself, like his brothers, had moved among the most distinguished minds at The Hague and Leyden and played an energetic part in the victory of Cartesianism. In addition, he showed such an astonishing gift for mathematics that the illustrious author of the *Discours de la Méthode* did not disdain to converse with him and suggest problems for his solution. Mersenne had already dubbed him 'Archimedes Batavus'.

While his two companions plunged into the whirl of Parisian social life and sought the society of courtiers and wits, aiming only to improve their art of conversation and extend their social contacts, Christiaan set about making the acquaintance of poets and artists, men like Scarron and Chapelain. The latter was not only the unfortunate author of a *Pucelle* that had been outrageously hissed, but also a man who was very well informed in scientific matters and whose pleasure it was to play the intermediary between scientists and those in power. Now, Christiaan Huygens had been favourably spoken of in scientific circles even before his arrival in France. On the preceding 25 March he had discovered a satellite of the planet Saturn[1] with the aid of a telescope he had made himself. This discovery caused a considerable stir among men of science, and when introduced by Chapelain the young astronomer was enthusiastically received by Gassendi, Boulliaud, Roberval and other celebrities of the period.

Nowadays we find it hard to imagine science being such an easy matter and a scientific reputation so quickly established. At the present time no one can claim to have discovered anything new in a particular field of study until he has mastered the whole contents of that field— and this is a great deal vaster than in Huygens's day. Moreover, apart from certain purely abstract studies, such as relativity and wave mechanics, research on any scale calls for a great deal of experimental equipment. Consequently, though there is no comparison between the Mount Palomar reflector and the tube with two lenses by means of which Huygens discerned Jupiter's satellite, we may be sure that the discovery made with this insignificant instrument created more stir than anything yet achieved by Hale's colossus.

[1] The one we now call *Titan*.

The Mount Palomar mirror is 16 feet across; the young Dutch-man's object-glass was 4 inches at most. The fact that he ground it himself shows that at this period every amateur astronomer was more or less an instrument-maker as well. After the monopoly claimed by Galileo, which lasted till his death, instrument-makers multiplied, especially in Italy and France. Unfortunately this increase in quantity was not followed by an improvement in quality.

By the middle of the century there was still no means of over-coming the two great faults that vitiate the use of simple lenses, *chromatic aberration* and *spherical aberration*. The first arises from the fact that the lens acts somewhat like a prism and breaks up the white light —hence the iridescence round the edge of the image. As a result of the second, only the light rays that pass through the lens close to the centre converge at the focus, so that to obtain a clear image the rest have to be cut out by stopping down the lens. Descartes proposed a means of overcoming this aberration, but it seems from this letter written by Chapelain to Huygens that he never succeeded in passing from theory to practice:

'At one time M. Descartes promised to make lenses of such perfection that with their aid it would be possible to examine the disc of the Moon and see whether it was inhabited and what shape the animals were if any existed. . . .'

His young correspondent amply justified the French poet's hopes, but it must be recognized that in the meantime, despite the primitive nature of their instruments, a number of scientists continued with honour along the trail blazed by Galileo.

As was natural, since it is the closest luminary and the one that exhibits the most details, their attention was particularly drawn to the Moon. The Frenchman Claude Mellan in 1636, Scheiner and Rheita in 1645, and the Belgian Langrenus (1600–75) at around the same time published maps of the Moon that owed less and less to imagination. Then a complete *Selenographia* appeared under the signature of Riccioli and with the collaboration of another Jesuit, Grimaldi. Their nomenclature, which gave the names of scientists to the features of lunar topography and distinguished 'seas', mountains, valleys and craters, won acceptance all over the Continent after 1651. It is still in use.

Without a doubt, however, the best lunar map was that drawn in 1647 by a Danzig amateur called Johannes Höwelke, or Hevelius (1611–87). The son of a wealthy brewer, this amateur had plenty of leisure and an excellent observatory in which to pursue his favourite occupation. The observatory consisted of a group of small towers with revolving roofs built on top of his house. He equipped his observatory with a quadrant, a sextant and telescopes, the largest of which was 16 feet long, while the lower storey housed a printing press destined to spread the master's discoveries. The description of the Moon that emerged from this model establishment was very much superior to all earlier studies. Its accuracy was such that it was even possible to demonstrate and calculate the phenomenon of *libration*, which makes our satellite appear periodically to tilt slightly on its axis.

Hevelius's book in the library of the Paris Observatory, *Machina Coelestis*, a magnificent folio volume embellished with engraved plates, shows the care with which this astronomer conducted his investigations. But let us be under no illusions: his lenses were rudimentary, and he was probably aware of the fact, since in drawing up a catalogue of the stars he observed solely with the naked eye, using sighted alidades. No wonder, then, that when Huygens joined the ranks of the explorers of the firmament he asked himself whether it would not be possible to employ more powerful instruments— Hevelius's magnified thirty or forty times—and to eliminate the aberrations that diminished their efficiency still further.

The only way to reduce the two aberrations was to construct lenses that were less curved. This meant lengthening the focal distance: as may easily be verified with the aid of a simple pair of field-glasses, the less convex a lens is, the farther away lies its focus. Around 1650, therefore, Huygens, aided by his brother Constantijn, began to grind for himself lenses with a very long focus.

Some of the 150 object-glasses produced by the two brothers during their lifetime and signed either by Christiaan or, more often, by Constantijn, are still preserved at Leyden, Utrecht, Brussels and

London. The first, the one with whose aid Christiaan discovered the
satellite of Saturn, had a focal distance of 12 feet; the second of 21 feet.
As results were achieved, ambitions grew. There sprang from the
hands of the two clever opticians lenses with a focus of 40, 50, 62 feet.
The latter, which measures 5·8 inches in diameter is one of the trea-

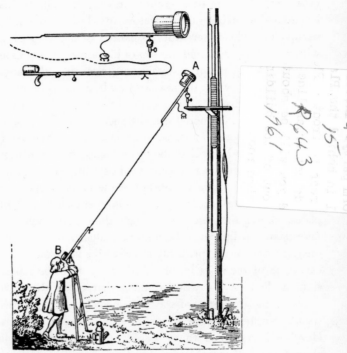

Fig. 6 HUYGENS'S GREAT REFRACTING TELESCOPES
The object-glass A and the eye-piece B were attached by a cord, so that as
long as this cord was taut the two lenses were exactly opposite one another
(after H. Michel, *Ciel et Terre*, 1946, p. 125).

sures of the Brussels Observatory at Uccle. It bears the date 15 March,
1685–6, and Constantijn's signature engraved with a diamond.

Naturally, it was not possible to hold such instruments in the hand
as Galileo used to do, even if they were supported on a window-sill or
a tripod. Observers adopted the course of suspending them by a cord

running on a fixed pulley at the top of a pole. In this way the astronomer could train them in any direction. When the focal distance was too
great, the tube had to be dispensed with. The telescope then consisted of a simple rod bearing at one end the objective and at the other
the eye-piece. One drawback to this system was the considerable
resistance the apparatus offered to the wind. Therefore, when the
Huygens increased the focal distance still farther, they were obliged
to invent a new method of construction.

The focus was now 80, 100 or 150 feet. The Royal Society possesses
a lens signed by Constantijn measuring 9.4 inches in diameter and
having a focal distance of 224 feet! Christian hit upon the idea which
enabled lenses of this size to be used in 1683, and expounded it in detail
the following year. It may be seen in Fig. 6. The object-glass, in its
tube, is attached to the end of a metal rod carried by a shelf that can be
raised or lowered along the pole. The observer holds the eye-piece
in his hand. This eye-piece is also fixed to a metal rod, which is
joined to the objective rod by a wire. It is only necessary to pull the
wire taut to bring the optical axes of the object-glass and the eye-piece
into line with one another. However great the operator's skill, experience and perseverance, only a man possessed by the sacred fire could
have undertaken serious observations with such a contraption.

It was with a more modest object-glass, of only 21 feet, that
Huygens made in 1655, immediately on his return from France, his
resounding discovery of the rings of Saturn. Up to that time the
curious appearance of this planet had defied explanation—we may
remember the agony of mind it caused Galileo. Apparently it still
seemed dangerous to reveal the existence of these rings even in 1656,
since Huygens veiled his disclosure in an anagram. It was not until
three years later that he provided the key and so enabled everyone
to admire the splendid planet in full knowledge of the facts.

Science gains prestige under Louis XIV

This discovery was widely talked of in the Paris salons, especially
those where scientific discussions were the order of the day. Chief
amongst these was Habert de Montfort's, frequented by the astrono-

mer Auzout, the geometer Desargues, the physicist Rohault and the physician Pecquet, all of them convinced Cartesians. Other circles were concerned particularly with experimental science; among these were Auzout's, notable members of which were the mathematician Frénicle, Guerderville, the Master of Petitions, and Abbé Charles; and Rohault's, the finest ornaments of which were Mme de Guerderville and Mme de Bonnevaux, who herself presided over a 'scientific' salon. Thanks to these coteries, which, we must not forget, gave a lead to Europe, science spread and became fashionable. Great lords, dukes, ambassadors were not afraid to take a hand in the work themselves, to put together a telescope or carry out experiments on the pendulum or 'the force of rarified water in pipes'.

Science was no longer a puny offshoot of scholasticism and theology, a pastime for unoccupied noblemen, retired magistrates and scholars who did not take the matter too seriously. It began to appear as an independent social force. It won respect by its ability to humble powers hitherto believed invincible—such as the Church in the case of Galileo—and to stimulate ideological movements capable of convulsing a kingdom—like the so-called 'freethought' movement, Cartesianism and seventeenth-century 'pre-scientism', which led to the 'age of enlightenment'.

Public authorities could no longer ignore an activity that conferred upon scientists such incontestable prestige. It was not by reason of birth, fortune or display that Descartes and Newton aroused the enthusiasm and admiration of everyone who mattered. And it was significant that a young foreigner thrilled the whole élite of Paris by his discovery of a satellite and ring to the planet Saturn. In 1702, that fine and profound mind, Fontenelle, affirmed the pre-eminence of science and proclaimed the superiority of the scientist over the statesman and his faith in a future society governed by knowledge.

Colbert, appointed general superintendent of finances after Mazarin's death and interpreter of the wishes of Louis XIV, was the first statesman officially to recognize this new social power and to translate such recognition into action. Remember the pensions granted to men of science and letters in accordance with a list supplied by Chapelain; the founding of the *Journal des Savants* (1665), the first scientific review in the world; the creation of the Académie des Sciences (1666), and the great minister's eagerness to attract to France the outstanding specialists from neighbouring countries.

Huygens was one of the first to benefit from this rise in scientific stock. Colbert and Chapelain were looking for 'persons of eminent quality, geniuses suited to carrying out an experiment and having sufficient clarity of mind to appreciate its results'. This shows how removed the new outlook was from the esoteric vaticinations of the philosophers and how closely such realistic and unmetaphysical thinkers as Huygens corresponded to the new definition of a scientist.

We shall return later to the highly important work done by Huygens during his stay in Paris from 1666 to 1681. Optics had ceased to interest him and he left his brother Constantijn to go on grinding object-glasses of exaggerated focal distance. Observational astronomy no longer concerned him either. He wrote in 1673: 'M. Cassini was the first to note Saturn's two new companions, after we had the telescopes from Rome. For over a year he has lodged at the Observatory and never allows a clear night to pass without contemplating the Sky; to which I have no wish to subject myself, resting content with my former discoveries, which are worth all those that have been made since.'[1]

Cassini, man of the world and creator of physical astronomy

Around the three orbs of the first magnitude that illumined Europe at the end of the seventeenth century gravitated a quantity of stars, men like Boyle, Wallis, the Bernoullis, Hevelius and Cassini. Though he did not succeed in drawing to Paris either Newton or Leibniz, as he had done Huygens, when he attracted Cassini Colbert brought off a master-stroke that proved more profitable than at first seemed likely.

In 1668, after Huygens had already come to Paris, the reputation of the Italian astronomer Giovanni Domenico Cassini began to spread across the Alps. He was professor of astronomy at the University of Bologna, an illustrious centre of learning at which Copernicus had studied a hundred and fifty years earlier. He was born on

[1] Quoted by E. Doublet, *Histoire de l'Astronomie* (Doin, 1922).

8 June, 1625, at Perinaldo, a village on the Gulf of Genoa, was appointed to his chair at Bologna at the age of twenty-five and immediately embarked upon a series of important studies.

Continuing the observations initiated by his compatriot Fontana in 1636, he took a particular interest in the planets. He discerned spots on the disc of Mars, saw them move slowly from east to west and deduced from this that Mars turns on its axis in the same way as the Earth. He estimated the period of this rotation at 24 hours 40 minutes—a very accurate calculation, bearing in mind that the precise figure is 24 hours 37 minutes 23 seconds, and that Cassini's primitive telescope cannot have given him an image much larger than a shilling seen from a distance of forty yards.

On Jupiter, Cassini had perceived the large red spot that so intrigues astronomers today. Seeing it disappear at the western edge and reappear some hours afterwards on the eastern, he assessed the period of rotation at 9 hours 56 minutes. He also observed tiny dark spots moving across Jupiter from time to time, and an effort of imagination suggested to him that these must be the shadows of the satellites as they passed in front of their planet. Perhaps it was these curious phenomena that gave him the idea of drawing up tables predicting the times of the eclipse of these satellites. In any case, it was these tables (published in 1688) that set the seal on his fame and induced Louis XIV, at the suggestion of Colbert, to invite him to come and work in France.

We have mentioned earlier the stifling conditions surrounding intellectual activity in Italy and, by contrast, the irresistible upsurge it was enjoying in France. In 1659 Cassini dedicated to the Pope a planisphere on which the planets were to be seen revolving around the Earth. Was this great scientist really a geocentrist? This is scarcely credible and we can only suppose that prudence alone compelled him to adopt an anti-Copernican position. The diplomatic adroitness astronomers had to exercise in this hornets' nest is evident from the simple fact that all Cassini's precautions did not save him from seeing the *imprimatur* refused to a new work of his in 1661. When he received Louis XIV's offer, therefore, he was no doubt very willing to throw off a yoke that had become unbearable. There can be no better testimony to the relative liberalism prevailing in France than the fact that the 'First Evening' of Fontanelle's *Entretiens* bore the unequivocal title, 'The Earth is a planet that revolves upon itself and around the Sun.'

Historical anecdote tells us of the Italian scientist's arrival in Paris, on 4 April, 1669, and his reception by the King. It shows him in the high position created for him, a prince of science living like a prince by birth, on familiar terms with the greatest figures at court, quickly naturalized French, marrying a Frenchwoman and founding his line of descendants at the château of Thury, near Clermont, Oise. A now famous print shows him conducting the sovereign and his suite round the Observatory—lace cannions, plumed hats, flowing wigs, canes, rustling embroideries and gold-braid amidst the odd assortment of instruments that constituted the equipment of an observatory in those days.

Such anecdotes must not, however, blind us to the important historical facts, just as drawings showing M. de Cassini in society ought not to eclipse those which originated from his own hand, on clear nights, when he spent tranquil hours observing heavenly bodies. For Cassini was a great deal more than a man of the world, and if he wasted much of his days in the salons, his nights were spent in the Observatory garden with his eye glued to the ocular of one of the giant telescopes perfected by Huygens.

One expert in the subject, Eugène Antoniadi, holds the view that as an observer Cassini was infallible. 'His eye must have been free from astigmatism, his retina must have possessed an extreme sensitivity. He bears comparison with Herschel.' He might even have achieved results equal to those obtained by the British-naturalized Hanoverian a century later, if he had possessed equally efficient instruments.

In Cassini's day the leading manufacturers of object-glasses were the Italians Giuseppe Campani and Eustachio di Divini, and the Frenchmen Pierre Borel and Le Bas. A glass case in the museum of the Paris Observatory houses an objective ground by the former having a diameter of 5.4 inches and a focal length of 35 feet. With an eye-piece of 3 inches focus it gave a magnification of 120 to 140 times. This was an ordinary means of observation, but Cassini owned more powerful ones. His great 70-foot telescope consisted of a skeleton tube triangular in section—like three ladders joined side by side—suspended by cords from a pole.

This system was satisfactory as long as object-glasses under 100 feet long were employed, but when the tubeless telescopes introduced by Huygens became current some other method had to be devised. A wooden tower 118 feet high was brought to the Observatory, set on a base of masonry and fitted with a balcony, a staircase and a hoist. An object-glass was placed at its summit, while the observer stood down below with the eye-piece in his hand. The transport and construction of this tower took three years, from 1685 to 1688, and cost 10,000 *livres* (about £40,000 in modern currency). The objective itself cost around 1,000 *livres*—approximately £4,000. Its focus was something like 150 feet, it had a useful diameter of just under 9 inches and magnified some 600 times. It is, however, doubtful whether Cassini can have made frequent use of such magnification, which would have called for an atmosphere clearer than is usual at Paris.

Cassini entered the Observatory on 14 September, 1671, and in less than two months he had achieved his first feat and so confirmed his reputation. On 25 October he discovered a second satellite of Saturn (Iapetus). He even detected the periodical variations in brightness, which led him to suppose that this satellite might be condemned always to present the same face to its planet, as the Moon does with regard to the Earth. A year later, on 23 December, 1672, a third satellite emerged from the darkness (Rhea), then a fourth and fifth both at the same time (Tethys and Dione) on 21 March, 1684. Between-whiles, in 1675, he spotted the fact that Saturn's ring is really double, being divided into a dim and a bright ring by a dark band subsequently christened *Cassini's division*.

As discoveries seemed to come from his telescope as though by magic, it is easy to understand that Cassini was looked upon by his contemporaries almost as a wizard and even, by certain jealous spirits, as a charlatan. Nowadays he appears to us as no more and no less than the creator of physical astronomy. After positional astronomy, which astronomers had cultivated until the invention of the telescope—

too often for astrological purposes—after the first discoveries of Galileo, Cassini introduced the era of the physical study of the heavenly bodies. Up to that time the planets had been no more than slowly moving points of light, and the whole science of astronomy consisted in predicting their movements with the greatest possible accuracy. As seen by Cassini every point of light became a world, a globe that might resemble the Earth, rotating like the Earth about its own axis and presenting topographical features that might be continents and seas. In this way astronomy was transformed; from being an arid system of trigonometrical formulae accessible only to mathematicians, it was transmuted into a kind of 'geography' of the heavens, with all the horizons this conception offers to the imagination. We know the skill with which Fontenelle utilized these open horizons, how he led the lovely Marquise de la Mésangère to dream about the lands of the sky, their topography and their problematical inhabitants, and the way he popularized Cassini's investigations by his descriptions.

The sweep of the great Italo-French astronomer's labours is attested by their diversity. It was the same man who, after studying the surface of the planets and making an inventory of the lunar features, calculated the parallax of the Sun and initiated the triangulation of France. It was also he who explained as a mass of meteoric dust the pale light that is sometimes seen to rise at sunset on spring evenings among the nascent stars, the existence of which had already been recorded in 1601 by the English priest Childrey[1]—the *zodiacal light*. Finally, it is also to the author of the tables of the satellites of Jupiter that we owe indirectly that prodigious conquest, the measurement of the speed of light.

Roemer subjects light to mensuration

A visitor to the Paris Observatory around 1673 would have seen in the wake of famous astronomers like Cassini, Auzout and Huygens, a

[1] And possibly also by Shakespeare, declares P. Doig, basing his opinion on these two lines from *Romeo and Juliet*:

'Yon light is not daylight, I know it, I:
It is some meteor that the sun exhales . . .'
(Act III, Scene v.)

young man under thirty, tall and pale, who seemed particularly attached to Abbé Picard. He was a young mathematician whom this venerable scientist had brought back to Paris after a trip abroad, a Dane named Olaus Roemer, whom he lodged in his own apartment in the Observatory.

Born at Aarhus, near Copenhagen, on 25 September, 1644, at the age of twenty-eight Roemer had been adopted by Colbert. He was now the Dauphin's private tutor, a member of the Académie des Sciences and in receipt of a pension that rose in nine years from 1,000 to 4,200 *livres*—roughly from £4,000 to £17,000. Such was the generosity of the Sun King. And Roemer was still busy comparing observations of the satellites of Jupiter with the tables of these satellites drawn up by M. de Cassini in 1668.

It had long been recognized that this system of four satellites constituted an astonishing signalling apparatus. Almost every night it presents a characteristic phenomenon visible from all over one hemisphere simultaneously through the least powerful telescope: a satellite that is eclipsed, or rather that disappears behind the disc of the planet, or perhaps passes in front of another satellite so that the two of them form a single satellite. In short, a whole series of almost instantaneous signals that can be calculated in advance, and therefore serve as a means of telling the time in any part of the hemisphere.

It was no doubt the practical value of these phenomena that induced young Roemer to check the tables by observations—and to detect a serious discrepancy between them. When Jupiter (J in Fig. 7) appeared in opposition—that is to say, when the Earth was in the section E_1 of its orbit—the eclipses took place *earlier* than predicted; when it appeared in conjunction—that is to say, when the Earth was in the section E_2—they took place *later* than predicted. Roemer thought that if the eclipse appeared to occur later for the observer at E_2 than for the observer at E_1 this was because it took longer to become visible at E_2 than at E_1. He attributed the delay to the fact that the image was not propagated instantaneously from J, but that the path of light JE_2 took longer than the path JE_1.

That the speed of light was not infinite was a highly audacious hypothesis. It agreed with the opinion of Empedocles and Francis

Bacon, neither of whom was a very commendable authority, but had against it the majority of scientists and especially the Cartesians. For this reason Roemer presented his view to the Académie in very circumspect terms on 22 November, 1675. He stated that the discrepancy detected arose from the time taken by light to travel the diameter E_1E_2 of the terrestrial orbit. This time being 22 minutes for a distance E_1E_2 estimated at 69,500,000 leagues, it gave a speed of 52,650 leagues per second (about 130,900 miles).

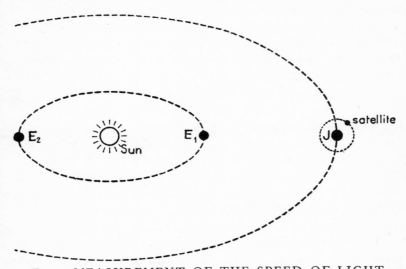

Fig. 7 MEASUREMENT OF THE SPEED OF LIGHT

The image of Jupiter J takes longer to reach the Earth when the latter is at E_2 than when it is at E_1, The difference in time naturally corresponds to the course E_1E_2, which is twice the distance Earth–Sun. It therefore becomes possible to calculate this distance after measuring the time taken by the passage of light.

We need not attach too much importance to the entirely relative accuracy of this latter figure—the 22 minutes are really 16 minutes 32 seconds, and the 130,900 miles, 186,000 miles—the cardinal fact is that a natural element as essential as light was henceforth subject to mensuration, in other words human intelligence was now in a position to cope with it.

Obviously no one at that time could foresee the importance Roemer's work would assume two hundred and thirty years later in the hands of Einstein, but the whole scientific world realized the added support it gave to the scientific conception of the universe. How remote now was the mystical and Aristotelian cosmos of yesterday, steeped in scholasticism and astrology! Galileo's resolutely experimental method, Descartes's stringent rationalism, as they awaited Newton's brilliant synthesis, had swept all irrational ideas from the minds of astronomers. To this offensive Roemer made a contribution whose importance no one underestimated. A fresh section of ancient supersitition collapsed. Astrology had disappeared. In the matter of religion, men of science generally contented themselves with an outward show of conformity, and the majority were either complete atheists, like Huygens, or professed a vague deism.

Death of Cassini, eclipse of physical astronomy

It seems quite legitimate to see the origin of this broad intellectual evolution in Cassini. By creating physical astronomy he showed that the planets were in no way different from the Earth, that their surfaces could be studied by the ordinary methods of geography, and their motions known with the aid of recognized mathematical formulae. He expelled mystery from this region of nature and replaced it by the most realistic visual knowledge. Physical astronomy appeared from the outset a weapon of intellectual emancipation, capable of helping man to free himself from his ancient prejudices and purely intuitive beliefs.

Cassini, the founder of this new science, was a happy and powerful man. He enjoyed considerable prestige with the King and had at his disposal an observatory adapted to his views, giant telescopes and a large staff. He was the head of a family distinguished by its intellect, which worthily prolonged his lineage until the middle of the nineteenth century. He himself, after going blind in 1711, lived to the age of eighty-seven, gossiping with his friends and dictating Latin verses till he departed this life on 14 September, 1712; but he left his son Jacques (p. 193) to maintain the heritage of his great name; the latter entrusted the same mission to one of his children, César-François, known as Cassini de Thury (p. 195), who handed it on to his son Jean-Dominique. The latter preserved the family's intellectual patrimony through the tempestuous days of the Revolution and passed away at the advanced age of ninety-seven, in 1845—four years after the birth of Clemenceau.

To this line of descent we may add that of the Maraldis, represented by Giacomo Filippo, called from Italy by his uncle Giovanni Domenico to work with him in 1687, and Giovanni Domenico, who likewise came to Paris in 1727 to join his uncle Giacomo Filippo. And it might be thought that, supported by such guarantors and kept alive by such a large and powerful family, physical astronomy, Cassini I's claim to fame, would have spread and overrun classical astronomy.

Such was not the case. No sooner was Giovanni Domenico dead than it faded and vanished. No one took the great astronomer's place at the eye-piece of the great telescopes. The observation tower was not demolished till 1753, but it had long since ceased to be used. And the old classical astronomy had long since re-established its former supremacy. Divided circles had ousted the 'terrifyingly long telescopes' again, scientists had lost interest in the surface of the planets and the cartography of the Moon and were once more concerned solely with their motions, as in the days of Tycho Brahe and Kepler, as though Giovanni Domenico Cassini had never existed.

Physical astronomy died out, in spite of its spectacular character and the fantastic panoramas it opened to the imagination; positional astronomy, composed of figures, measurements, formulae, and lacking any attraction to the layman, was resuscitated. How is this double phenomenon to be explained? Simply by the fact that the former had no roots in material existence and served no utilitarian purpose, whereas the second was closely linked to the progress of navigation. Under Louis XIV physical study of the heavenly bodies was no more than a pastime; it did not lead to any form of practical application, nor was it connected with any technique. We must remember, as these pages have repeatedly shown, that scientific progress is made up of a perpetual interchange between pure and applied science, the former providing the means of improving the latter, which in return furnishes the former with more powerful weapons.

Being devoid of any practical significance, physical astronomy was necessarily condemned by the indifference of the public authorities to wilt and wither. Not until the middle of the nineteenth century did new economic conditions restore a certain value to progress in this field and remind people of the useful information to be acquired by star-gazing.

Now the political power of the three countries that counted in Cassini's day, France, Britain and the Netherlands, depended less on force of arms than on economic prosperity. In France manufactures were started or increased, aimed, above all, at producing quality goods for export. The van Robais textile factories, the Tourlaville and Saint-Gobain glassworks, ironworks, iron and coal mines developed, employing hundreds of workmen and encouraged and favoured by official regulations. In Britain large-scale industry had commenced its reign and wealthy capitalists had set about concentrating undertakings. Mines, foundries, breweries and textile factories had invaded social life to the detriment of agriculture. The Netherlands were enriching themselves by their shipbuilding and their wool, cloth and china industries. In all three countries the government realized that economic prosperity depended upon technology. As technology was, in its turn, a superstructure of science, they henceforth paid far more heed to the latter than in the days when it was a mere exercise of the wits.

This development is illustrated by the organization of academies of science. Before Charles II created the Royal Society and Louis XIV the Académie des Sciences many other academies had existed—the Academy of the Secrets of Nature, the Accademia del Cimento and the Accademia dei Lincei in Italy, the Academy of the Curiosities of Nature in Germany, the society directed by Roberval and Etienne Pascal, and Habert de Montmort's salon in France, and so on. In every case, these were private bodies whose members chatted about philosophy and discussed scientific problems for their own delectation. They could not live, because they had no roots in reality and no concern with utilitarian questions. The organizers of the Royal Society and the Académie des Sciences had very different ends in view. There was no question of indulging in abstract debate or purely theoretical speculation. The Paris Académie, for example, was given the thoroughly concrete tasks of drawing a map of France, tracing out roads and canals and keeping a check on the machines used by iron-masters, glassmakers and cloth manufacturers. Colbert's main aim was to ensure the commercial supremacy of France by breaking that of the Netherlands and combating the rising competition from Britain. To this end he mobilized scientists by directing their energies towards technological research. To this end, also, he did everything in his power to bring about a rebirth of the navy and the mercantile marine.

We need not relate here how the great minister produced from nothing, in ten years, an active fleet with its officers and men, its armaments and its dockyards. But it is obvious that, having created this fleet, he had to provide it with the means of navigation, and with better means than those in use elsewhere. Naturally, therefore, Colbert encouraged astronomy—not physical astronomy, which described the 'seas' on the Moon or the spots on Mars, which were of no interest to mariners, but the good old astronomy of the ancients, whose object was to foretell the movements of the Sun, Moon, and planets with increasing accuracy. To Colbert's mind this astronomy, which was essential for taking bearings at sea, was the only useful one.

When, in 1665, while the reorganization of the navy was in full swing, he communicated his wishes to the astronomers, they were much embarrassed. In 1665 Huygens was just beginning his life's work and had not yet settled in Paris, while Cassini was only a humble professor at Bologna. The French astronomers were Picard, Auzout, Richer, Buot, Frénicle. They possessed neither an official nor a private observatory and were content to set up their instruments in gardens or on balconies. To tell the truth, the building of observatories had gone out of fashion long ago. The splendid establishments of Ulugh Beigh and Tycho Brahe were nothing but a memory. Apart from Hevelius's observatory at Danzig, there was only the tower erected at Copenhagen in 1637 by the King of Denmark for Longomontanus, Tycho's former pupil.

The French astronomers therefore replied to Colbert's request by calling for an observatory. Their petition was presented to the King by Adrien Auzout (6122–91). It was immediately agreed to and the observatory was built between 1667 and 1672 to Perrault's design. Cassini, who arrived in France while the work was in progress, suggested certain modifications, and we know the use he made of the finished building.

The Royal Observatory, Greenwich, founded in 1675, came into being for the same reasons. The sea was already the main concern of the British and the determination of longitude a major and as yet unsolved problem. The idea of working out the time by the angular distance from the Moon to the nearest stars had certainly been thought of, but an astronomer had pointed out that this method was rather inaccurate, in view of the fact that the true position of the Moon generally differed by one-third of a degree from that given in the astronomical tables, and that Tycho Brahe's star catalogue, being nearly a century old, no longer answered the needs of the day. All in all, a bearing was unlikely to be less than 300 leagues out.

Naturally this conclusion, set down in a hard-hitting report by Flamsteed, the Astronomer Royal, made a great impression on King Charles II. Busy as he was—principally with hunts and gay parties—he was nevertheless aware of the needs of the realm. He too decided, in 1675, to build an observatory. The site was to be a hilltop at Greenwich; the cost—£520—was to be covered by the sale of a stock of damaged gunpowder. The Royal Warrant for the payment of his salary directed the Astronomer Royal 'forthwith to apply himself with the most exact care and diligence to the rectifying the tables of the motions of the heavens, and the places of the fixed stars, so as to find out the so-much-desired longitude of places for perfecting the art of navigation'.

The building did not bear comparison with its homologue at Paris. It was no more than a simple octagonal tower of two storeys, the lower one serving as a residence for the astronomer and the upper for observations. Moreover, it was exclusively an astronomical observatory, the staff of which was kept to a strict programme of work. The Paris Observatory, on the contrary, was more of a general scientific institute, in which it was possible to carry out physical experiments as well as anatomical dissections and where men of science worked independently without being answerable to any director. The instruments were plentiful and of excellent quality; Colbert personally ordered the best lenses from Campani or Divini; whereas at Greenwich they were conspicuous by their absence. Charles II had appointed a director to take charge of an observatory that had neither staff nor instruments. The Astronomer Royal began his functions in two empty rooms, and when he wished to start the work for which he was being paid—a meagre £100 per annum—he had to obtain instruments at his own expense.

What instruments were available to the astronomers of the day? The most representative work was the star catalogue drawn up by Hevelius in 1661. It comprised some 1,500 objects, whose co-ordinates were certainly much more exact than in Tycho Brahe's catalogue. Nevertheless, and although he possessed refracting telescopes which he had employed in drawing his map of the Moon, Hevelius made his observations exclusively with the naked eye aided by divided circles fitted with sighted alidades.

One day he and Halley, the great English astronomer, who had come to visit him, made an experiment. They both observed the same stars at the same time, Hevelius with his sights, Halley with a telescope. The latter was no little surprised to see that Hevelius's series of observations was no less accurate than his own.

In spite of this meritorious accuracy, the founders of the Paris and Greenwich Observatories were understandably hesitant about following the Danzig astronomer's example. The precision attained by the latter was a unique feat. Instead of viewing with the naked eye through sights, it seemed much more profitable to view through a telescope revolving on the divided circle.

This idea of replacing the alidade by a telescope seems to us self-evident, although it was not adopted until more than half a century after the invention of the latter. The French astrologer Jean-Baptiste Morin suggested it in 1634, but nothing came of his suggestion. It was actually his compatriot Jean Picard who put it into effect and spread its use.

Science owes Picard several debts. It was this priest, a professor at the Collège de France, who brought Roemer to Paris—an event which led to the measurement of the speed of light; it was he who measured the radius of the Earth by triangulation—and so paved the way for the discovery of gravitation by Newton; it was he who initiated the *Connaissance des Temps*, the official French astronomical tables that have been published without interruption since 1678;[1] it was he, finally, who introduced use of the telescope for taking sights in positional astronomy and geodesy. Thus when he undertook in 1669 to measure the meridian arc intercepted between Sourdon, near Amiens, and Malvoisine, south of Paris, he used a quadrant of 3 feet 4 inches radius on which a graduation in transversals[2] enabled him to read the minute of arc. Increased accuracy in sighting was afforded by a telescope bearing a *reticle*, that is to say a network of fine lines in the focal plane of the object-glass, in place of the alidade. With a base line of 5,663 *toises* (a *toise* being a trifle under 6 feet) measured along the road from Villejuif to Juvisy, and a system of thirteen triangles whose apices were marked by fires, Picard found that this arc Sourdon-Malvoisine was 1° 21′ 54″ and measured 78,550 *toises*. This made 57,060 *toises* to one degree, or 370,700 feet, a value slightly higher than the true one, which is 364,605 feet. We know that this approximation did far more than any earlier measurement to help Newton verify his hypothesis of universal gravitation.

His success in the field of geodesy naturally encouraged Picard to apply the same technique to astronomy. As soon as he was installed at the Observatory, in 1673, he fitted his divided circles with telescopes. Then, having adopted the method of calculating the right ascension of stars from the time of their passage across the meridian, he devised an instrument by means of which the instant this passage took place could be exactly registered. This instrument, produced in 1683, was

[1] Similar astronomical tables are, in England, the *Nautical Almanac*, which has appeared since 1766; in Germany, the *Astronomisches Jahrbuch* (since 1774); and in the United States, *The American Ephemeris* (since 1849).

[2] The *vernier*, although invented by Pierre Vernier (1580–1637) in 1631, did not become generally used until around the middle of the eighteenth century.

the *mural sector*, a quadrant of 5 feet radius fastened to the wall of the Observatory's western tower in such a way that the telescope swept over the meridian.

Some years earlier the reticle had been improved to form the *micrometer*. In 1666 Auzout had the ingenious idea of making one of the vertical spider-lines movable. It could be moved with the aid of a very exact screw, so that by framing an orb like the Sun or Moon between this mobile spider-line and a fixed one it was possible to assess its apparent diameter. To be accurate, it seems that a young Englishman named William Gascoigne (1612–44) had already devised a similar instrument, but had kept it secret. The priority of Gascoigne's invention was hotly asserted by his countrymen when Auzout arrived at it independently twenty-six years later and, unlike Gascoigne, immediately made it public property.

In 1690, when Roemer returned to Copenhagen after nine years absence and, in order to obviate the drawbacks of the mural sector, devised the *transit instrument* which swung in the meridian between two fixed pillars, positional astronomy was in possession of all its basic instruments. By 1700 Newton had already supplied the principle of the sextant, which Hadley put into effect in 1730. This ushered in the reign of a whole pleiad of instrument-makers, most of them English, who vied with one another in the art of graduating circles. Chief among them were Graham, Sisson, Cary, Bird, Ramsden and Troughton. Not until 1804 did the Continent produce, in Germany, a worthy rival. Finally, thanks to Huygens, mechanical horology was born.

Huygens, the father of precision horology

Until the approach of the Renaissance the only means of measuring time were procedures that had been in use since antiquity. Sundials were everywhere. The King of France was compelled to remove them from Paris, at the same time as the posts for tying up horses, because they interfered with the traffic.[1] For short spaces of time the sandglass or the candle was employed—the latter practice has been perpetuated in auction sales 'by inch of candle'. Monasteries, on occasion,

[1] Jean Granier, *La Mesure du Temps* (Presses Universitaires, 1943).

employed monks to recite psalms of predetermined length that served as an alarm clock. But the most practical appliance remained the clepsydra. In the most highly perfected model, the water flowing regularly from a reservoir moved a wheel that actuated a needle in front of a dial.

Around the beginning of the fourteenth century it occurred to an unknown craftsman in Lombardy that, instead of having the wheel turned by a flow of water, it would be more convenient to employ a falling weight. To brake and regularize the fall of this weight he devised an oscillating beam whose to and fro movement periodically halted and restarted the descent of the weight. Thus mechanical horology was born.

The oldest extant mechanisms of this type are the relics at Beauvais (prior to 1324) and at Dover (now in the Science Museum, South Kensington, and dating from 1348). They have neither dial nor hand and their sole purpose was to strike the hours. Clocks with dials did not appear until the end of the fourteenth century. One of the earliest examples, constructed under Charles V between 1364 and 1370, may be seen on the Law Courts in Paris.

From this time on, clocks became works of art that were used to embellish cathedrals. The clock at Padua dates from 1344, that at Strasbourg from 1354, those at Frankfort and Lund from 1380, that at Rouen (the Great Clock) from 1389, and so on. Very soon a clock-work figure representing a watchman who struck the hours was added; this was the ancestor of the Jack-o'-the-clock. Then the mechanism was given the task of recording not only the time of day, but the day of the week, the phases of the Moon and the courses of the Sun and planets. Clocks developed into wonderful monuments on which animated statues depicted religious scenes—and which gained or lost as much as an hour a day.

In the middle of the seventeenth century, with the invention of the so-called 'balance-wheel' escapement, which may still be seen in certain old clocks, the daily error dropped to a few minutes. This was all very well for the needs of everyday life, but still fell far short of the requirements of astronomy. Since the weak point in this system was the irregularity in the fall of the weight, a son of Galileo had the idea, in 1649, of assuring the regularity of this fall by the swing of a pendulum. No doubt this idea was 'in the air', for it was taken up again seven years later by young Huygens, then twenty-seven. For this device and for that of the spiral watch-spring, which he published in 1675, Huygens deserves to be called the father of precision horology. It must, however, be added that the true solution to the problem was not found until 1680, when the anchor escapement, adumbrated by Robert Hooke (p. 130), was brought into actual use by the English clockmaker William Clement. Accuracy was thereby increased to a point at which the daily error was reduced to less than one second. This was the case, in particular, with John Harrison's timepieces, which may still be admired in the National Maritime Museum at Greenwich (p. 189).

The first inventory of the stars

Huygens, who retired to his own country after being banned from France by Louvois, passed away on 8 July, 1695. His discoveries in horology, optics and, together with Newton, in mechanics had paved the way for a positional astronomy such as was desired, because of the needs of their navies, by both Louis XIV in France and Charles II in Britain.

We shall not trace here the progress of this nautical astronomy, which lies outside the scope of this book; but we must examine the contribution it made to the conquest of the skies. We must first picture the King of Great Britain and Ireland reading Flamsteed's report on the problem of longitude at sea (p. 160), horror-struck at learning how seriously it was impeding the development of the British navy and deciding that an 'astronomical observator' should be appointed to deal with it. 'Who is this astronomical observator to be?' he was asked. 'The person who drew up the report,' replied the King. Thus Flamsteed was appointed director of Greenwich Observatory.

There was nothing outstanding about either the person or the work of John Flamsteed (1646–1719). This astronomer was neither a great genius like Newton, nor a great nobleman like Cassini, nor a man of pronounced character like Galileo. He was only twenty-nine when Charles II entrusted him with the task that was to make him famous, but he was already the retiring, ailing, pious and conscientious clergyman he remained for the rest of his life. When he started work at the Royal Observatory on 29 October, 1676, this Observatory contained nothing that belonged to the King except the walls. The two clocks and the great sextant were a gift from Sir Jonas Moore; the small quadrant had been lent by the Royal Society and the rest belonged to Flamsteed himself. He later calculated that in thirty-four years he had spent £2,000 on assistants and instruments out of a salary of £100. Not until 1689 was he able to install a good mural circle that enabled him to measure the position of the stars by observations on the meridian.

Flamsteed has been defined as Tycho Brahe plus the telescope. In Tycho's case the probable error of an isolated observation amounted to 1 minute of arc; it was no more than 10 seconds with Flamsteed. This shows how conscientiously he discharged the task which the King had set his astronomer. He laboured at it throughout his forty-four years at the Observatory, gradually amassing the data for a catalogue of 3,000 stars down to the seventh magnitude. This catalogue was published in 1725, six years after its author's death, posthumously edited by his assistant Joseph Crosthwait. The delay was due to Flamsteed's excessive perfectionism, which involved him in quarrels with all his contemporaries and especially with Newton and Halley.

It is surprising to see astronomers, from Hipparchus onward, undertaking this never-ending and monotonous task of cataloguing the stars. The fact is that as each century passed mariners demanded greater and greater precision in taking bearings. That was why astronomers, for ever observing the same stars with increased accuracy, sought again and again to improve on their predecessors' work.

Nor was it enough to give an ever more accurate description of the northern skies. Ships just as frequently sailed the southern seas, and the needs of navigation were no less imperious here. At the moment when Flamsteed set to work, this need struck Edmund Halley (1656–1742). We have already referred to Halley on page 130, and we know that it was he who encouraged Newton to publish his *Principia*. But at the period we are speaking of (1676, eleven years before the

Principia) he was only a young man who, thanks to the fortune of his father, a wealthy soap manufacturer, had the means to indulge his taste for astronomy. This young man of twenty was bold enough to put before Charles II his plan for a catalogue of the southern skies. The sovereign received him graciously and provided him with the necessary funds. Halley embarked for St. Helena in November 1676.

He remained there almost two years and on his return published a catalogue of 341 southern stars. This was not a very impressive number, and Halley was not an observer of Flamsteed's calibre. Nevertheless, this work placed his feet on the ladder. On his return he was dubbed the 'Southern Tycho', and elected to the Royal Society; in 1720 he succeeded Flamsteed as Astronomer Royal. Yet it was not until 1763 that navigators came into possession of a description of the southern firmament comparable to those of the northern firmament. This was the posthumous work of a French astronomer named La Caille, and it comprised some 10,000 stars.

Nicolas La Caille (1713–62) may be regarded as the prototype of those scientists who, being as modest as they are hard-working, do not attach their name to any sensational discovery and yet build by their patient and unnoticed labours an unshakable foundation for the discoveries of tomorrow.

La Caille entered the field of astronomy in 1736, at the age of twenty-three, when he was introduced to Cassini. King Louis XV was on the throne of France, Flamsteed had been dead for seventeen years, Newton for nine, and Halley, aged eighty, was director of Greenwich Observatory. La Caille, like Flamsteed, was a modest and conscientious little priest, but unlike his English colleague he enjoyed robust health equal to every trial. These traits of character are illustrated by two anecdotes, one of which depicts him returning from his expedition to the southern hemisphere and giving back to the Treasury the sum of 855 *livres* 15 *sous* which he had saved out of the 10,000 *livres* allocated to him; the other represents him falling off his horse in the Pyrenees, rolling into a torrent, changing his clothes and immediately starting work on his observations.

We shall read later (p. 174) what great aims La Caille set himself when he embarked at Lorient, on 20 November, 1750, for the Cape of

Good Hope. In those days such a voyage was no small enterprise. It took him no less than five months, following a detour via Rio de Janeiro. The scientist got down to work the moment he landed. One hundred and twenty-seven nights were sufficient for him to observe the co-ordinates of 9,766 stars down to the seventh magnitude. Thanks to him, the southern sky ceased to be a jumble of unorganized stars. It was arranged in constellations, and La Caille displayed the full measure of his methodical and down-to-earth mind by giving them names like *The Compasses*, *The Pneumatic Machine* and *The Chemical Furnace*—very different titles from such poetic appellations as *The Lyre* (given by Eudoxus), *The Little Horse* (Hipparchus) or *Berenice's Tresses* (Tycho Brahe).

Bradley establishes the positions of the stars

Two men may be regarded as the originators of our modern knowledge of the starry sky: Flamsteed in regard to the northern hemisphere and La Caille in respect of the southern hemisphere. Thanks to them, a regular inventory of the stellar universe was drawn up. All the visible stars were catalogued and their co-ordinates established to within about ten seconds. It may reasonably be assumed that such a level of accuracy—an angle of ten inches is equal to the thickness of a hair seen from a distance of two yards—satisfied the wishes of mariners: it was more than they required for taking bearings. We might have thought it would also be sufficient for astronomers, who are more exacting in this connexion. In point of fact, however, several of the latter noted changes in the position of certain stars. Abbé Picard, for example, observed that the polar star shifted twenty seconds to either side of its mean position in the course of the year. Hooke and Flamsteed had spotted similar cases. Was this the effect of atmospheric refraction? If so, a star at the zenith ought not to be affected, since its light passes through the atmosphere perpendicularly. To settle the matter, a London amateur astronomer, Samuel Molyneux (1689–1728), decided in 1725 to follow the star γ Draconis, which passes at the zenith of London. He was no little surprised to find that it moved forty seconds in the course of the year, as though it traversed a small ellipse centred on its mean position. He undoubtedly confided his perplexity to his friend Bradley, for the latter henceforth dedicated himself to this problem and further observations relating to it.

The Rev. James Bradley (1693–1762) occupied the Savilian chair of astronomy at Oxford. His first idea was that the curious annual shift of γ Draconis was an effect of parallax reproducing the annual orbital movement of the Earth—just as, if we move our head to and fro as we look out of the window at a distant house, the house seems to move to and fro in the opposite direction. But in the case of the stars, this explanation was untenable, since the maximum movements to north and south, instead of occurring in June and December as expected, took place in September and March.

The key to the mystery fell into Bradley's hands one day in September 1728, while he was sailing on the Thames. He noticed that every time the boat tacked the burgee at the masthead changed direction, as the movement of the boat combined with that of the wind. It immediately struck him that the light, as it fell from the stars, must combine its speed with that of the Earth in its orbit, just as vertical rain forms slanting streaks on the windows of a moving car. The 'light-rain' from a star must also appear slanting, so that the image carried by it must change place in proportion as the Earth itself moves along its orbit. Bradley had thus discovered the *aberration of light*, without knowledge of which the estimated positions of the stars would have been out by plus or minus twenty seconds of arc. This was also the first mechanical proof that the Earth was in motion.

This discovery Bradley supplemented twenty years later by the no less vital discovery of the *nutation of the Earth's axis*. In 1741 this great astronomer became director of Greenwich Observatory. His appointment was one of the last acts of Robert Walpole. Although convinced that he had fully explained the anomalies of γ Draconis, he continued to watch this star. Hence he was not taken by surprise when, in 1747, he noted that even after deducting the aberration, the co-ordinates of γ Draconis continued to display slow variations. These took place over a period of eighteen and a half years and involved a shift of no less than ten seconds.

Eighteen and a half years—the figure at once called to Bradley's mind another phenomenon that occupied the same space of time: a particular movement of the lunar orbit as it turned on its axis. It then occurred to him that the Moon, as it changed position in eighteen and a half years in relation to the stars, thereby gradually modified its attraction on the bulge along the terrestrial equator. Since the Earth was drawn in a perpetually changing direction, each of the stars must appear to describe a small circle every eighteen and a half years.

This new factor, nutation, rendered the picture of the universe considerably more complex. Every star, instead of being a rigidly fixed point, was affected first by the aberration of light, which caused this point to describe in a year an ellipse whose major axis measured forty seconds. Then account had to be taken of the precession of the equinoxes, which led it to follow a circle of forty-seven degrees diameter centred on the pole of the ecliptic every 26,000 years. Finally, the nutation of the Earth's axis resulted in the star embroidering on this circumference a kind of annual scallop of eighteen seconds amplitude.

This complexity was, in fact, fortunate, since it made it possible to give a description of the celestial topography that was now extremely accurate. The best proof of this may be seen in the fact that the catalogue drawn up by Bradley between 1750 and 1762, published in 1798 and reprinted in 1818, remained the basis of Auwers's study of the motions of the stars in 1894.

Resumption of planetary exploration

The pursuit of an accuracy of one second in the position of the stars may cause the layman to smile, striking him as a total waste of effort. Yet it was not concern for pure science that impelled Colbert and Charles II to finance the investigations of either Picard and La Caille, or Halley and Bradley. We know that for them the improvement of navigation was a political necessity, so that, paradoxical as it may seem, the progress of the most disinterested of sciences was ultimately due to the most materialistic considerations.

The benefits of this progress were not confined to navigation; it was also the underlying factor in the drawing of the new maps that had been so long demanded by soldiers, travellers, merchants and manufacturers. That these new maps were no luxury is evident from the monstrous errors which blemished those of Louis XIV's time, where France appeared half a degree too long and one degree—forty-five miles—too wide, which placed Rennes almost in the position of Saint-Nazaire off the Ile d'Yeu. In fact the Sun King regarded the re-drawing of the map on the basis of a new measurement of the meridian as the most important achievement of G. D. Cassini and his team-mate Philippe de la Hire (1640–1718).

Even simple surveying and levelling owed a debt to astronomy. Sighting instruments and spirit levels inherited the same improvements as had been made in the great instruments of the observatories, so that this highly practical occupation also benefited from the gain of a few places of decimals in the sidereal co-ordinates.

In short, the major branch of the science of the skies—positional astronomy—was above all utilitarian. Its function was that of a mere technique in the service of such important activities as navigation, cartography and levelling. Even such eminently disinterested spirits as Picard and La Caille could satisfy their taste for pure science only in directions that led to some practical application.

But the time had now come in which the pendulum of history already referred to on page 157, which ceaselessly swings between research and application and thanks to which science periodically draws new vigour from industrial progress, moved in the direction of pure astronomy. Navigation and surveying, in whose interests the astronomer had been working almost continuously, now repaid him with their instruments, their methods and their subsidies. Thanks to them, the tradition of speculative astronomy enjoyed a fresh lease of life—watched by an industry hopeful of deriving new profits from it.

If we continue to term 'utilitarian' that part of astronomy which is concerned with measuring the position of the stars, it is reasonable to dub 'pure astronomy' that which is aimed at determining their nature, topography and distance. Granted that stellar co-ordinates are useful to navigators, geographers and explorers; it is nevertheless difficult to see the practical value of locating the spots on the planet Mars, or knowing that this globe is farther from the Sun than the

Earth and closer than Jupiter. But from its collaboration with commerce and the gains it had afforded trade, astronomy acquired the wherewithal to ensure it provisional independence. It was free to resume its traditional path without bothering whether it paid its way or not. As a result, the study of the planetary system roughed out by Cassini was progressively, at first timidly, taken up anew. In the luminous dots, of which they had hitherto confined themselves to determining the position, astronomers began once more to discern worlds, sisters to the Earth.

When an explorer sets foot in an unknown land, his first thought, before identifying its fauna and flora or geological structure, is to map it. Astronomers, the explorers of the solar system, had long been trying to map this system. For millennia they had placed the Earth in the centre and set the Sun, Moon and planets revolving round it. The first problem, then, was to find out whether this was a true picture, whether it was really the Earth, and not the Sun, that occupied the centre. The heliocentric solution did not begin to impose itself until Galileo's time, and even in Picard and La Caille's day it was still not accepted unanimously.

A second problem was to ascertain in what order the seven planets and the Earth were arranged, and this was finally solved by Kepler. His third law (p. 115) provided the means not only of determining the situations of the planets in relation to the Sun, but also of calculating their relative distances. It was known, for example, that the distance from Mercury to the Sun is approximately 0.39 times that from the Earth to the Sun; the distance from Venus to the Sun, 0.72 times; from Mars, 1.5 times; from Jupiter, 5.2 times; from Saturn, 9.5 times.

Astronomers were in a position to draw a rigorously accurate diagram of the planetary system. In this diagram there was only one blank space—the corner in which the *scale* is normally given. The scale was lacking. This was a regrettable gap. In many instances it was not enough to know that Mars was one and a half times as far from the Sun as the Earth: it was necessary to know what this distance was in leagues. It was fine to be able to express, with a very fair degree of accuracy, the distance of the planets from the Sun in terms of the

Earth's distance, which was thus raised to the level of an astronomical unit of distance; but it was also necessary to know the absolute value of this unit in leagues, *toises* or feet.

Naturally, the problem of the Earth's absolute distance from the Sun was far from new. We saw at the beginning of this book how it haunted the ancients from the height of Greek antiquity. We remember, too, that the first solutions to the problem advanced were based on mystical and magical considerations totally alien to science. Anaximander estimated it at twenty-seven or twenty-eight terrestrial diameters. Aristarchus of Samos was the first to attempt a rational solution, and he calculated it at 170 to 190 diameters. Then Hipparchus appeared, and by reckoning the breadth of the cone of shadow cast by the Earth, raised the latter's distance from the Sun to 1,146 terrestrial diameters. Hallowed by the great scientists' authority, the same method was employed one after the other by his successors, Ptolemy, Tycho Brahe (who raised the figure to 1,150), Longomontanus (1,288) and Copernicus (1,179).

It is true that at the point we have now reached, the mid-eighteenth century, astronomers were becoming aware of the defects of the Hipparchian method and the inaccuracy of the resulting data, which had such a troublesome effect on the final outcome of the calculation. They were in possession of instruments—quadrants, transit instruments and theodolites—which allowed far more accurate measurements than in Kepler's day; they had long been conversant with trigonometry and the techniques of geodesy and they began to ask themselves whether these various factors did not open up an approach to the problem completely different from Hipparchus's.

The Moon, the first step in surveying the planets

This was the moment at which the first great national map appeared, produced by Cassini. The progress of geodesy had revised the methods of cartography from top to bottom, and we know, in particular, how greatly it changed the picture of France. It was natural to ask why geodesy, which had measured distances as great as that from Dunkirk to Bayonne, should not tackle even greater distances.

Since the science of triangulation appeared all-powerful, what was to prevent it from attacking the cardinal problem of celestial distances? Was it not possible to construct a triangle whose base could be measured on the Earth and whose apex was a star?

That such a project could actually be put into effect was shown, in 1753, by La Caille. We have already seen, on page 167, how this scientist set out from Lorient for the Cape of Good Hope at the terribly slow speed of the sailing-ships of the day. When the Académie des Sciences sent him on this trip they entrusted him with a threefold task: first to map the southern sky; then to determine the longitude of the Cape of Good Hope, an essential stage for ships sailing east; and, finally, to calculate the distances of the Moon, the planets and the Sun.

Since the Moon was the nearest orb, it seemed best suited for application of the classical method of triangulation. As a base, La Caille chose the chord of the terrestrial sphere joining Berlin to Capetown. Why these two towns? Because they are on almost the same meridian and their latitude differs by approximately ninety degrees, which gives a base line about 6,000 miles in length. If one observer in Berlin and another at Capetown simultaneously took sights on the Moon, it would be easy to measure the two angles at the base of the triangle. An elemental trigonometrical formula would then give the distance sought.

That was why La Caille set sail for the Cape of Good Hope, after requesting his colleague Charles Le Monnier (1715–99) to go and make corresponding observations at Berlin. This astronomer doubtless had no taste for the journey, for he sent in his place his pupil Jérôme de Lalande (1732–1807), a student of nineteen! King Frederick, to whom he was presented by Maupertuis, then president of the Berlin Academy, was highly astonished to see such an important mission entrusted by France to such a young man.

The pupil seems to have done credit to his master, for the enterprise was crowned with success. The parallax of the Moon—that is to say, the angle under which the radius of the Earth would be seen from the Moon—was found to be fifty-seven minutes (the value adopted nowadays is $57' 2 \cdot 7''$) and the corresponding distance 240,000 miles.

This victory, which was hailed as a triumph of science, encouraged La Caille to extend it and pass on from the Moon to the Sun. He was certainly not the first to cherish the plan of measuring the parallax of the Sun by trigonometrical methods, nor was he the first to realize the difficulties. Even at this time, the Sun was looked upon as being much farther away than the Moon. Hence the triangle to be constructed was much more tapering; in fact the base was so small in relation to the height that it was completely impossible to calculate the angle at the apex. We know today that this angle is little more than eight seconds. La Caille would have found great difficulty in estimating it with his instruments, efficient as they seemed to him.

To measure the distance of the Sun by means of triangulation alone was therefore totally impracticable. The difference between the distance of the Moon and of the Sun was too great to span in one jump.

But astronomers had long ago realized the impossibility of reaching the Sun with a single triangle and come to the conclusion that it could probably be done by placing two triangles end to end. This operation could be carried out if an intermediate point in space could be utilized. Obviously, this intermediate point must be a planet and preferably a planet very close to the Earth. The procedure would then be to determine its parallax and distance and then employ these to reach the Sun.

Of the planets that come relatively close to the Earth there were Mars, which passes within 35,000,000 miles of the Earth at its opposition, and Venus, whose conjunction takes place at a distance of 24,700,000 miles. These distances were themselves too great to contemplate measuring them by La Caille's method of triangulation; but eighty years earlier the great Cassini had proposed an ingenious solution, which he had himself employed in tackling the same problem.

In 1672 Mars was in opposition, that is to say the planet lay in a straight line with the Earth and the Sun (Fig. 8). Cassini took advantage of the fact that his colleague Jean Richer (d. 1696) was leaving for Cayenne to ask him to observe Mars simultaneously with himself.

From Paris, Cassini (at C in the diagram) saw Mars in the direction CMM'. The difference between the two directions could be worked out. Knowing the base CR (the chord joining Paris to Cayenne) to be 4,443 miles, it was possible to deduce from it the distance of Mars.

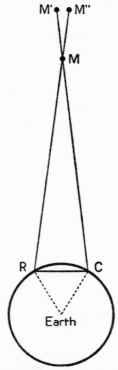

Fig. 8 HOW CASSINI MEASURED THE DISTANCE OF
THE PLANET MARS

Cassini at Paris (C) and Richer at Cayenne (R) saw Mars projected at different points in the sky, M' in the case of the former and M" in the case of the latter. By measuring the angle M'MM" it became possible to determine the triangle MCR and consequently its side MC or MR.

Cassini made this distance 32,900,000 miles, corresponding to a parallax of twenty-five seconds.

The first triangle was therefore established. It remained to construct the second, the one which, resting upon the first, would reach the Sun. Cassini called to his aid Kepler's third law, which relates the duration of the revolution of the planets to their distance from the Sun. Since the distance from Mars to the Earth was known, as well as the duration of its revolution (1 year and 322 days), it was easy to work out the distance from the Earth to the Sun: 86,500,000 miles, corresponding to a parallax of 9·5 seconds.

For the first time a reasonable figure had been produced (the real distance is 92,900,000), since Kepler himself had estimated it at only 27,875,000 miles. The only drawback to the method was the necessity of relying on the estimate of the parallax of Mars. It was easy for error to slip into the evaluation of an angle as small as the angle CMR in Fig. 8. For this reason later astronomers checked Cassini's calculations—and produced different results. His nephew Maraldi found a parallax of 10 seconds, not 9·5, La Hire of 11·4 seconds, and Bradley of 12 seconds. The distances ranged from 41 to 136 million miles. This was how things stood when La Caille took the matter in hand in 1753. Before leaving for the Cape, he had carefully co-ordinated his operations with those of Bradley at Greenwich and Grishov in Moscow. Unfortunately, he was no more able than his predecessors to free the data of observation from their basic uncertainty. The value which he published for his parallax, 10·2 seconds, gave just over 80 million miles.

The difficulty lay in the fact that Mars was too far from the Earth to afford a good intermediate point. Why, then, had it been chosen, instead of Venus, which was closer by 10 million miles? For the simple but compelling reason that Mars, at its shortest distance, is visible in the middle of the night and therefore easy to locate in relation to the Stars, whereas Venus, when it is nearest to us, is right between the Sun and the Earth and therefore, like the new Moon, totally invisible.

The transit of Venus: adventures and misadventures

A great many astronomers probably racked their brains for a way out of this impasse after 1672. The solution was found in 1678 by the great and productive English astronomer whose name has repeatedly cropped up in these pages, the perspicacious Halley. He did not announce it, however, till 1716, when he was sixty and knew that it could not be put into effect until forty-five years later, when he would certainly be dead. He was a long-term prophet of great celestial events and had already predicted the appearance in 1758 of a fine comet, which his eyes would never see but whose flight through space science enabled him to follow.

When the Moon passes between the Earth and the Sun, in the course of its passage round the former, it is in a dead straight line between these two orbs. It then hides the Sun from us and there is a total solar eclipse.

Halley perceived that Venus also came into a geometrically straight line between the Earth and the Sun. Of course, it is much too far away to hide the latter from us, but with the aid of a telescope it can be seen as a black dot travelling by its own motion across the blazing disc. It seemed to Halley that the best moment to measure the parallax of Venus was while it was thus passing across the face of the Sun. He proposed to place two astronomers as far apart as possible and let them trace the planet's path across the solar disc. By virtue of the same effect of perspective as in Cassini's method, this path would not be exactly the same for both observers. As in the case of the parallax of Mars, it would be sufficient to measure the angular discrepancy between the two paths in order to obtain the distance of Venus.

The drawback to this procedure is the fact that the transit of Venus in front of the Sun takes place at very long intervals—every 113 years plus or minus 8 years. The records show the following curiously spaced dates: 1631, 1639, 1761, 1769, 1874, 1882, 2004, 2012. Halley, who had propounded the theory, could not hope to see any of them. At least we may regard as a tribute to his memory the enthusiasm with which astronomers prepared to observe the transit of Venus on 6 June, 1761.

This event was the occasion of the first great astronomical expeditions. Modern science has made us familiar with these sensational undertakings. Every time there is a total eclipse of the Sun, we see expeditions set off into the remotest corners of the world and devote a

wealth of patience, ingenuity—and money—to the study of a phenomenon that lasts only a few minutes and has long since ceased to be of
anything but purely scientific interest. Knowing the cardinal importance acquired by science, we are no longer surprised by these
commandos sent out at great expense into lands many of which are
little more than a wilderness. But we must picture the state of mind
obtaining in 1760 and the wild excitement of scientists confronted
by a problem in pure science from which no immediate material gain
was to be expected. Most European countries were determined to have
their own astronomers on the spot, and the phenomenon was observed
from no less than seventy-two stations distributed among three of the
five continents.

The need to observe from widely separated points led scientists to
take up positions in Siberia as well as Tahiti, in India as well as
Finland. As regards the French, Abbé Chappe d'Auteroche (1728–69)
was sent to Tobolsk; Pingré (1711–96) to Rodrigues Island off
Madagascar; Le Gentil (1725–92) to the Indian Ocean; Cassini de
Thury to Vienna and La Caille to Charenton with Turgot, the future
minister, as his assistant.

The records tell us of the tribulations of these missionaries
despatched to the confines of the world on voyages which in some
cases lasted for years. We will take as an example the especially
picturesque adventures of the unfortunate Le Gentil.

Le Gentil left Lorient in March 1670 and disembarked in July on
Mauritius, where he waited seven months for a frigate to take him on
to Pondicherry. As they were about to land, after battling for a week
against contrary winds, the commander learned that the town had just
been taken by the British. There was nothing for it but to turn back.
Le Gentil put about and headed for Mauritius. He had the bitter
consolation of watching Venus passing in a cloudless sky across the
radiant disc from the deck of the ship.

Did he resign himself to returning to France? No, because the
planet was due to pass a second time, on 3 June, 1769. Le Gentil
resolved to wait eight years and make good his loss. To increase the
chances of fine weather he decided to establish himself on Manilla.
In 1766, therefore, he boarded a Spanish man-o'-war that was sailing

to this island and landed upon it without let or hindrance. But his troubles began afresh. He was pestered by an interfering governor, who finally compelled him to leave the island and take refuge at Pondicherry, which was now no more than a heap of ruins. Le Gentil nevertheless made preparations to observe the phenomenon, confident in the limpidity of the sky, which had been serenely blue for months. He was sadly disappointed, for an unfortunate coincidence sent a single cloud drifting across the sky at the crucial moment, so that the unlucky astronomer saw even less of Venus this time than the last.

This was not the end of his troubles. After embarking for France in 1770 he was held up for four months at Mauritius. Then, no sooner had the vessel that was carrying him set sail, than a storm drove her ashore. There were no regular sailing routes in those days, and a voyager whom bad luck threw into some out-of-the-way port might wait there months, or even years, before some kindly captain would consent to take him aboard. Thus Le Gentil lost another three months, at the end of which time a Spanish ship afforded him a passage to Europe. She took another four months over this, after spending a fortnight rounding the Cape of Good Hope in a raging storm. All in all, the adventurous scientist did not return to his estate until 1772. Then it was to find that the confidential agent he had left to manage his affairs had robbed him outrageously and that his heirs, thinking him dead, were preparing to divide what was left of his possessions.

On the scientific plane, the results obtained by the other expeditions, both in 1769 and 1761, were not in keeping with the effort expended. Collation of all observations of the first transit gave a mean parallax of the Sun of 9 seconds. The second transit, after all the data had been collected by Pingré, gave 8·75 seconds. To tell the truth, this last figure was marvellously close to the value accepted today, 8·8 seconds. But Pingré's contemporaries were unaware of the fact, and this 8·75 seconds was probably merely the result of an extraordinary concatenation of circumstances in which the errors happened to cancel one another out. After 1769, therefore, the majority of astronomers stuck to a value of 8·91 seconds. This made the distance of the Sun appear to be 91,700,000 miles—a figure that was too small by approximately 1,200,000 miles.

6

Laplace and Herschel: the explanation and picture of the universe

Newton frees the mind by putting the stars in chains—The founding of celestial mechanics—The Moon and the problems of longitude—Clairaut disciplines the comets—The shape of the Earth—Newton's law weighs the world—Laplace, legislator of the heavens—The universe? A perpetual-motion apparatus—Herschel, or the passion for seeing—Uranus: the solar system draws back its frontiers—A stride towards the stars—The Sun is drifting in the sky—An inventory of the nebulae—The plan of the universe—A gauge for the skies

O N 10 February, 1778 a piece of news spread like wildfire through Paris: the King had just returned to his capital. The population was shaken by a tremendous outburst of enthusiasm. Not only did all the nobility of France appear at the levee, not only did the Académie Française, the Académie des Sciences and the Comédie Française come in a body to pay homage to their sovereign, not only did the social élite of France, the rank and fashion of Paris and Versailles, hasten to add their acclamations to the general rapture, but the very populace, the populace especially, the newsmongers, the street-porters and artisans, gave the monarch a delirious ovation. The triumph reached its climax on 30 March, when the King appeared in a box at the Comédie Française and the spectators rose to their feet, the actors placed the hero's bust in the centre of the stage and crowned it with laurels, and noblemen and commoners, intoxicated by a fervour of admiration, bore him to his carriage as he cried, overcome with emotion: 'Do you want to suffocate me with roses?'

It was not, of course, King Louis XVI, but Voltaire. 'Which sovereign do you fear most in Europe?' somebody once asked Frederick the Great. 'King Voltaire,' he replied.

Exactly a hundred years earlier, in 1678, Louis XIV had forbidden the teaching of Descartes's system, thus giving a further turn to the iron-collar that imprisoned free thought. Prison, torture, death awaited the bold or thoughtless writer from whose pen some allusion escaped that might be thought injurious to the authority of King or Church. It was not so long since Galileo's profanities had been forced down his throat, and the majority of thinkers preferred to keep their ideas to themselves, rather than risk the wheel, or at least indefinite incarceration in the Bastille, as a result of publishing them.

It took less than a century for the picture to change utterly. Voltaire crowned, Voltaire deified, achieving in 1778 the spectacular feat of being acclaimed simultaneously by the populace, the philosophers and fashionable society on the look-out for novelty—it was free thought that showed itself in broad daylight and the Inquisition, impotently raging, that retired into the shadows. There could be no better indication that power was beginning to change hands. The Sorbonne and Parliament thundered and threatened in vain; what could they do against the irresistible force of public opinion? Come wind and high water, Diderot continued to publish the *Encyclopédie*, Buffon the *Histoire naturelle*, and Helvétius, d'Holbach and Toussaint impious books whose success was assured by the scandal they aroused —not to mention a plethora of tracts, lampoons, pamphlets and broadsheets, carried and sold by a crowd of hacks and hawkers with the complicity of the police, censors and customs officials. And this social transformation was not restricted to France, but extended over most of Europe—think of Frederick II's Prussia receiving Voltaire and Maupertuis and Catherine II's Russia opening its doors to Diderot.

We know the cause, the motive power of this intellectual revolution that preceded the Revolution itself: the advent of reason. Philosophers no longer demanded obedience to antiquated traditions, outworn superstitions, fictitious deities, but to reason pure and simple. It was for lucid logic and positive reasoning to dictate decisions, based on facts established by strict observations of the laws of nature, and no longer for arbitrary powers speaking in the name of occult and unknowable forces.

According to the philosophers, rational science was substituting for the traditional universe, governed by God in accordance with His whims, a universe ruled by impersonal mechanical laws. This universe was nothing but a vast machine whose cogs, once imposing in their mystery, were shown up one after the other by the bright light of science. Yesterday, man trembled with fear at the thought of his smallness and weakness in the midst of this enormous world over which reigned almighty God. Now humility gave place to pride: why should man humble himself before a machine? Ought he not rather to feel proud of having penetrated a world that was so grandiose, of having unravelled laws that were so complex, of having been able, merely by solving a few equations, to predict the courses of the planets?

Newton frees the mind by putting the stars in chains

Thus, during the latter years of the eighteenth century, the universe appeared in a new guise. Only yesterday it had seemed, in the light of scholasticism and unbending religious dogma, a clock whose very existence, as Voltaire put it, postulated a Clockmaker. Now the most imposing manifestations of this universe—the motion of the Sun, tides and eclipses—proved dependent not upon an arbitrary will, but upon material laws capable of being translated into mathematical formulae. What had been taken for an intentionally arranged harmony of nature turned out to be nothing but the outcome, for good or ill, of a combination of disparate forces, while the existence of the Clockmaker himself seemed questionable. Let there be no doubt about the importance of this change of outlook: the whole spiritual turmoil, the tornado of revolution and the new equilibrium in Europe sprang from it.

The new ideal dictated by the Newtonian theory called upon men to turn away from everything that was not the outcome of reasoning based on experience and to remould society in this pattern. Since science was capable of plotting the course of worlds through the heavens, how could anyone dispute its right to regulate the affairs of a tiny globe like the Earth? Fundamentally, it was the mathematical order of the planetary system that the philosophers wished to transplant on to the Earth. The rigid order of this system became the model for the turbulent social forces of the late eighteenth century. The conquest of the skies, of which Newton had just completed the first stage, necessarily brought with it the conquest of the Earth—the conquest of matter, achieved by technology raised on the foundations of science and liberty.

In 1778, when the Parisians crowned Voltaire amidst transports of enthusiasm, Newton had been dead for half a century. There had been time for the impetus he had imparted to science to communicate itself to the whole of Britain. British society, down-to-earth and realistic, lived exclusively by commerce. It had freed itself from absolute kings and adopted constitutional monarchy, linking the sovereign to the nation by a tacit contract. Newton's theory could scarcely have fallen on more fertile soil. For this people concerned solely with matters of imports and exports and navigation, for whom business was the primary activity and who believed only in objects they could touch or in documents that bore the guarantee of an unimpeachable signature, what philosophy could have been better suited than Newton's? It subjected the heavens to the same formalism, the same rigorous orderliness as the world of business. This was the philosophy that reached the Continent, thanks especially to Voltaire, and we know how contagious it proved when it got there. What scientist, what philosopher did not hunger for the ability to explain everything, as Newton did when he analysed every detail of the motion of a planet?

The founding of celestial mechanics

If Newton's work was behind these social tidal waves, the latter, in their turn, reacted upon the work. Newton, as he said himself, had supplied the 'principles', illustrating them by a few particular cases. It was up to his successors to apply them; up to them to generalize the rational explanation of the universe step by step.

The *Principia* had demonstrated the law of universal attraction and, as a corollary, the mechanism of the circulation of each planet round the Sun and of the Moon round the Earth. But this was only the first step. The author had confined himself to studying the cases in which only two heavenly bodies were in interaction; the law of gravitation is then very simply expressed by the following equation, in which F represents the force of attraction, M and m the mass of each of the two bodies, r the distance between their centres and G a certain constant;[1]

$$F = G \frac{M\,m}{r^2}$$

But this, obviously, could only be a theoretical case, since in reality far more than two bodies are in interaction. For example, the movement of the Moon around the Earth is regulated not only by the attraction exercised by these two masses upon each other (that of the Earth naturally being preponderant), but also by the action of the Sun. This means that there are three bodies in interaction, and that the force can no longer be expressed in the same simple manner as before. Newton's law governing the relationship of the Earth and Moon is falsified by disturbances, by *perturbations*, caused by the distant but enormous mass of the Sun. Similarly, the precession of the equinoxes cannot be explained entirely by the Moon's attraction on the Earth's equatorial bulge; here again the influence of the Sun has to be taken into account (to the extent of about one-third). What happens in the case of a planet that has several satellites, like Jupiter or the solar system as a whole? The perturbations effected by each planet on the others are superimposed upon the attraction of the Sun in an inextricable network of pull and counter-pull.

Newton had found the key that enabled him to decipher the world of the heavenly bodies, in which for long mankind had seen only mystery and chaos. A valorous Theseus, he had discovered the entrance to nature's labyrinth. But now this labyrinth had to be traversed to the very end along the path which he had mapped out. The moment had come to translate into clear the cryptogram written in the sky by the intricate dance of the planets, after grasping the key proffered by Newton. In other words, the task now was to rise above particular cases and reach the general case, to acquire the ability to predict accurately the path of any celestial body whatever. The broad

---

[1] G is a universal constant, called the *constant of gravitation*; its value in c.g.s. units is $6 \cdot 70 \times 10^8$.

outlines of a future science of *celestial mechanics* were already beginning to appear, built up on Newton's law.

Reduced to its most elementary form, the problem consisted in supposing two material points, that is to say two infinitely tiny masses, in interaction; in calculating the attraction they exercised upon one another; and in determining, section by section, the path along which this attraction pulled them. The solution is contained in the three letters F = mg, formulated on p. 129 and written in the shape of a *differential equation*, as Newton had taught. This equation applied only to an infinitely small portion of the path, but all that was necessary to obtain this path in its entirety was to add up all the individual parts. It was, above all, Leibniz (1646–1717) who taught how this operation was to be carried out, that is to say how to find the *integral* of the differential equation. As there are three directions in space, the proper way to acquire a complete description of the movement was to calculate its three components, that is, to draw up an equation for each direction. The problem boiled down to one of pure mathematics, the integration of a system of three differential equations.

Newton and Leibniz did not carry their mathematical work to this point, but the relay was taken over by three great Swiss mathematicians, the two Bernoulli brothers, Jacques (1654–1705) and Jean (1667–1748), and especially Leonhard Euler (1707–83). It was they who laid down the rules for the integration of various types of differential equations. In 1744 Euler took the major step of clearly posing the general problem of planetary perturbations when the interacting bodies number *n*. He showed that the differential equations representing the motion of these *n* bodies are finally reduced to ten integrals.

The Moon and the problem of longitude

This, as may be seen, was pure theory. Astronomers were in a hurry to pass on to application, to utilize these new methods in an attempt to solve the great riddles of the skies. The most important of these was the riddle of the Moon.

It is usual to say that the Moon revolves around the Earth. In reality, however, the sun affects it with perturbations that disturb its elliptical motion. These perturbations are revealed by a whole series of little apparent irregularities which successive astronomers have recorded through the ages. We may recall that Hipparchus discovered one (p. 74), Ptolemy a second (p. 77), Tycho Brahe a third. . . . The Danish mathematician Hansen (p. 229) counted no less than a hundred such irregularities, while Brown, in 1926, brought the number to 1,500! It is easy to understand that such distortions of the Keplerian motion should have raised doubts as to whether the Moon was really subject, like the planets, to Newton's law, so that a careful check seemed to be called for.

This check was published in 1752 by the Frenchman Alexis Clairaut (1713–65). Clairaut was a man who may be said to have passed through life with long strides: the author at sixteen of a brilliant treatise on geometry, elected to the Academy at eighteen, sent to Lapland with Maupertuis at twenty-three to measure the meridian, he led a frenzied life in which work alternated with social amusements and amatory feats, and died at fifty-two. It was after ten years' study, at thirty-nine, that he succeeded in accounting for the chief inequalities in the lunar motion by means of the Newtonian principles.

To search laboriously for the origin of such minute variations may seem a gratuitous exercise without practical utility. At bottom, this meticulous dissection of our satellite's path was not as disinterested as might appear. In its regular movement past the constellations the Moon is like the hand of an enormous clock—a hand which, as it meets one star after another, tells a whole hemisphere the time. When we recall that the time was the stumbling block that barred the solution to the old problem of longitude at sea, we shall appreciate the practical value of an accurate lunar theory.

For little or no progress had been made with the longitude problem since Greenwich Observatory was created for that very purpose in 1675. Yet it was so important, of such vital significance to navigation, trade and economic prosperity that, one after the other, King Philip III of Spain, the States General of Holland and the British Parliament offered prizes to anyone who could find a solution. Spain offered 100,000 crowns, Holland 30,000 florins and Britain £20,000.

At first sight it looks a simple matter to determine local time by the stars encountered by the Moon in its passage across the sky, since this luminary's motion is such that it traverses approximately 13 degrees along the zodiac daily. Unfortunately, as Flamsteed pointed out in his report to Charles II, this motion is blemished by the irregularities we have referred to. As the slightest error in the prediction of the Moon's positions is augmented by the conversion of the angular measurement into time, it is easy to believe that, as La Caille said, the resulting inaccuracy in the longitude might amount to 97 leagues.

There was the case of the French ship *Le Glorieux* which, in 1763, while heading for the Cape of Good Hope, looked for the Cape Verde Islands to the west when they were to the east, and being unable to find them was forced to put in at Brazil; the case of the British *Union* (1775) whose master believed he was 40 miles off Cape Finisterre (in north-west Spain) and then ran aground off the Ile de Ré; that of the squadron commanded by Suffren (1782), who found himself in the middle of the ocean with no land in sight when by his calculations he should have been 30 miles inside the African continent. . . .[1] The loss of time, money and human life, the shipwrecks and accidents of all kinds brought about by such stupendous errors, are beyond counting. No wonder the British made it a matter of state and instituted the competition of 1714.

As Clairaut expounded a brilliant theoretical solution to the problem in 1752 it may seem strange that he did not submit it to the British jury. The reason was simple: it was only a theory. What the British wanted was not a learned treatise on mathematics to be enjoyed only by erudite manipulators of integral equations, but elementary and practical tables by means of which the least educated of sea dogs could read the position of the Moon and deduce from it his longitude. Neither Clairaut's work nor a similar memoir by Alembert met these requirements.

Then, in 1762, the British Parliament received a manuscript. It was signed by a very well-known name, that of the German astronomer Tobias Mayer (1723–62), director of Goettingen Observatory. Mayer was a conscientious and modest scientist. For ever striving after

[1] A. Thomazi, *Histoire de la Navigation* (Presses Universitaires, 1947).

unattainable perfection, he would never have agreed to submit his work, the fruit of his own observations. It was his wife who did so, after his death at the age of thirty-nine. The jury did not award her the prize, but gave her a recompense of £5,000. In any case, the widow's finest reward was to see Tobias Mayer's *Tables of the Moon* used in drawing up the *Nautical Almanac* and the *Connaissance des Temps*. It was not until 1905 that they were dropped from this latter publication.

As for the prize of £20,000, it was awarded in 1772 to the English clockmaker John Harrison (1693–1776) after thirty years of reiterated checking. The chronometer he constructed maintained correct time long enough to ensure that the error of longitude did not exceed 30 miles.

Clairaut disciplines the comets

The foundations of celestial mechanics were laid by Newton—an Englishman.

The materials for the construction of the edifice were amassed by men of various countries, such as the Bernoullis, Euler, Riccati, Taylor, L'Hospital.

The edifice itself was built by Clairaut, d'Alembert, Lagrange and Laplace—four Frenchmen.

Pure chance?

Perhaps not, if we agree that scientific discoveries appear in the ground best prepared to receive them. Realistic and commercially-minded Britain was the most fertile soil in which Newton's ideas could have grown. France, at the end of the eighteenth century—philosophical, ratiocinative, pitiless in its pursuit of logic, eager to expel the least whiff of mysticism from every corner of nature—was the ideal ground for those astronomers who aspired to know everything. For such was the ambitious aim of the Frenchmen whose names we have just listed: to show that the universe was nothing but a machine functioning in accordance with the laws of mechanics, without having recourse to the intervention or changing will of the Deity.

To be exact, little doubt remained on this point in the eyes of scientists and of those philosophers who prided themselves on having a scientific outlook. Newton had proved irrefutably that the planets were nothing but inert masses obeying the mathematical law of gravitation; Clairaut and d'Alembert had extended this proof to the Moon. The whole solar system would be included within the same formula once it had been imposed upon the comets.

This problem, too, had been tackled by Newton. Linked to the Sun by its power of attraction, the comets could not do otherwise than describe ellipses round it, however elongated these ellipses might be. They must all, therefore, return periodically into its vicinity—unless, of course, they exploded and vanished on the way. When one of them appeared, it was difficult to tell whether it was an already known comet, or a comet that had come into view for the first time after traversing an immensely long orbit. The only way to find out was by calculating the newcomer's path and checking to see whether it coincided with that of any heavenly body already catalogued.

This is what Halley did in respect of the fine comet of 1682. Having worked out the details of its orbit (position in relation to the orbit of the Earth, shortest distance from the Sun and so on), he perceived that these elements coincided with those of two earlier comets, that of 1607, observed by Kepler and Longomontanus, and that of 1531, observed by the German Bienewitz, called Apianus. It was tempting to assume that it was the same object which had appeared three times, at intervals of about seventy-five years. Confident in his data, Halley did not hesitate to predict its return in 1682 + 75, that is to say in 1757 or 1758.

When the date for the fulfilment of this prediction approached, the English astronomer had been dead for several years, and his successors were no longer so sure that it would come true. A comet, in fact, is an object of trifling mass whose lengthy orbit may carry it through a large part of the solar system. It passes within varying distances of many planets, coming so close to some that they inflict profound perturbations upon it. Subjected to so many conflicting influences, it is rather like a feather at the mercy of the wind. No doubt it is not impossible to foretell its route, but this involves estimating all its perturbations. Such a task is frightfully complicated and terribly long, but nothing can better corroborate Newton's law and prove that the capricious comets are also obedient to it.

This was the task undertaken by Clairaut in respect of Halley's comet.

According to the orbit originally foreseen by the great English astronomer, the comet would cross the whole of the planetary system then known, passing beyond Jupiter and Saturn. It was therefore bound to undergo particularly strong perturbations originating from these two great globes. These perturbations must be assessed before an ephemeris of the comet could be drawn up. Clairaut laid down his programme and set the equations and formulae. Then he left it to his collaborator Lalande—who had also been La Caille's assistant in 1753—to replace the letters by their numerical values and to work out the figures.

This task was as protracted as it was irksome. We can form some idea of its complexity when we consider that it involved, in particular, calculating the comet's distance from Jupiter and from Saturn successively for each degree and for a hundred and fifty years. He was, however, aided by the most charming of assistants, Hortense Lepaute (1723–88), wife of the famous clockmaker, a delightful mathematician who had been Clairaut's pupil. Clairaut was full of enthusiasm for his feminine disciples. One day he shut himself up with Mme du Châtelet in order to give her a lesson in mathematics. But Voltaire took the matter very badly, broke into the house, kicked down the door and blasted master and pupil with a stream of invective.

It took Lalande and Hortense Lepaute six months, working from dawn till dusk and sometimes during meals, to arrive at a result. From it Clairaut inferred that the perturbations due to Jupiter would delay the comet by 518 days and those due to Saturn by 100. He gave the day on which it would pass through the perihelion (that is to say, its shortest distance from the Sun) as 13 April, 1759, adding that it might be one month out.

This proved to be the case. Keeping her date with the scientist, the traveller appeared one night at the end of 1758 as a nebulous whitish patch. She grew clearer, came closer and reached her perihelion on 12 March, 1759, with the delay foretold by Clairaut.

We can scarcely imagine the popularity which this prediction won for the great mathematician. To trace the path of an invisible orb, to foresee the moment at which it will come into view, seems to us a commonplace feat: after Clairaut, Le Verrier discovered Neptune in the same way, and modern astronomers foretell, with an assurance that is never challenged, the return of Halley's comet, Encke's comet and many others. But in 1759 Clairaut's success was the first of its kind. It confirmed that the heavenly bodies, even the comets, which are the most flighty, obey no other powers than the laws of mechanics. It proved that the universe held no secrets from the eyes of science, and that science, which had so demonstrably triumphed in the domain of the celestial bodies, was indubitably the power best equipped to govern the material world.

The shape of the Earth

The problem of longitude and the extension of the empire of science into the heavenly regions were not the only points in connexion with which the efficacy of the tool forged by Newton and his successors became manifest. There was reason to suppose that it would also provide pointers to the Earth's mass, shape and radius. There is no need to stress the importance of the latter. Since Newton's day the terrestrial radius had been the unit of distance for the heavenly bodies. And its practical value was no less, because upon the length of this radius depended that of the circumference of the globe, and hence that of the minute of arc, which is nothing else than the *nautical mile*. During the Middle Ages the unit of length used in navigation was the *Mediterranean mile* of approximately 1,350 yards, then, in the time of the Spanish supremacy, the *legua*, of which there were $17\frac{1}{2}$ to one degree. After the sixteenth century the *nautical league* was employed, numbering 20 to the degree. Hence the length ascribed to the terrestrial circumference gave that of an important unit of distance, and we can guess what attention skippers and shipowners paid to the latter when an error of only 20 yards in the value of a minute of arc might mean, after thirty days' sailing, a total error of 60 miles.

This uncertainty made itself painfully evident in maps. During the second half of the eighteenth century the position of Newfoundland differed by 9 degrees, say 600 miles, as between English or Dutch maps; there was an error of 4 degrees—277 miles—in the longitude of Iceland, 500 in that of Cape Horn, and maps showed two St. Helenas and three Galapagos archipelagos.

Obviously, there was a major task of expurgation to be carried out. It was all the more urgent because this was the age of a great rush to new lands, of the expeditions led by Bougainville, Wallis, Cook and La Pérouse. Expeditions from which very little profit could be derived so long as the exact shape and dimensions of the globe remained uncertain.

What? the reader may ask. Was there still doubt regarding the Earth's shape? Was it not unanimously agreed to be a sphere? Yes, indeed, but questions were already being asked about the regularity of its sphericity. Some observers wondered whether it was really a perfect sphere. In 1672, the physicist Richer noted that a pendulum swung less rapidly at Cayenne than at Paris. Did this not prove that gravity was less there, in other words that the surface of the Earth was farther from the centre at Cayenne than at Paris, which meant in effect that the Earth had an abnormal bulge at this point?

The existence of a bulge at the latitude of Cayenne was very well explained by the adherents of Newton. If it was accepted that the globe was originally fluid, it followed that centrifugal force caused it to bulge at the equator and hence grow flat at the poles.

Unfortunately, this inference did not accord with certain other facts. Jacques Cassini (1677–1756), son of the great Giovanni Domenico, announced in 1720 that the Earth must, on the contrary, bulge at the poles, not at the equator. He based his assertion on the measurement, made between 1683 and 1718, of the French meridian from Dunkirk to Perpignan. This measurement seemed to show that degrees of meridian grew shorter and shorter the farther north they lay. This could only mean that the planet was egg-shaped, the major axis of the egg being the line of the poles.

A conclusion so contrary to their doctrine threw the Newtonians into a rage, and resounding arguments ensued beneath the vaulted ceilings of the venerable Académie des Sciences. Clairaut, Maupertuis,

Bouguer and Désaguliers opposed Jacques Cassini, who was supported by Maraldi, Mairan and Eisenschmid. In 1735 Maupertuis decided to put the question to the test of renewed observation. Since the crux of the matter was whether the degrees of meridian increased from north to south or from south to north, the best way of solving the problem was to send out two expeditions, one to a point near the pole, the other to a point near the equator. Each would measure a degree of meridian, and it would soon be seen which was longest.

The expeditions were immediately fitted out. The one headed for the equator set sail for Peru in May 1735. Its chief members were the physicist Pierre Bouguer (1698–1758) and an amateur who was the party's man of action, La Condamine (1701–74). The polar expedition left for Lapland the following year. It was led by Pierre Moreau de Maupertuis (1698–1759), an ex-officer who had become a distinguished mathematician, and it included such illustrious figures as Clairaut, Le Monnier and the Swedish physicist Celsius.

The Peruvian expedition was away for twenty-nine years and its members passed through innumerable vicissitudes. Established on the uplands of the Cordilleras, where they were victims of the climate, the arid soil and the Spaniards who ruled the country, they nevertheless succeeded in triangulating an arc of meridian that gave 56,732 *toises* to one degree.

Meanwhile the Lapland expedition, which took little more than a year, had carried out its task and arrived at a value of 57,437 *toises*. The matter was now settled: the degree of meridian was greater by 700 *toises* at the pole than at the equator, the Earth was shown to be flat at the poles and to bulge at the equator. Newton had been proved right.

The outcome of these investigations was formulated by Clairaut in 1743. In his book *Théorie de la figure de la Terre tirée des principes de l'Hydrostatique* he explained mathematically how a fluid mass, such as the Earth must originally have been, had been flattened by rotation at the extremities of its axis. He showed how the varying thickness of the Earth's crust produced a variation in gravity, which in turn was revealed by variations in the speed of oscillation of a pendulum.

Not, of course, that the flattening was very great. According to Clairaut the polar diameter and the equatorial diameter of the Earth were in the ratio of 177 to 178, which is very near the truth. But this slight flattening, this imperceptible equatorial ridge nevertheless had important consequences. It was this ridge which, by exercising a special attraction on the Moon and Sun, was responsible for the precession—and also for the nutation that had just been discovered by Bradley.

At this point the stage was taken by another eminent mathematician, Jean d'Alembert (1717–83). This great man, the natural son of Mme de Tencin and the Chevalier Destouches, abandoned by his mother on the steps of the church of Saint-Jean-le-Rond (the baptistry of Notre-Dame de Paris), had a singular destiny. He was adopted and raised by the wife of a poor glazier and continued to live with his humble family until he was forty-seven. Here this incomparable geometer, member of all the learned societies of Europe, whom the salons fought over and whom Frederick the Great and Catherine the Great both tried to attract, who had transformed mechanics with his *Traité de Dynamique* and who, together with Diderot, launched against the government the colossal engine of war of the *Encyclopédie*, remained for ever 'the foster-child'!

In 1749 d'Alembert published his *Recherches sur la Précession des Equinoxes*, a generalization of Clairaut's approach. In it he considered the Earth as a solid body in movement round a fixed point and reduced its motion to a system of known forces. From the equations of this motion he then deduced the phenomena of precession and nutation.

Other results—of a more practical nature—followed from the new knowledge of the Earth. Jacques Cassini's view had, of course, to be abandoned. His son, Cassini de Thury (1714–84), forthrightly renounced the family error. Then, from 1739 to 1740, he worked with La Caille on the task of remeasuring the French meridian, which had given rise to such polemics in 1718. This new triangulation was the point of departure for the famous map of France known as 'Cassini's map'.

But perhaps the most important practical consequence of the Newtonian theory was the metric system, adopted by the Constituent Assembly in 1791. It was actually based on Bouguer's triangulation in Peru and a new measurement of the French meridian carried out by Delambre and Méchain.

The last doubts were thus removed. Newton's law was indeed the supreme key to the solar system. Thanks to this 'open sesame' astronomy was in a fair way to explain its machinery from top to bottom. As for our own little globe, not only had astronomy revealed first its precise form and then its exact radius, but now it actually weighed it.

The prologue to this new feat took place in 1738 in Peru, where the members of the famous expedition were at work. Bouguer noticed that at the foot of Chimborazo, a mountain of 20,790 feet, the plumb-line was not completely vertical. Was this to be blamed on a deviation due to the attraction of the equatorial bulge? No, because four miles west of the massif, that is to say at the same latitude, the plumb-line resumed its normal direction.

The true significance of this observation was not grasped until thirty years later, by the director of the Greenwich Observatory, Nevil Maskelyne (1732–1811). Unlike Bouguer, La Caille, Halley and many other adventure-seeking astronomers, Maskelyne was of a sedentary disposition. One of the only two journeys he ever made was to Scotland, but at least this journey was particularly profitable to science.

By Mount Schiehallion he repeated Bouguer's experiment and found that when he was north of the mountain the plumb-line deviated from the vertical southwards, while to the south of Schiehallion it deviated northwards. It was exactly as if the mountain attracted it. This was undoubtedly an illustration of Newton's law, the huge mass of the mountain was attracting the little ball of lead at the end of the line. By a skilful application of the formula of attraction, the scientist succeeded in calculating the mountain's mass, then, by estimating its volume he arrived at its density. He thus laid bare an unsuspected vein of unparalleled richness, for his discovery made it possible to calculate the mean density of the terrestrial globe and therefore its mass—in other words, science was in a position to weigh the Earth.

There was no counting the triumphs of Newton's theory, which a genius of a different type from Maskelyne seized upon to explore and illumine the last remaining dark corners of the planetary system. This was the deep-thinking Lagrange (1736–1813), one of the greatest mathematicians of all time, who was born in Italy of a French father, but did not settle in France until he was fifty-one.

Honest and good-natured, but reserved and uncommunicative, Lagrange offers a typical example of the prestige which the mathematical genius enjoys in the eyes of those who are very often least able to understand him. Few men did less than Lagrange to attain worldly honours, yet few received so many. He was on familiar terms with Frederick II; sought after by Louis XVI and received with respect by the King and Queen, as he was later by the Revolution and later still by the Emperor. Perhaps Napoleon alone was capable of appreciating the broad sweep of his work—a sweep that extended as far as Saturn, since he identified the perturbations of our satellite and of the planets and showed that, in their diverse forms, all the minor variations affecting the motion of these heavenly bodies were only the outcome of Newton's law. Even the four satellites of Jupiter, upon which Lagrange placed the Newtonian chains in an epoch-making memoir published in 1767—the same year in which a young Norman of nineteen alighted in Paris and knocked timidly at d'Alembert's door.

Laplace, legislator of the heavens

In the heart of fertile Normandy, a few miles from Deauville and Pont-l'Evêque, the village of Beaumont-en-Auge drowses on the rolling slopes of the pastureland. A village like so many others, with its petrol pumps and the inevitable statue in the square. 'Some local celebrity,' thinks the tourist pressing his foot down harder on. the accelerator.

Yet readers of this book would experience no little emotion as they approached the statue, deciphered the name carved on the plinth and, taking a few steps towards one of the ugly houses in the vicinity, read on a plaque these lines by Chênedollé:

Sous un modeste toit ici naquit Laplace,
Lui qui sut, de Newton, agrandir le compas,
Et, s'ouvrant un sillon dans les champs de l'espace,
Y fit encore un nouveau pas.[1]

This pathetically insignificant verse, sole vestige of a monument that once stood on the site of the house in which Laplace was born, this fine statue, unveiled in 1932 by Ernest Esclangon, a few canvases, a few books—that is all which remains of the loftiest genius France can boast, of the 'French Newton', the legislator of celestial motions. Newton rests at Westminster Abbey; Laplace lies in the Père Lachaise cemetery, lost in a crowd of unknown dead. France, who has conducted to the Panthéon so many celebrities of an hour, did not consider her greatest scientist worthy to sleep there alongside his friend Lagrange.

In the last resort, what does it matter? If our ephemeral glories require a monument to prolong their fame for a few decades, this is not so with Laplace—any more than with Kepler, Galileo or Newton. The statue at Beaumont-en-Auge, the monument in the village cemetery and that in the cemetery of Père Lachaise may disappear—Laplace's name will none the less continue to be spoken by all who matter among the human race. It is engraved in the sky, linked with the machinery of the heavenly bodies, and the scientists and school-boys of future ages will pronounce it, century after century, when the whole of our present-day civilization has crumbled into dust.

Nothing in his native village recalls today the landscape that revealed itself to the childhood eyes of Pierre-Simon Laplace—save, perhaps, a grey wall pierced by narrow windows, a relic of the old Benedictine priory in which the young man received his education till he was sixteen. There this son of a well-to-do farmer, born on

Here beneath a modest roof was born Laplace,
Who Newton's compass spread and made more wide,
Ploughing a fresh furrow in the fields of space
And taking through them a new stride.

22 March, 1749, learned to love Latin and theology, the prelude to the flowering of a transcendent genius for mathematics.

History casts little light on this flowering. The only landmark it has to cling to is this: when Laplace, having finished his studies first at Beaumont and then at the University of Caen, left Normandy to try his luck in Paris, he was already in full possession of his powers. A memoir, which he submitted to d'Alembert in lieu of a letter of introduction, staggered the latter, then the highest French scientific authority. Laplace was just twenty; he was appointed professor at the École Militaire Royale, and without losing a moment plunged into that ocean of theoretical astronomy in which he disported himself until his death.

1770. Little Napoleon Buonaparte had been born one year earlier in Corsica; the future King Louis XVI had just married Marie Antoinette; the British colonies in America had risen against George III. Euler was sixty-three, d'Alembert fifty-three, Lagrange thirty-four and Clairaut had been dead five years. With the audacity of his twenty years, young Laplace went straight at the heart of the problem which the greatest geometers had only tackled piecemeal—the problem of the solar system as a whole and its ultimate future.

1770. It was only 137 years since the Church condemned Galileo. Newton had published his *Principia* less than 100 years ago, and Laplace himself had received the traditional Scholastic training. That is to say, in spite of the efforts of the scientists, the problem of the planets had not yet been cleared of the metaphysical fog that had obscured its solution since Greek times. The consensus of opinion was that the planetary system resembled a machine, but it nevertheless seemed necessary for God to give it a push from time to time in order to keep it running properly. This was Newton's view: afflicted as it was by perturbations of all kinds, he thought the solar system could not continue to exist without occasional divine intervention. This opinion was shared by Euler. Even Clairaut and d'Alembert were half inclined to believe that, under the influence of the neighbouring orbs, the Moon might eventually fall on to the Earth and the Earth, like several other planets, on to the Sun.

This persistent doubt regarding the stability of the planetary machinery showed that Newton's law did not suffice to explain and foretell everything. This machinery had undergone minor improvements at the hands of Clairaut, d'Alembert and Lagrange. These improvements showed that the Newtonian interpretation was only a first approximation, and their authors were resigned to seeing the finger of God in the perpetual preservation of the harmony of the cosmos.

This was the problem Laplace set himself at the age of twenty: to demonstrate that the circulation of the planets can dispense with all supernatural intervention, that it depends exclusively upon the principles of attraction, and that the Moon, Earth and planets are therefore destined to pursue their present motions indefinitely without falling on top of one another.

The young professor at the École Militaire was certainly the right man for the job. 'Laplace was born to improve everything,' wrote Fourier, 'to make everything deeper, to push back all limits, to solve what might have been thought insoluble.' He possessed the tool that was needed: a mathematical inventiveness equal to that of Lagrange. And his superiority over all his contemporaries shone forth from the fact that he was not only a star of the first magnitude in the firmament of analysis, but also an equally profound philosopher. Unlike the pure mathematician Lagrange, Laplace was a Cartesian who ardently sought the secret of things behind the beautiful order of equations. He was a man of universal curiosity in whose study portraits of Descartes and Galileo were flanked by reproductions of Raphael, and who after writing a memoir for the Academy, found relaxation in reading Racine. He was also a man of tenacious character who set himself a single problem at the outset of his career and spent his entire lifetime in solving it.

Powerful brains, like Leibniz and Arago, dispersed their energies in a multitude of investigations without carrying any to their ultimate conclusion.

Laplace, on the contrary, remains 'the man of celestial mechanics', the man who, come wind and high water, in the face of political events, wars and revolutions, pursued his purpose without allowing himself to be halted by any consideration whatever. Nothing diverted him from the path he had mapped out for himself. What importance could reverses of fortune or political upheavals have for this man whose aim was to prove that the motions of the heavenly bodies would continue for ever and ever?

Two years after his arrival in Paris, Laplace already enjoyed an enviable reputation and he was within an ace—at the age of twenty-three!—of being elected to the Académie des Sciences. The Revolution, though it forced him to make a 'tactical withdrawal' to Melun, did not deflect him from his work, since he profited by his enforced retirement to write his *Exposition du Système du Monde*. An ardent Bonapartist under the Consulate, which made him Minister of the Interior, then under the Empire, which made him a Count, a Chancellor of the Senate and a Grand Officer of the Legion of Honour (the highest degree at the time), he was a royalist again under the Restoration, which turned him into a Marquis. No doubt he cared little for these changes of label, so long as the government of the day supplied him with the means to prosecute his investigations.

He had, in any case, no particular talent for politics, to judge by his setbacks as Minister of the Interior. And the fact that, when the Convention reformed the calendar, he proposed to date our era from 1250, the year when the major axis of the terrestrial orb was perpendicular to the line of the equinoxes, showed that he had little sense of opportunism. . . .

The universe? A perpetual-motion apparatus

It happened in 1773. Laplace was twenty-four. The first result fell into his hands: he showed that the small divergencies noted in the motions of the planets did not accumulate with time, but consisted of alternating variations in both directions. Instead of becoming progressively distorted, the orbit of each planet did not leave a fixed plane and its major axis was invariable.

Nor was there any risk of the Moon crashing on the Earth, Jupiter falling on to the Sun or Saturn flying off into space: the slight inequalities that inspired these pessimistic prognostications were also periodic. And it was the same with the oscillations displayed by our globe: they gave no reason to fear that the pole would shift so far that Europe would develop an arctic climate and disappear beneath a sheet of ice, nor that the amplitude of the tide would increase until the ocean flowed all over the continents. In short, by the time he had completed his investigations Laplace had proved that the solar system was perfectly stable. It was an enormous machine of regular action and set to run indefinitely.

After the passage of fifty years this conclusion doubtless seems a trifle over-optimistic and even illusory. Its author did not possess all the data we have at our disposal today; he was unaware of the existence of Uranus, Neptune, Pluto and the minor planets, and consequently did not take their perturbations into account. Nor did he possess the figures and theories regarding the Moon elaborated by Delaunay, Hansen and Brown. But the Laplacian synthesis came far closer to reality than any previous theory, and we can picture the enthusiasm with which its precision and soundness were received by his contemporaries. It was the first time they had been presented with an explanation of the universe in which metaphysics had no place. Laplace's assertion of the stability of the solar system was a deduction arrived at through a strict chain of mathematical reasoning, which showed no fissure through which the slightest trickle of the supernatural could penetrate.

And there was more to it than that. The starry vault, which only yesterday had been the ideal field for religious meditiation, the heavenly bodies whose movements seemed the most tangible proof of the existence of God, now suggested exactly the opposite. The circulation of the planets, regulated by differential equations obtained from Newton's law, did not prove there was no God; it simply ignored him.

Laplace was not an atheist, but the advocate of a nebulous deism. When Bonaparte, after glancing through the *Mécanique céleste* with which the scientist had just presented him, remarked, 'Newton often spoke of God in his book. I have looked through yours, but I did not see this name once,' Laplace replied, 'Citizen First Consul, I did not need that hypothesis.' Hearing of this answer one day from Bonaparte, Lagrange sighed, 'And yet it was a fine hypothesis: it explained so many things!'

Not only had Laplace demonstrated the stability of the solar system, but, in the process, he had made a number of discoveries whose importance the future was to show. For example, Halley had previously noticed that the speed of the Moon's motion was continually increasing—in fact it was this *secular acceleration* which gave rise to the fear that our satellite would eventually fall on to the Earth. Laplace proved that this acceleration was really periodic and arose from the fact that the terrestrial orbit is more or less eccentric over a span of time. This explanation was correct but, as we now know, very incomplete. In this instance the whole interest of Laplace's explanation lies in what was missing from it. For the important factor in relation to the acceleration of the Moon is not so much that the latter speeds up as that the Earth slows down (p. 229).

Laplace gathered together all his findings, as well as those of his forerunners that had been of use to him, in a book that was to become the *Almagest* of the nineteenth century, the astronomers' Bible, his *Mécanique céleste*. The first two volumes, published in 1798 and 1799, consisted of a preliminary exposition of the general theories; the two subsequent volumes (1802 and 1805) contained the essence of his work, the application of these theories to the heavenly bodies; a final volume, published in 1825, was devoted to certain special investigations.

Nowadays we look upon the *Mécanique céleste* as one of those books which, throughout the ages, have changed the course of civilization, like the *Almagest* itself, the *Discours de la Méthode* or Newton's *Principia*. It marked the end of the mystical phase in the history of science and the beginning of the determinist and rationalist phase. Before its appearance, mankind could not shake off the idea that natural phenomena were arbitrary, that they might change at any moment in response to a superior will. After its appearance, the universe seemed like a vast but simple machine, subject to the same mechanical laws as industrial machinery. On this point, too, the future was to bring many reservations, but none of these were foreseen at the time. For the past hundred years Newton's *Principia* had been a bedside book for scientists and had set them their tasks. Laplace's *Mécanique céleste* took its place during the next hundred years. The scientific ideal which it propounded, the imposition of a mathematical formalism upon nature, became the model and aim of all the sciences and dominated the rising century.

Covered with glory and honours, surrounded by the unanimous admiration of the world, Laplace died at Paris on 5 March, 1827—a century after Newton. He had dismantled the works of the universe, spread the parts out on the table and explained their action as fully as scientists could wish.

He even addressed this explanation to laymen in an *Exposition du Système du Monde* (1796), which was continually reissued with growing success. Not content with painting a picture of the planetary system, he even sketched out a hypothesis regarding its origin. The same thing had already been attempted by Buffon in 1749 and Kant in 1755. As may be supposed, Laplace approached the task in a far more realistic spirit. No doubt every reader of this book knows the famous Laplacian Cosmogony or Nebular Hypothesis, the theory that the planets were formed from rings of fluid matter which, after being produced by the rotation of the original nebula, progressively condensed. He did not, incidentally, accord his cosmogony the importance subsequently attached to it by others, but his contemporaries may be excused for deeming that the great astronomer had thus set the seal on his mechanical theory of the universe.

After Laplace there seemed to be no more dark corners in the sky. The *Mécanique céleste* had cast the light of scientific knowledge everywhere, and thanks to it human intelligence now felt equal to the most formidable of puzzles.

Herschel, or the passion for seeing

On 27 April, 1781, the *Journal de Paris*, in an article signed J. de Lande, reported an event that certainly left most of its readers cold. An amateur astronomer in England, a Mr. Hertstchel or Herschell, a musician of Bath, had, on 13 March, spotted a comet. The curious thing was that this comet had no tail.

Nowadays, when news of this kind reaches astronomers it touches off a well-established mechanism. Observers look for the newcomer through their telescopes; they keep it in view as long as they can and measure its co-ordinates; then they pass these on to their mathematical colleagues, who set about determining the orbit and ascertaining the identity of this new member of the solar family.

The same thing happened when the aforesaid Mr. Herschel made his discovery. He at once notified Mr. Maskelyne, the Astronomer Royal, and the news soon spread from Greenwich to scientific circles on the Continent. The French expert on comets, Charles Messier (1730–1817), who had studied forty-six of them, began to shadow the luminary; the President of the High-Court, Bochart de Saron (1730–93), who found relaxation from his Parliamentary duties in calculating cometary orbits, tried to fit it into his equations—and found that it did not go: the data furnished by observation did not agree with a parabolic orbit. Was it not a parabola, but a greatly elongated ellipse? That was highly improbable. Then Laplace took over. He quickly showed that the comet's path was quite simply a prolate ellipse and, consequently, that the supposed comet was neither more nor less than a planet.

To comprehend the stir this news created in the cultured world we must recall that, since earliest times, the planetary universe had always been limited to the five known orbs, Mercury, Venus, Mars, Jupiter and Saturn. It no more occurred to the great Newton than to Galileo, Kepler, Copernicus, Hipparchus or Aristotle that there might be others. Science, philosophy, scholastics, theology—St. Thomas Aquinas, Halley the atheist and the pious Flamsteed—had always been convinced that the solar system was confined to these five units. The time was past when there were believed to be seven orbs in the sky because there were seven openings in the head, seven deadly sins and the candlestick of the Temple had seven branches; but that there were only five planets was an article of faith as indisputable as Euclid's postulate, the sphericity of the Earth or that 2 and 2 make 4.

The discovery of a new planet was a thunderclap in the peaceful sky. All at once the discoverer's name spread around; people asked each other curiously who this Mr. Herschel could be, how a musician came to make a discovery that had been overlooked by the Astronomer Royal, M. de Cassini and all the pundits of science, and the stages in his astonishing career were related with amusement.

Today the feelings of scientists towards Herschel have developed somewhat. It is not so much his revelation of the planet Uranus that arouses their admiration as his staggering prescience in the field of stellar astronomy. The spotting of Uranus is now considered only a prologue to a series of discoveries that transformed classical astronomy and laid the foundations of modern astrophysics. But a century passed before this was realized and the impressive scope of Herschel's work appreciated.

Some readers may have been surprised to see the names of Laplace and Herschel linked at the head of this chapter. But such a marriage is entirely characteristic of the universe of their day. The great French geometer explained this universe entirely by deductive reasoning, without any recourse to the telescope; while the great Hanoverian astronomer furnished a complete and objective picture of it. Laplace was the brain, Herschel the eyes. The former, trusting only to pure mathematical reasoning, defended himself against anything that might be an illusion of the senses or a figment of the imagination; the latter, an incomparable observer, drew a faithful picture of the firmament, but without forbidding himself such fanciful hypotheses as that of the *island universes*.

Laplace and Herschel—two parallel lives, since they were born and died a few years apart, since they were interested in the same object seen from two opposite sides, but how different humanly speaking. If Laplace was the born scientist, the official figure brought up on classical studies, who won fame with epoch-making discoveries as soon as he was launched in life, Herschel represented the poor amateur who picked up his knowledge where he could find it, a scientific outsider who, ablaze with the sacred fire, embarked upon his career at an age when other people are already thinking of retirement.

Herschel was not a priest, as most earlier scientists had been, men like Flamsteed, Bradley, Maskelyne, Picard, La Caille, Pingré, Boscovich—even Laplace began by studying theology All his early work was done as an amateur, without the use of any official observatory and with no concern as to whether his discoveries might benefit navigation or geography, which gave him all the greater freedom to devote himself to pure science. All these characteristics, which distinguished him from his pre-Revolutionary forerunners, made of the 'father' of Uranus a scientist of the nineteenth rather than the eighteenth century and, in spite of chronology, brought him closer to Shapley, born one hundred and fifty years after him, than of Cassini IV, his contemporary.

William Herschel, who was born in Hanover, Germany, on 25 November, 1738, was the son of a gardener turned musician. He himself was a musician turned astronomer. At thirty-five, having immigrated to England, he was still a poor organist at Bath, earning a living by playing the organ and giving lessons and an occasional concert. But at night, after a sixteen- or eighteen-hour day, the musician found relaxation in reading a popular work on astronomy.

The book was written by Ferguson, an amateur who had kept sheep till he was fourteen and had preserved his taste for contemplating the night sky. No doubt he communicated his enthusiasm to his reader, for Herschel was henceforth devoured by impatience to see for himself all the wonders described.

For this he needed a telescope. The musician made several, the length of which increased with his ambitions. We can imagine how awkward to manage these enormous tubes must have been (the longest was 30 feet), and the organist did not have the resources of an official observatory to enable him to use them in comfort. One day he tried a reflecting telescope, found it infinitely handier and, as his purse would not run to buying one, decided to make one for himself.

Little has been said so far of the reflecting telescope. Since the first experiments made by the Jesuit Zucchi (p. 122) it had been submerged by the popularity of the refracting telescope. In the reflecting telescope the image from the sky, instead of being received by a lens (the object-glass), falls upon a concave mirror. After magnification by this mirror, it may be further magnified and examined with the aid of a lens serving as an eye-piece. As a mirror presents only one surface, whereas an object-glass has two, it is easier to manufacture large reflectors than large refractors, so that the former can be made to give far brighter images.

Why then, since they were invented at the same time, did the refracting and the reflecting telescope have such different destinies, in spite of the latter's incontestable advantages? Because the reflector had certain drawbacks. There was the minor difficulty of training it on a heavenly body, because in order to see this body in the mirror the observer had to turn his back towards it. This problem was solved by reflecting the image in the principal mirror on to a small secondary mirror, which in turn reflected it towards the observer (a system employed by Gregory, Newton and Cassegrain). More serious difficulties were connected with the bronze used for the mirror. It was as yet impossible to make this of glass and so white bronze was employed, composed of copper with thirty-five per cent tin. This white bronze was a hard alloy, unaffected by the atmosphere and easy to polish, but very heavy and very brittle. Nevertheless, mirrors several times as wide as the 4-inch object-glasses usual in refracting telescopes could be produced from it. The supremacy of the refractor must, therefore, have been firmly anchored in tradition not to have succumbed to the obvious superiority of its rival.

This superiority did not escape Herschel; that was why, in 1773, he set about grinding a mirror.

Nowadays we can hardly imagine a private individual turning himself into a metallurgist for such a purpose, building himself a furnace, stocking up with metal and coal, working out the proportions of the alloy, moulding a thick disc, then polishing the surface of the disc and transforming the spherical concavity into a parabolic concavity to less than 1/14,000 of a millimetre. Yet that was the task undertaken by this musician—an organist by day, entrancing his audience with the gentle harmonies of cantatas and oratorios, at night struggling with solid matter in his kitchen that had become a foundry and his drawing-room now an optical workshop.

Uranus: the solar system draws back its frontiers

Only those readers who have themselves ground mirrors—nowadays of glass—will understand William Herschel's delight when, on 4 March, 1774, he was able to train upon the skies the first instrument made by his hands. It was only a small reflecting telescope 5 inches in diameter, but it immediately disclosed to him the nebula of Orion. Straight away music lost its hold, his violin lay neglected in a corner and books on astronomy and celestial charts piled up on his piano in place of scores. Pupils continued to come for lessons, but it was not unusual for the master, seeing the sky clear in the middle of a lesson, to spring to his feet as though electrocuted and, unable to resist the temptation, run to his eye-piece, leaving his pupil to struggle with double crotchets.

Herschel's first telescope had a focal length of 5 feet 6 inches; a second followed with 7 feet; a third with 10 feet, a fourth, then others, dozens, hundreds of others. . . . In twenty years, more than 400 mirrors came out of the little workshop at Bath. The astronomer used some of them; the rest he sold to amateurs capable of benefiting from them—and paying for them.

It was with his reflecting telescope of 7 feet focus and 6 inches useful diameter, with a magnification of 200 times, that Herschel was exploring the constellation of the Heavenly Twins, on the evening of 13 March, 1781, when he caught sight of a star that was larger than the others and not shown on the charts. Was it a comet? The astronomer hastened to inform the director of Greenwich Observatory. . . . And we know what followed, how the supposed comet became a planet, the planet Uranus, and the sensation it caused among scientific circles of the day.

The planetary system, the frontier of which had hitherto been marked by Saturn at a distance $9\frac{1}{2}$ times greater than that from the Earth to the Sun, now expanded to more than 19 times this distance. It was suddenly doubled in extent, enlarging the rule of Newton's law and the area within which globes were subject to the Sun to 1,782 million miles.

Herschel derived great fame from revealing this new world to mankind. But honours do not keep body and soul together, and Herschel had reached an age—he was now forty-four—when a man grows tired of living from hand to mouth and seeks to place his existence on a solid foundation. Nevertheless George III had to be lavish with grants, pensions and donations before the organist consented finally to abandon music for astronomy. Then he left the little house at Bath and moved into more spacious quarters in a pleasant property at

Slough, near Windsor Castle, where the open horizon allowed him to employ the full power of his telescopes.

At Slough Herschel completed his inventory of the planetary world. The balance-sheet showed a handsome profit: two satellites of Uranus discovered in 1787, two satellites of Saturn in 1789. Yet it was little compared with the prodigious harvest he reaped when, a Columbus of infinite space, he set out to conquer the vast world of the stars.

A stride towards the stars

Let the reader glance back over the 209 pages that precede this one; let him recall the investigations of Ptolemy, Kepler, Galileo, Newton, Laplace; let him visualize the mass of studies which, by the end of the eighteenth century, had laid the foundations of astronomy—he will see that this vast accumulation of effort, these observations and theories, concern only the solar system. The heavens, from Thales to Laplace, meant the world of the planets. It alone counted; it alone offered a grip by means of which it could be geared to mathematics. Beyond it lay the stars—true, but of what interest were they except as a guide to navigators? The universe consisted of a few planets, satellites and comets, strictly regulated by the laws of mechanics, against a back-cloth of myriads of stars, simple points of light, mere landmarks on charts of the sky.

Similarly, the section of the town or the village in which he was born seems to the little boy who first lets go of his mother's hand the whole universe, while what lies beyond is only a confused mass of objects from which no good can come.

There is no cause for surprise at this. Whereas the planets, Sun and Moon presented to the astronomer varied surfaces with a visible and sometimes changing topography, whereas their motions, orbits and eclipses posed any number of fascinating problems, whereas every amateur, stimulated by a popularizer like Fontenelle, could picture these worlds resembling the Earth and give his imagination free rein concerning them, the stars offered nothing of all this. Even in the most powerful refracting telescopes they appeared only as dots of no size, they never shifted in relation to one another, and their only claim to attention was their fixity, which made them stand out conspicuously on the mariner's sextant and the geographer's theodolite.

Fascinated by the study of the motion of the planets, the greatest scientists, from Galileo to Laplace, rarely took any heed of the stars, which raised no problems. Their sole function was to figure in tables of co-ordinates. While the planets raised serious problems, from the vagaries of astrology to G. D. Cassini's diagrams and Laplace's equations, the stars appeared to men of science only as severe rows of figures in the column of right ascensions and declinations.

No, there is no cause for surprise. Things were bound to be like this while the poor refracting telescopes of Herschel's day remained useless for any other tasks than those of positional astronomy. To attack the empire of the stars required instruments of far greater range and luminosity. To discern that this empire might be of importance, that it might be worth studying, also required an intelligence which was not the slave of inflexible discipline, which allowed itself to be swayed by imagination and hypothesis and was capable of combining these two in the right proportions.

These things required the genius of William Herschel.

The latter was now at Slough, a member of the Royal Society and cynosure of all the astronomers of Europe. His appetite for seeing and knowing found satisfaction in the construction of giant reflectors. The earlier ones of 10 or 20 feet focus were now succeeded by huge appliances of 30 to 40 feet. In his garden, visitors viewed with respect a strange scaffolding carrying a tube over 40 feet in length and 5 feet in diameter, which was raised and lowered by pulleys and pivoted on roller bearings. The observer perched on a movable platform at the orifice of the tube, which was a reflecting telescope of 5 feet 10 inches aperture. He shouted his instructions to two assistants at the crank-handles of the winches. The magnification? It may have been 3,000, 4,000 or 5,000 times . . . . With such a means of sounding the heavens at his command, how could Herschel, after exploring the solar system, fail to be tempted by the more distant stars?

The first time a layman looks at a star through a telescope he is profoundly disappointed. All the planets show apparent discs, Saturn displays its rings, Jupiter its satellites, the Moon its 'craters', and we can let our imaginations play around the greenish patches on Mars and the mysterious surface of Venus. But a star shows nothing of this sort. Even at the most powerful magnification a star remains a point. It is not this dimensionless point that impresses the layman; it was not this which provided the spur to Herschel's activity. The wonderful thing is that this star, which appears to the naked eye to be alone in a dark corner of the sky, when observed through the eye-piece is only a unit in a field of stars stretching as far as the eye can see.

If the naked eye counts less than 7,000 stars in the two hemispheres, a simple pair of field-glasses shows 23,000, a 4-inch refractor 1,000,000, while Herschel's reflector revealed to him, in certain regions of the sky, serried ranks of stars as close together as blades of grass in a meadow. What were these stars? How many of them were there? How far did they stretch? What place did the planetary system occupy in the sidereal system? This was the first time that the sidereal universe had disclosed itself and enabled a human being to ask himself these questions. It was to these questions that Herschel sought an answer.

Motionless on his little platform from dusk to dawn, he began a 'review of the stars' that was to take years. His assistants kept the machinery in continual movement, following the motion of the stars. The icy nights of winter were the clearest, and the astronomer indefatigably prosecuted his celestial inventory, keeping his face and hands warm by massaging them with raw onion.

At his feet, seated at a small desk barely sheltered from the cold, his secretary took down his observations as he dictated them. His secretary, that is to say his sister Caroline (1750–1848), a gentle spinster, who had shown herself a talented musician while her brother was a musician, and now that he had been metamorphosed into an astronomer also changed into a gifted astronomer. She had first helped William to make mirrors, putting the food into his mouth when he could not take his hands from the surface without risk of damaging it; now, disregarding her fatigue and the cold that froze the ink in the ink-well and numbed her fingers, she faithfully jotted down the information dropped to her from the darkness above. In her spare time, she too observed with her little reflecting telescope that magnified twenty times, discovered eight comets and published a short catalogue of stars.

The Sun is drifting in the sky

The first problem Herschel set himself was both the loftiest and the most difficult: how far away are the stars? It had long been known that no process of triangulation had any chance of success in their case. The stars appeared to be incomparably farther away than the most distant planet. Herschel, however, considered that remote as they were their distances nevertheless varied. Some were closer than others and was it not possible that an effect of parallax between the more distant and the nearer stars might be obtained?

Let us imagine, as we did on page 69, that we are looking out of a window at a post standing at the edge of the pavement and an electric pylon on the horizon, both lying in the same direction. When we move from one part of the room to another, the post seems to shift in relation to the pylon. Similarly, Herschel wondered whether, if two stars at varying distances were seen in the same direction, the oscillation of the Earth would produce a parallactic shift between them.

For this purpose, pairs of stars had to be found that were sufficiently close together from the viewpoint of the observer. Since Riccioli (1650), astronomers had known of the existence of *double stars*, that is to say stars which looked perfectly normal to the naked eye, but became double when seen through the telescope. Huygens, Hooke and Bradley had sighted several of these heavenly couples. When Herschel took the matter up, the harvest was vastly more abundant. By 1782 he had recorded 260, whose angular divergence he had measured, while by 1803 the total had reached over 800.

He sought in vain, however, to discern any parallax effect in these double stars. He found nothing of the kind, but nature presented him with a consolation prize: he noted that in some pairs one of the stars seemed to revolve around the other, as if it was really attached to it by gravitation. In 1803 he became convinced that there were two sorts of double stars: one lot were only 'optical couples', the components of which might be very far apart and only brought together by perspective; the others were really 'mechanical couples', *binary* stars, linked to one another by Newton's law and composed of a satellite star revolving round a sun star.

As a matter of fact, the possibility of such pairs had already been suspected some years earlier by the German Christian Mayer and the Englishman John Mitchell, but it was Herschel's achievement to convert this suspicion into certitude. He observed stars such as Castor (of the Twins), γ Virginis, and γ Leonis, calculated the rotation period of the satellite star around the principal star (342 years in the case of Castor, 708 of γ Virginis, 1,200 of γ Leonis), showed that these motions were regulated by Kepler's laws exactly like those of the planets and, consequently, that Newton's law retained its full force even at these stupendous distances.

After this, the traditional 'fixity' of the stars seemed highly dubious. It was only a first approximation that made them appear eternally immovable. The 800 double stars listed by Herschel showed that in hundreds of cases the immense distance alone prevented the motion from being perceptible.

What else might this distance not also conceal? Was it not possible that the stars might move about the sky? On this point, too, the absolute fixity of the stars had been an article of faith since the Mesopotamians. They had been regarded as absolutely motionless since the very earliest times; if the catalogues of Hipparchus, Ptolemy, Tycho Brahe, Flamsteed and Lalande all ascribed to them the same place in the sky—after taking into account precession and aberration—if geodesists and navigators confidently relied on their co-ordinates, this was because their stability was a law that brooked no exception.

And yet. . . .

Yes, since Halley exceptions had been known to exist. The fact that, as Halley noted in 1718, there was a difference of about one degree in the position of Sirius, Aldebaran and Arcturus as between Hipparchus's catalogue and Flamsteed's might be due to an error. But when Lalande reported similar discrepancies in 1781 and showed, after close study, that they could be attributed neither to errors nor to periodic phenomena such as precession, there was no escaping it—these stars had moved. True, the annual shift was infinitesimal: the greatest displacement would have been covered by the width of a needle seen from six yards; but in 1,800 years the displacement of Arcturus, for example, amounted to no less than $1°\,7'$. This meant the downfall of a dogma that was as old as the world and upon which nobody had hitherto dared to cast doubt: the absolute fixity of the stars could no longer be accepted as a fact.

When we are sitting in a stationary train standing alongside another and the latter begins to move, we at once ask ourselves whether it is this train which is starting or our own. Similarly, when we learn that the stars have shifted slightly in the sky, we are entitled to ask whether it is really the stars that are moving—or is it the Earth, or rather the solar system? In the case of the train there is a simple means of settling our doubt. We have only to look out of the opposite window: if it is our train that is starting up, all outside objects will seem to be flying away behind us at the same speed. In the case of the stars, the problem is naturally far more complicated. Johann Lambert (1728–77), a former tailor's apprentice from Alsace, was the first to envisage it. In 1761 he came to the conclusion that the movement of the stars might very well be real; but as the Sun seemed also, in the last analysis, to be a star, it must also be moving. The apparent shift of the stars must therefore be due both to their own motion and to that of the Sun.

Twenty years later, this problem was tackled by Herschel. Thanks to Maskelyne he possessed certain meagre, but reliable data: the movement of a dozen stars, notably Sirius, Castor, Pollux and Arcturus. It was the direction of this movement that gave him the solution. Remember the example of the starting train: all outside objects seem to fly away behind us. Herschel realized that if it was our solar system that was in motion, all outside objects—that is to say, the stars—must appear to fly away behind it. In other words, it was up to observation to supply the answer. If it showed that all the stars moved in the same direction, this would mean that the solar system was moving in exactly the opposite direction.

The Slough astronomer discovered in 1783 that such was indeed the case. Apart from their proper motion, the apparent shift of the stars reflected, by a simple perspective effect, a certain movement of the solar system in space. In 1805 he located the direction, the *apex*, of this movement. It was a point in the constellation of Hercules close to star γ. Towards this point the Sun, drawing its retinue of planets, had been heading since the beginning of time at a velocity which it was left to the future to determine.

An inventory of the nebulae

There is certainly no need to emphasize here how greatly Herschel's scientific method differed from the classical method. He did not regard positional astronomy, with its tables of co-ordinates and its star catalogues, as anything but an indispensable base of operations. He resolutely escaped from the planetary domain which had hitherto constituted the sole playground of astronomers. He launched out into the empire of the stars and resolved problems his predecessors had never thought of. We must bear in mind that the very moment when Herschel was working on his review of the heavens at the eye-piece of his giant reflectors, official observers were still glued to their divided circles and fussing over decimal places. Herschel forged ahead, plunging every evening deeper and deeper into space. He was soon pointing out to Caroline nebulous areas of whitish light, of all shapes and sizes, dotted about among the stars.

As we may imagine, Herschel was fully conversant with the observations already made on these *nebulae*. Since Peiresc discovered that of Orion in 1610 and Simon Marius that of Andromeda in 1616, several others had been added to the list: the *Trifid* nebula in Sagittarius, the clusters in the Centaur and Hercules—six in all according to Halley in 1714; three hundred according to Messier in 1781. This latter astronomer, whose private observatory was in Paris, at the palace of Cluny, drew attention to himself first by his discoveries of comets, then by his catalogue of nebulae, the first of its kind. He himself had discovered sixty-one of them. Contrary to what might be thought, this catalogue is not only of historical interest: even now astronomers continue to refer to certain clusters and nebulae by their number in Messier's catalogue. Baade, like Herschel, knows the nebula of Andromeda as *Messier 31*, or *M 31*, and that of Orion as *M 42*.

Herschel resumed Messier's work, but on a totally different scale. In 1786 he presented to the Royal Society a provisional list of 1,000 nebulae and clusters, which increased by another 1,000 in 1789, and by a further 500 in 1802. This total of 2,500 included a wide variety of objects. The most typical were, on the one hand, the clusters of stars—such as the Pleiades (*M 45*) which appear to be six in number when seen with the naked eye, but become 200 when looked at through a telescope; and on the other, nebulae like that of Orion, which are hazy, without clear outlines, resembling a cloud with ragged edges. Between these two extremes Herschel established a sort of gradation, from clusters of distinct stars through more and more compact groups to agglomerations in which the stars were far too crowded to be separable. The last stages of these agglomerations were milky patches of curious shape, looking like a piece of lace, a horse-shoe, a crab, a ring, the clapper of a bell or a comet.

Imagine that we are flying in an aeroplane sufficiently high above a town for the pedestrians and cars to have disappeared from sight, while all the streets are still visible. Rising higher, we see only the main thoroughfares. Higher still, the town becomes a dark patch with a more or less broken outline and criss-crossed by thin light-coloured threads. At the maximum height the threads disappear, leaving only the patch. Whether this is round, oval or quadrilateral, we shall have no hesitation in declaring, 'That's a town,' even if we cannot identify it. Suddenly, after showing us several patches of this kind, the pilot interrupts us and says, 'No it isn't, the patch you are looking at is not a town, but a lake.'

When Herschel set about listing nebula after nebula and watched them, as he saw them at increasing magnifications, break down into stars, he thought at first that all of them, even those that consisted of nothing but a vague luminous mist, were made up of stellar agglom-erations of which the stars were confused by distance. But in 1791 he changed his mind. Some of them seemed so far removed from having a stellar structure that he could not believe them to be composed of stars. He came to think that, if many of these objects were really asterisms, others might be true clouds, more or less ragged and luminous. Perhaps, even, there were some which were completely black? He actually found, to his surprise, certain areas totally devoid of stars, like 'holes in the sky'. The riddle of these blank spaces was not solved till later, but the great astronomer was inclined to believe that they were in the nature of screens, opaque clouds masking what lay behind them. Anyhow, and confining himself to the visible agglomerations and nebulae, there must be two kinds: those which were *resolvable* into stars, and those which were made up of some mysterious 'phosphorescent matter' and remained *unresolvable*.

Inventory, classification, study of the nebulae, whether resolvable or otherwise, discovery of the binary stars, revelation of the proper motion of the Sun—the very listing of such achievements is enough to distinguish Herschel from the astronomers who were his predecessors or contemporaries. How alien to him was the problem of longitude. With what disdain he regarded the Moon, that miserable suburb of the Earth, he who felt at ease only in the limitless expanses of stellar astronomy. What concerned him were not the usual practical applications—telling the time of day, determination of co-ordinates, map-making—nor even those fundamental theories of planetary astronomy to which Laplace had devoted his life; what occupied his mind were questions to which, hitherto, only philosophers had dared to aspire. What is the universe? What place within it does the solar system occupy? What, above all, is this wide irregular band that girdles the night sky with its hazy light, the Milky Way? These were problems of unaccustomed breadth, which the ancient philosophers had treated with their usual presumption and their usual scientific ignorance, but which Herschel tackled, as may be imagined, in a very different spirit.

The plan of the universe

It was a long time since anyone, except the poets, had taken the stars for golden nails hammered into the vault of heaven. Huygens was the first to regard them as globes similar to our Sun. The starry universe seemed to him like an ocean of suns, scattered at incalculable distances from the Earth and one another.

This was a wildly audacious idea against which the Church was ready to hurl its thunderbolts. At first no one would express it openly save atheists like Huygens and Halley. It did indeed conjure up truly vertiginous possibilities. If every star was a sun, the Milky Way, which is a conglomeration of stars, became an accumulation of suns, each one of which might have its entourage of planets, perhaps inhabited by living creatures and even by human beings. . . . Was such a view tenable?

There can be no reader of this book who has not been struck, on some clear and moonless night, by the vast luminescent arc of the Milky Way. It stretches from one horizon to the other, enclosing whole constellations under its immense arch. It runs right round the Earth, varying in width and density from point to point and dividing in two when it enters the constellations of the Swan and Scorpion.

The first to consider that it was nothing but an enormous agglomeration of stars, too far away to be distinguished individually, was the Ionian philosopher Democritus of Abdera (b. *c.* 460 B.C.). His intuition was correct, but it was not confirmed until Galileo trained the first telescope on the Milky Way and saw it resolve into stardust.

This discovery raised a delicate question. If the Sun was really only a star, like any one of its myriads of brother orbs, what was its place in the whole complex? Since Galileo, astronomers had had the greatest difficulty in winning acceptance for the heliocentric system, that is to say in placing the Sun at the centre of the universe; now they had succeeded, the Sun was threatened, doubts were cast on the justice of its claim to this privileged position. Giordano Bruno was burned for less than that. . . .

But liberty of thought had made headway since 1600, especially in Protestant countries. Five hundred and fifty years later, an Englishman named Thomas Wright (1711–86), who had been in succession a clockmaker, sailor, mechanician, teacher and engraver on copper, propounded an idea that does not seem to us now so very unreasonable. He supposed that the whole mass of all the stars had the shape of a millstone or a girdle-cake. The Sun was inside the girdle-cake some-where near the centre, a position that explains the appearance of the Milky Way: when we look at the sky in the direction of one of the radii of the girdle-cake, our eyes traverse the latter at its greatest width and meet the maximum number of stars; these stars then seem to form a kind of girdle around the sky. Our eyes encounter the minimum number, on the contrary, when we look 'upwards' or 'downwards' in relation to the girdle-cake.

Five years later, in 1755, this hypothesis received powerful support from none other than Immanuel Kant. At the same time, since the illustrious Koenigsberg philosopher was not a man to accept someone else's work as it stood, he added his own. In Kant's view, the universe was not confined to the girdle-cake of the Milky Way, a solitary island in the ocean of the heavens; it was occupied by a multitude of islands scattered at immeasurable distances. The Great Universe became an archipelago of *island universes*, which were nothing else than the tiny whitish fleeces of the nebulae, of which Halley had recorded six examples forty years earlier.

We must admire this prescience on the part of the author of the *Critique of Pure Reason*, a prescience which forestalled by 170 years our most up-to-date conceptions. But let us not forget that this was pure speculation and supposition. There is no certainty that Kant ever put his eye to a telescope, and in any case his turn of mind forbade him to envisage any experimental method of ascertaining whether his grandiose hypotheses had the slightest basis in fact.

Even more gratuitous was the extravagant construction erected by Lambert in 1761. According to him, the Great Universe was a com-plicated system of partial universes one inside the other. The planets revolved round the Sun, the Sun round a certain star X, the latter, together with the whole of the Milky Way, round a super-centre, which in turn . . . and so on.

When, after Wright, Kant and Lambert, we come to William Herschel, we find ourselves once more on the firm ground of rational experiment. This great self-taught scientist was not hampered, like so many other men of science, by a rigid intellectual armour. He had not received, like Laplace, a basically Scholastic training, intended to curb untimely flights of the imagination and keep those of hypothesis to the paths of scientific orthodoxy. Laplace, too, was haunted by the great mysteries of the universe, but knowing them to be scientifically insoluble he did not allow his reason to dwell upon them. When he permitted himself to propound a cosmogony, he was careful to put it forward as only a supposition, against which he personally warned the reader to be on his guard.

But Herschel, who was not restrained by these considerations, saw no reason why a scientifically conducted investigation should not enable him to elucidate the riddles which obsessed him, the shape of the universe, its dimensions and the part played by the Milky Way. It was to these profound problems that he dedicated his labours. It was to solve them that he invented absolutely new methods of research, in which he was an original and solitary pioneer.

A gauge for the skies

How can we find out the shape of the universe, the shape of the fabulous agglomeration of stars in which the Sun is no more than a modest unit? How are we to know whether the stars stretch farther in one direction than another? Whether they extend latitudinally, so as to form the overall shape of a disc, as imagined by Wright?

Herschel based his investigations on two working hypotheses, regarded as sufficiently accurate for a first approximation. The first was that all the stars were roughly the same distance apart; the second that they all possessed roughly the same *absolute* luminosity.[1] Once these two postulates were accepted, all that was necessary in order to ascertain whether the agglomeration stretched farther in one direction than the other was to count the stars in each direction.

Herschel divided the northern sky into 3,400 small zones and set about enumerating the stars in each of them. These celestial *gauges* showed him that some parts of the Milky Way were a hundred times

---

[1] A distinction must be made between the *apparent* brightness of a heavenly body and its *absolute* brightness. The Sun appears to us 11,000 million times as bright as Sirius, but only because it is 568,500 times closer. If the Sun and Sirius were the same distance from us, the latter would really be 26 times brighter than the former. The *absolute* brightness of Sirius is therefore said to be 26 times that of the Sun.

more densely populated than others. In conformity with his basic hypothesis, he deduced from this that the stars extended a hundred times farther in the former areas than in the latter.

In 1785, he set down his initial conclusions in a treatise entitled *On the Construction of the Heavens*. Here the universe appeared, as in Wright's cosmology, as a roughly oval girdle-cake with irregular edges in which two cracks corresponded to the two bifurcations visible in the Milky Way. The Sun was not far from the centre, and Herschel estimated the maximum dimension of the whole as 950 times the distance Earth to Sun. There is no need to stress that this latter evaluation was entirely fictitious, since no one had ever succeeded in measuring the distance of a star.

The majority of British astronomers judged the whole of their compatriot's treatise to be fictitious. He was an outsider, he did not belong to any official body, he had not been brought up on the good solid diet of Newtonian mathematics; he was more interested in sketching out the structure of the cosmos than in adding another place of decimals to the co-ordinates of the stars. We can very well understand the reserved, indeed frigid reception his paper received from the Royal Society. For the latter, as for the majority of astronomers, the knowable universe was limited to the solar system. By his efforts to reconstruct the mechanism of the heavens, Laplace supplied the learned world with work enough to keep it busy for a century. How could his contemporaries fail to consider adventurous the views of Herschel, which were based not on the laws of mechanics and differential equations, but on the most dubious postulates?

In the last resort, neither Herschel nor the rest were wrong. If the others were right in wishing to unravel the problems of the planetary universe before tackling those of the stars, Herschel's only mistake was to be too far ahead of his time. One hundred years ahead, to be precise, since his work ties up directly with Shapley's in 1918.

The great astronomer became aware that his fundamental hypotheses were doubtful almost as soon as he had copyrighted his manuscript. He had supposed that the stars were distributed more or less equally everywhere. Observation showed him that, on the contrary, in certain areas, particularly in the Milky Way, they tended to congregate in special profusion. Therefore the density of their distribution was not a valid indication of the extent of the solar system in this direction. He had to abandon his attempt to reach the limits of the universe. It might even be limitless.

Herschel presented this rather disappointing conclusion in 1811 and 1817. This time it was received with the deference due to such a great man. He was just on eighty, the doyen of European astronomers, a member of the Institut de France and a foreign associate of innumerable learned societies, and in 1821 he was elected first President of the newly-founded Royal Astronomical Society. Meanwhile he had been knighted by the King and was now Sir William Herschel.

The good Caroline was still at the side of her illustrious brother, but the burden of housekeeping had been lifted from her shoulders by his marriage. William had waited till he was fifty before taking a wife—a widow, the daughter of a London businessman, who brought him a comfortable income. And he was already in his fifty-fourth year when he became the father of a son, who was also to be his successor, Sir John Herschel. Another thirty years of life remained to him after his son's birth, for he died on 25 August, 1822, at the age of eighty-four.

William Herschel rests in the cemetery of Upton, near Slough, and his tombstone bears a Latin epitaph meaning: 'He broke the barrier of the skies.'

7

A step towards the stars

From the conquest of the sky to the conquest of the universe—
France is bogged down in the Laplacian furrow—A planet at the
bottom of the ink-well—Birth of the modern object-glass—The
solar system becomes peopled with little planets—A profusion of
satellites—An abundance of telescopes for the exploration of the
heavens—Bessel, the man who codified observation of the stars—
The apex of the triangle touches the stars—The Struves, a dynasty
of astronomers—Balance-sheet before a fresh start

From the conquest of the sky to the conquest of the universe

THE death of an astronomer does not stop the Earth rotating nor even hinder people from going about their business. It is highly probable that the death of Herschel in 1822 and of Laplace in 1827 went unnoticed by the great majority. King George IV was reigning in Britain; in France, Charles X had succeeded Louis XVIII. Napoleon had just died and it was the eve of the battle of Victor Hugo's *Hernani*.

From the quarter of a century of struggle which the French Revolution brought to Europe it was Great Britain who emerged victorious. Her booty consisted less in territorial gains than in economic outlets, in openings for the immense volume of goods she was pouring out. Built on a soil containing an abundance of coal and iron, her manufacturing centres were transformed into true factories and this youthful industrial power quickly gained first place in the world and held it for the rest of the century.

It is no coincidence that the two countries which had so long been in the forefront of civilization, Great Britain and France, were also in the vanguard among the conquerors of the skies. Beside those giants, the Englishmen Newton, Halley, Bradley and Herschel, and the Frenchmen Clairaut, La Caille, Lagrange and Laplace, what weight did the Danziger Hevelius, the Italian Boscovich, the Swede Wargentin and even the German Tobias Mayer carry? The great British and French astronomers, by creating and organizing Newtonian dynamics, had presented engineers with the most effective means of harnessing nature. From celestial mechanics was derived mechanics as such, and the latter not only constituted the indispensable foundation for every technical achievement, but was also the formative influence in creating the mental outlook that characterized inventors.

Britain owes the success of her Industrial Revolution to Newtonian rationalism. Watt, Murdock and Trevithick were scientists who dealt scientifically with the problem of the steam-engine; Faraday was a great physicist who discovered the secret of steel alloys while waiting for the secret of induction; and it was a selenographic astronomer, James Nasmyth, who invented the steam-hammer.

It was to this same spirit that France owed the first triumphs of the Revolution. Quite apart from the geometer Carnot, the 'organizer of victory', remember Monge casting cannon and Lagrange working out ballistic trajectories.

Up to the first quarter of the nineteenth century the two countries had marched side by side in the conquest of the skies, one illumining every corner of the planetary mechanism, the other carrying out reconnaissance into the sidereal universe. The future seemed clear. It was for these two countries, so well supplied with knowledge and technical resources, to explore the vast expanses of the Milky Way, to bring under the control of Newtonian mechanics those stars which positional astronomy had hitherto regarded as merely insignificant points of light serving as landmarks.

Curiously, things did not happen like this. Britain alone continued the furrow ploughed by Herschel. She alone was bold enough to thrust on beyond the traditional domain of the planets. France barricaded herself inside this domain and refused to venture outside. To be sure, within this domain she celebrated splendid successes and established science's final grip on the motions of the planets, but she remained almost completely apart from that race to the stars run, behind Britain, by Germany and Russia.

Yes, the beginning of the nineteenth century saw a surprising phenomenon: France and Britain, which had hitherto kept pace along the same road towards the conquest of the skies, saw this road fork. One of the two forks—the one taken by British scientists and, after them, by those from the rest of Europe—led to stellar astronomy, the cataloguing of the stars and nebulae, investigation of their distance and shape, the constitution of the universe, all the great problems, the whole future. The other fork, taken by the French scientists, twisted and turned endlessly within the solar system and led those who followed it to resign themselves to chewing over and over, in a numberless series of special cases, the same everlasting problems of celestial mechanics that Laplace had solved once and for all. On one side of the Channel astronomers called to their aid the newest resources of science, technology and imagination, and spread out through the still virgin empire of the stars. On the other side, in Paris, they stood aside from these undertakings, deeming them risky; they shut themselves up inside the planetary redoubt which had been trampled over for so many centuries and in which nothing remained to be discovered but trifles.

How are we to explain this parting of the ways? Why was the conquest of the sidereal universe left to the British, the Germans, the Russians and the Italians, while the French got stuck in a blind alley where most of the thrilling and sensational discoveries had already been made?

There were several reasons for this, the first being that research as understood by Herschel called for considerable financial resources. The astronomer who is not content with pursuing indoor astronomy, as practised by Laplace, must procure a telescope, and if he wants to tackle the stars he needs telescopes of ever-increasing power. This naturally requires money, and also an industry capable of producing the necessary equipment. Britain had both, whereas France had been impoverished by the Napoleonic Wars and her industry hindered by lack of coal.

It must also be admitted that the country of Newton and Herschel prided herself on these two great men and bestowed a legitimate esteem upon science, whereas in France it was rather looked down upon. All the favours of power went to belles-lettres, and a deaf ear was turned to Arago when he declared before the tribunal: 'Fine words will not produce sugar beet, nor will Alexandrines extract soda from sea salt.'[1] Mathematics had an even worse press, and careful adherence to the beaten track was preferred to all the creative flights of science.

Since pure research appeared to the directors of French industry nothing but groundless speculation, this industry took care not to indulge in such a pointless activity—there was more profit to be had from resting content with things as they were and putting into practice Guizot's famous advice, 'Enrich yourselves!' Obsessed by its fear of taking chances, French industry allowed the more enterprising British to forestall them in applying the greatest inventions of the century: railways, gas lighting, electric telegraphy, steam and propeller navigation. For this reason, too, France had no part—except for photography—in the great discoveries that were to convulse the whole structure of science: spectrum analysis, the laws of energy, electromagnetism, non-Euclidian geometry, the kinetic theory of gases —every one of which proved the truth, where science is concerned, of the saying 'Nothing venture, nothing win'.

This retreat by French scientists is also explained by the persistence among them of a Cartesian spirit that had become a brake rather than a motor. Descartes had said, 'Common sense is the most widely distributed commodity in the world,' and he made this faculty the criterion of scientific reasoning. But what was splendidly audacious in 1637 was not so at all two centuries later. Sheltering under the success of such achievements as Laplace's, Cartesian rationalism enjoyed so much authority that anything that diverged from it seemed beyond the pale. To be a Cartesian and Laplacian meant to believe only in what could be seen or mathematically proved; it meant the pitiless elimination of hypothesis and the indignant rejection of the most timid suggestions of the imagination. It was by following this

[1] Robert Schnerb, *Histoire générale des Civilisations*, Vol. VI (Presses Universitaires, 1955).

policy that Laplace had disclosed the system of the world. Unfortunately, French scientists were still blinded by his brilliance; his distrust of hypothesis had become, in them, a hatred; his fear of everything that was not experiment or logical deduction, a phobia; and the creative Cartesianism which he had handled like a master, the prudence of a craven petty bourgeois.

We can now understand the cause of the divergence between French astronomy and that of the rest of Europe during the first quarter of the nineteenth century, and why the latter set out to attack the stars, while the former dared not leave the trail blazed by Laplace.

To tell the truth, the finishing touches it added to the trail were not without their value. Science is never finished. Even after Laplace had constructed the glorious edifice of celestial mechanics there remained details to be filled in and appendices to be added. The future even showed that some of these appendices were sufficiently important to gain the admiration of the world. But the solar system is a tiny district of the sky, containing a limited number of objects. Once these objects have been listed and the district mapped, little hope remains of discovering anything else of importance in it.

No scientist was thinking just then of pushing back the frontiers of the district. The whole ambition of the French, who prided themselves on being Laplace's continuators, consisted in tracing more precisely the movements of certain planets, accounting for certain perturbations and interpreting hitherto unexplained phenomena by the most recent discoveries in mechanics. Thus, throughout the century, the astronomy of this country was represented by a succession of eminent 'mechanicians', from Denis Poisson (1781–1840), who perfected Laplace's theory of the invariability of the major axes of the planets, to Henri Poincaré (1854–1912), who proved that this invariability was not as complete as had been thought and equipped the celestial workshop with an impressive set of new mathematical tools.

The memorable page written during this century by the French specialists in precision astronomy lies outside our field, but we will nevertheless extract a passage from it. It will show the unexpected repercussions that sometimes follow from the most disinterested discovery.

We refer to the theory of the Moon. A great deal has already been said about lunar theory in the course of this book and we may recall its importance in connexion with the problems of navigation (p. 187). We may also remember that Tobias Mayer drew up in 1762 tables that deserved the prize offered by the Board of Longitude in 1714. In these tables the possible error in the right ascension of the Moon was reduced to two minutes of time (as opposed to five or six in Halley's day)—but at the cost of a minor adjustment made by Mayer to the the theory to bring it into line with observation.

Naturally, this adjustment was, if we may so express it, a disastrous grain of sand in the works of the celestial machinery. Laplace strove to get rid of it. But his efforts were in vain, as were those of his continuators, the Frenchman Baron Marie-Charles-Théodore de Damoiseau de Montfort (1768–1846) in 1824, and the Dane Peter Andreas Hansen (1795–1874) in 1853. The latter, especially, made a valiant attempt to record all the perturbations to which the Moon was subject. But even after calculating a hundred of them he was obliged to reintroduce the fatal adjustment, in the shape of an empirical correction. Nor did it disappear when another distinguished mechanician, Charles Delaunay (1816–72), took account not of a hundred, but of thirteen hundred perturbations. . . .

Astronomers had to bow to the evidence, as Simon Newcomb (1835–1909), an American, did in 1878, when he stated that our satellite was subject not only to the Newtonian force of attraction, but also to some additional unknown influence.

The key to the riddle was provided in 1926 by another American mathematician, Ernest Brown (1866–1938). He realized that if the Moon was never in agreement with the theory this was not only because, due to undergoing a number of perturbations, it was getting farther and farther ahead of its time-table, but also because the Earth was slipping back. As Kant foresaw in 1752, and as Delaunay suspected, the rotation of our globe was retarded by the friction of the tides.

This conclusion has now been fully confirmed. The Earth slows down to the extent of 17.51 seconds a century, so that the duration of a day is growing imperceptibly longer. Furthermore, the invention of new types of clock, more accurate than the Earth-clock, have disclosed varying fluctuations in the diurnal rotation. Finally, contemporary astronomers recognize the impossibility of predicting the period of this rotation to within less than 1/100 of a second. This means that the legal unit of time to which industries like that of the radio, radar and atomic energy work, the second, has become insufficiently exact. According to the latest intelligence, the task of defining this unit will be left to the *atomic clock* instead of to the rotation of the globe, which is far too crude a method.

A planet at the bottom of the ink-well

We have just jumped more than a hundred years; now we must go back to the beginning of the nineteenth century, to the moment when the towering figure of Laplace dominated the whole of celestial mechanics. This great man believed he had fully explained the system of the universe. Having cast the net of his differential equations over all the inhabitants of the solar domain, he was quite convinced that he had accounted for all their movements by the law of attraction and that none of them would dare to disobey him.

We know that he was to some extent deluding himself so far as the Moon was concerned. If the five planets known since ancient times seemed far more docile—with the possible exception of Mercury—this was not so with the last-born, the famous Uranus, discovered in 1781 by Herschel. Once it had been registered as a planet, astronomers were naturally eager to calculate its orbit and determine its trajectory in the years to come. Unfortunately, observation did not accord with their predictions.

Establishing the orbit of a planet is rather like plotting the trajectory of an aeroplane. If we know its co-ordinates, its altitude and its velocity at well determined intervals, we can deduce from them the curve it will probably follow and the moment at which it will reach such and such a point in space—it is upon these conjectures that the theory of anti-aircraft defence is based. In the case of a planet the task is obviously simpler, because the moving body is not guided by the arbitrary will of a pilot and the curve is inevitably an ellipse. But account must be taken of the fact that it may be slowed down or speeded up by perturbations due to other planets. For this reason the influence of the large neighbouring planets, Saturn and Jupiter, had to be reckoned with when the tables of Uranus were calculated.

These tables were the work of a French mathematician called Alexis Bouvard (1767–1843). A little fellow from Savoy, who came to Paris as a servant, he patiently worked his way up from the free courses at the Collège de France to election to the Académie des Sciences. A born arithmetician, of the kind of which we shall see an even more remarkable specimen in a minute, he took great pleasure in carrying out the calculations required by Laplace for his *Mécanique céleste*, and it was with the same passion that he set to work on the tables of Uranus in 1820.

By this time, forty years of observations were already available. Since this planet revolves round the Sun in eighty-four years, this meant that it had already been followed along almost half its orbit. At first sight, therefore, determination of this orbit did not seem to offer any difficulty, even taking into account the action of Jupiter and Saturn. However, it was not long before a discrepancy between Bouvard's tables and reality became manifest and began to increase alarmingly, half a minute of arc in 1832, two minutes in 1845. To appreciate the full horror of this discrepancy we must recall that the positions of the other planets were being foretold, at the same moment, to within a few seconds.

One thing was certain, since Uranus went so far off its track it must be subject to other perturbations than those of Jupiter and Saturn. There must be another, and unknown, planet lurking somewhere in space, the mass and proximity of which were sufficient to bring about the deviations recorded. The director of Greenwich Observatory, George Bidell Airy (1801–92), resigned himself to believing in this planet X in 1835, the great German astronomer Bessel in 1840, and François Arago (1786–1853), director of the Paris Observatory, in 1844.

But there was a world of difference—literally—between suspecting the existence of planet X and discovering it. It had never been discerned through the telescope. The only hope of locating it lay in studying the perturbations it imposed upon Uranus. From the magnitude and direction of the perturbing force it should be possible to deduce the mass and location of the perturbing planet.

This possibility was clearly evident to astronomers. Fundamentally, it was the reverse of the usual problem, that of calculating the perturbations which a planet induced in another planet when the mass and position of the first planet were known. But, although they could clearly envisage the problem and knew quite well how to tackle it, the most celebrated mathematicians one after the other declined the honour of solving it. It was purely a numerical calculation, but a calculation so intimidating that it was more than even the most voracious figure-eaters dared to get their teeth into. Let those readers who are mathematicians visualize several dozen formulae, one member of each of which is a polynomial of some hundred terms, all of them taking the form $119,427.34 \sin (6a - 5b)$, or something of that sort; let the rest imagine thousands of multiplications of numbers of fifty digits, each one governing the next, so that an error in one is enough to render all the rest of the calculation useless.

Men capable of executing such a task were to be traced in every country. In Germany, Bessel found Flemming; in England, Airy found Adams; in France, Arago found Le Verrier. Flemming died with his task hardly begun; John Couch Adams (1819–1892) finished it in 1845, but his results, though perfectly correct, remained locked up in Airy's drawer: Le Verrier alone not only brought it to a successful conclusion and published it, but obtained the most spectacular confirmation through the discovery of the mysterious planet with the telescope.

A Norman from Saint-Lô and a student at the École Polytechnique, Urbain-Jean-Joseph Le Verrier (1811–77) did not at first have very definite plans for his future. At the age of twenty-six, while an engineer with the Tobacco Department, he applied for a post as lecturer in chemistry at the École Polytechnique. When this post was given to someone else, Le Verrier accepted that of lecturer in astronomy, which was also vacant. There could be no doubt that he was now on the right path, for this was the start of a spate of writings on celestial mechanics that appeared unceasingly in the transactions of the Académie des Sciences.

Unlike such mathematicians as Henri Poincaré, who was a deplorable computer—he boasted that he had never got an addition right in his life—Le Verrier, like Euler, Bouvard or Gauss, was passionately fond of arithmetic. 'When he wished to relax his mind he took a large sheet of paper, wrote down one above the other two numbers of fifty (and sometimes a hundred) digits, found the product and then divided this product by the first number. He regularly ended up with the second number as quotient and remainder nought.'[1] When really worn out he used to sit down on the floor with his violin—he was an accomplished musician—and play for half an hour. It seems that these varied talents did not make him stuffy, if we are to believe his pupil Emile Gautier who wrote in July 1845: 'This evening my boss (Le Verrier) and I indulged in the lark of throwing a handful of balls of phosphorus salt into the Luxembourg pond, where they exploded in the water like pretty little stars . . . a pyrotechnic exhibition that alarmed the public and the police. . . .'

July 1845—the very moment when he was getting to grips with the enormous problem set him by Arago.

On first scanning the lie of the land, he found that of the 120 minutes of arc by which Uranus deviated from its path only 20 could be attributed to Jupiter and Saturn. The remaining 100 were due to perturbations caused by the unknown planet. He then formulated the problem on the basis of certain probable data: he supposed that the planet X, circulated, like the others, in the plane of the ecliptic, that its distance from the Sun was 38 times that of the Earth (in accordance with the Titius-Bode law, which we shall discuss on page 238), and so on. The learned, and even the not so learned, public followed with interest the progress of his work, the successive stages which he reported to the Academy as he accomplished them. But no one quite believed in this attempt to discover a planet by means of equations and logarithms.

Nevertheless, Le Verrier announced his results with unshakable confidence on 31 August, 1846: the planet sought for must revolve round the Sun in 217 years and its mass must be approximately 1/9,300 of the solar mass. If a telescope were directed towards the

[1] Jacques Duclaux, *L'Homme devant l'Univers* (Flammarion, 1949).

point of the ecliptic at longitude 326° 32' (near star ι Aquarii), this planet would be seen as a small disc of 3 seconds apparent diameter.

The German astronomer Johann Gottfried Galle (1812–1910) happened to possess a recent map of this region of the sky. Everyone knows how, on 23 September, 1846, he found in the field of his telescope a star that did not appear on his map and was none other than Le Verrier's planet, less than 1 degree from the position stated. Everyone knows, too, the enthusiasm unleashed by the great French scientist's feat. The result was to be publicly announced on 5 October. On this day 'the door of the Academy, access to which was normally easy, was blocked by the crowd. Great excitement reigned in the hall, and the noise of private conversation drowned the voice of the secretary reading the minutes of the last meeting. M. Leverrier's name was on every tongue. "Where is he sitting? Point him out to us," said the outsiders, and at a gesture from some regular participant in the Academy's meetings, all eyes were turned towards a pale young man at the end of the green table, whose health, once robust, had given way beneath the weight of his crushing labours. . . .'[1]

This planet which Le Verrier had found 'at the tip of his pen', according to Arago, or 'at the bottom of an ink-well', as some humorist put it, this planet that was christened *Neptune*, surrounded the astronomer with an unparalleled halo. Admittedly, the discovery was of no practical use. 'It did not open up to science such broad vistas as other, almost contemporary, discoveries,' writes M. Danjon; 'it had no future; it aroused no hope of fresh progress in the human condition. But what a victory of mind over matter, what a spectacular demonstration of the power of science!' The greatest astronomers of the day, men like Airy, Encke and Littrow, sent their congratulations, while the discoverer was covered in ribbons and medals and all the avenues of fortune lay open before him.

Let us cast a veil over the polemic that ensued with the British (John Herschel and Challis), who were furious that the honour should have been lost to Adams and gone to a Frenchman. Their unfortunate compatriot's only fault was to have had to do with Airy, who saw his

[1] Transactions of the *Institut National* (7 October, 1846), quoted in *Le Verrier et son temps*, catalogue of the Le Verrier Exhibition (Paris Observatory, 1946).

work as no more than a laborious student's exercise. France was accused of annexing part of the firmament; the two sides reproached one another with stealing planets, and the astronomers came down from the skies to very earthy abuse.

Meanwhile Neptune pursued its slow advance under the watchful gaze of observers. The radius of the solar system, which had already been doubled by the chance discovery of Uranus, was now quadrupled by the acquisition of Neptune, the result, this time, of brilliant and systematic labour. The frontier of this system, formerly situated 887,100,000 miles from the Sun at Saturn, then 1,785,000,000 miles at Uranus, now moved back to 2,797,000,000 miles. It was the instrument forged by Laplace that had made this enormous enlargement possible. Le Verrier had taken over the Laplacian heritage and used it to push back the limits of the solar system.

Birth of the modern object-glass

The discovery of Neptune was the grand finale of celestial mechanics. It was also its swan song. No further opportunity offered for a feat of this magnitude nor to create so much public sensation. The discovery of Pluto in 1930 is no exception to this, since it seems to have been due to chance rather than to Lowell's calculations (page 285). Lagrange had already sighed: 'Newton was very lucky to have had a system of the universe to discover. Unfortunately there is only one. . . .' The experts in celestial mechanics might have given vent to a similarly disillusioned exclamation on the subject of Le Verrier and Neptune, for at this period they were out on a limb. Throughout Europe the powerful current of stellar astronomy was spreading, while the birth of astrophysics, which was to change the whole face of civilization, was in secret preparation.

Despite the obstinacy of French mathematicians, celestial mechanics was destined to lose more and more of its importance, to be less and less talked about. At that very moment observatories were being built everywhere equipped with modern equatorial telescopes; everywhere astronomers were exploring the sky directly and returning from their amazed reconnaissance of the sidereal world laden with discoveries. What did our tiny planetary kingdom, already known down to the last detail, matter to them? Just as the dramatic advent of Galileo's telescope had swept away the old astronomy of former times, so the spread of new optical appliances reduced mathematical planetary astronomy to the status of a dusty antique.

It must not be forgotten that at the base of all astronomy there lay the indispensable telescope. It served equally for measuring the stellar co-ordinates required by positional astronomy and for studying comets, for cataloguing stars or listing nebulae. No telescope, no astronomy.

What had become of this telescope since Cassini's day? We have lost sight of it for nearly a century; had its two serious drawbacks been overcome, chromatic and spherical aberration (p. 144)? Had the outsize instruments popularized by Huygens been reduced to reasonable lengths? This cannot have been the case in 1750, since Euler wrote in that year: 'At Paris they have a telescope of 120 feet, and in London one of 130 feet; but the terrible difficulties of mounting and directing them almost nullify the advantages promised from them.' Three years later, however, an obscure English amateur, Chester Moor Hall (1703–71), an Essex magistrate, solved the problem that Newton himself had declared insoluble.

The great weakness in the object-glasses of that period was their lack of achromatism. As white light is made by the fusion of a series of basic colours, the image of a star breaks up in the object-glass into so many coloured images scattered along the optical axis. Instead of being reduced to a point, it appears as a small iridescent circle. How could accurate measurements be made on such an object? The only remedy, as we have seen, was to lengthen the focal distance. But this cure was worse than the disease, since it led to telescopes so long that it was impossible to manipulate them.

In 1753 Chester Moor Hall had the following idea: since the biconvex lens forming the objective gives a different image for every colour, another must be added that would fuse all these images into one single one. He cut the Gordian knot by fixing another lens on to the front of the objective. This new lens was biconcave, made of very heavy glass with a lead base and highly refractive, so that all the images were brought back to the mean focus.

Achromatism had been achieved. The images shed their iridescent halo and telescopes could be shortened. The same year, 1753, the Essex magistrate constructed one 20 inches long with an aperture of 2½ inches.[1] Achromatism had been achieved . . . but it was another man than Hall who claimed to have invented it.

Just as the telescope first constructed in Holland was not used for astronomy until adapted by Galileo, so the achromatic objective, invented by Hall, did not really come into use until distributed by Dollond. John Dollond (1706–61), a silk manufacturer of French origin who had emigrated to London, learnt of the combination of lenses devised by Hall in 1758, and at once turned optician in order to profit from it.

The importance of the discovery is evident. As telescopes diminished in length, falling from, say, 15 to 5 feet, observation gained increased accuracy and the object-glass could be made wider, and hence more powerful, without the instrument becoming unmanageable. The tremendous progress made by modern astronomy was all contained in embryo in Dollond's achromatic lenses. The theory behind these lenses was established by Clairaut and d'Alembert, who worked out their refractive index, radius of curvature, and diameter.

One practical detail alone hindered the spread of the new objectives at the outset: it was almost impossible to manufacture the glass. The biconvex lens had to be of *crown*, a white glass with a silica base; this was not too difficult to get hold of. But the highly refractive *flint* that formed the concave lens was almost unobtainable. In spite of the prices offered by scientific societies, it was only by chance that a piece of the material large enough and pure enough to grind a lens from was extracted from the melting-pot.

Here again, the problem was solved by an amateur. It was a clockmaker, not a glassmaker, who found a means of regularly obtaining large blocks of flint—the Swiss Louis Guinand (1748–1824). He

[1] According to A. Danjon and A. Couder, *Lunettes et Télescopes* (Revue d'Optique edit., 1935).

devoted to it seven years of effort, patience and poverty. But in 1799
he was able to show Lalande flint discs that were wonderfully limpid
and 4 to 6 inches in diameter. Six years later he was called to the great
optical firm founded in Munich by von Reichenbach, and the career
of the achromatic object-glass began.

The solar system becomes peopled with little planets

The nineteenth century's contribution to the conquest of the skies
may be summarized as having consisted, on the one hand, in completing and clarifying the description of the solar system, and on the other,
in initiating the discovery of the stars. This latter undertaking we shall
discuss later. For the moment we shall merely remark that exploration
of the solar system was carried out in two different ways: by celestial
mechanics and by the telescope. Celestial mechanics led to the triumph
of tracing Neptune; the telescope provided the opportunity of coming
upon an unknown heavenly body by chance. This was a far less
spectacular method of exploration, but it nevertheless enabled a large
number of units to be added to the classical list of members of the
planetary kingdom.

We have said, on page 205, how greatly the discovery of Uranus
surprised astronomers. No one had ever imagined there might exist
another planet besides Mercury, Venus, the Earth, Mars, Jupiter and
Saturn. The irruption of Uranus shattered this conviction. It showed
that the solar system as described by the ancients was by no means
inviolable. It was no longer considered sacrilege, nor even absurd,
to believe in the existence of other globes that would one day be
extracted from the darkness. An exceedingly active German astronomer, by name Johann Elert Bode (1747–1826), director of Berlin
Observatory, made himself the champion of this thesis.

In a work published in 1772 by his countryman Johann Daniel
Titius (1729–96), Bode had come across a footnote which, thanks to
him, achieved great celebrity. By arbitrarily breaking down numbers,
Titius had hit upon a curious empirical law: the respective distances
of the planets from the Sun may be represented by the following
numbers:

Mercury: 0·4	... : 2·8
Venus: 0·7	Jupiter: 5·2
Earth: 1	Saturn: 10
Mars: 1·6	... : 19·6
	... : 38·8

Now, when Herschel had found Uranus and the distance of this planet was known, astronomers noticed that it corresponded to 19·2 times that of the Earth to the Sun—almost the figure indicated by Titius's law.[1] This coincidence filled Bode with enthusiasm. He propagated the law, which was henceforth known as 'Bode's law', and did not hesitate to predict that, since a planet had appeared to occupy the position opposite 19·6, there must certainly be another to fill the space in front of 2·8. If it had never been found between Mars and Jupiter that was merely for want of looking.

Bode's advice was acted upon by a Hungarian, Baron François-Xavier de Zach (1754–1832). He was an ex-officer who, attracted to astronomy and backed by Duke Ernest II of Saxe-Gotha, had established an observatory close to the town of Gotha. In general, the merit of this astronomer lies less in his scientific achievements than in his activities as publicist and letter-writer. Living as he did at a time when scientific exchanges were neither rapid nor easy, Zach, who made discoveries, inventions and theories known from one end of Europe to the other by his writings, is entitled to a special debt of gratitude.

To him was due the first congress of astronomy, held at Gotha in 1798. In the course of this congress the question was raised of searching for the hypothetical planet assumed to gravitate between Mars and Jupiter. The discussion led, two years later, to the creation of a commission composed of six German astronomers, a kind of celestial police force entrusted with the task of tracking down the mysterious fugitive.

The celestial police force had not even begun their investigations when they heard that the fugitive had been run to earth—by, if we may so express it, a private detective.

[1] As may be seen, this law gives 38·8 for the distance of a planet situated beyond Uranus. This was the figure employed by Le Verrier in his calculation. In reality the distance of Neptune corresponds to 30·11.

He was discovered, quite by chance, by the Italian astronomer Giuseppe Piazzi (1746–1826). This scientist was a monk who, after teaching science, philosophy or theology as occasion offered in various religious establishments in Italy, finally accepted a professorship in mathematics at the University of Palermo.

It so happened that the viceroy of Sicily was a great devotee of science and aspired to enrich his capital with an astronomical observatory. Whom should he put in charge of this institution? Obviously the professor of mathematics at the university. Thus Father Piazzi was turned into an astronomer.

However, it is only in fairy stories that such metamorphoses are accomplished at one stroke. As the viceroy had no magic wand, he was obliged to send his mathematician to serve an apprenticeship with the astronomers. Piazzi therefore spent several years learning his new science, with Lalande at the École Militaire, Paris, and with Maskelyne at Greenwich. By 1791 he was ready and able to embark upon his duties at the new Palermo Observatory.

The great date of his life was 1 January, 1801—the first day of the nineteenth century. He was working on a stellar catalogue when his attention was caught by a small star of the eighth magnitude in the constellation of the Bull that seemed to have moved from one evening to the next. Was the Uranus affair going to start all over again? Piazzi was wise enough to doubt it, and he merely announced to a few colleagues, Lalande, Bode and Oriani, director of the Milan Observatory, the discovery of a new comet.

We can guess Bode's reactions to the letter he received. This was 'his' planet, the one whose existence between Mars and Jupiter, at a distance from the Sun corresponding to 2·8, he had foretold. . . . At least, his intuition assured him so. The problem was to demonstrate it, that is to say prove that the body in question was moving along an elliptical orbit. To this problem the experts applied themselves. It would probably have baffled them, since the new object could no longer be picked up by their telescopes, if the solution had not been furnished by an unknown investigator, a young Brunswick student who eked out a meagre existence by teaching mathematics. This student was called Karl Friedrich Gauss (1777–1855), and nobody at the time foresaw that he would be one of the greatest mathematicians of all time, on a par with Archimedes, Newton, Lagrange and Laplace. Gauss tackled the problem before which the most learned among his contemporaries flinched—because now that Piazzi's orb had become invisible, they lacked reliable data for their calculations—by the 'method of least squares', which he had just invented, and solved it. The object was indeed a planet and it did gravitate at a distance of 2·8 from the Sun.

This new member of the solar family was discovered on 1 January, 1801. It was not seen again until 31 December, at exactly the point indicated by Gauss. This rediscovery was the work of a Bremen amateur, the physician Heinrich Olbers (1758–1840). It did not arouse as much enthusiasm as might have been expected. Unlike Uranus, which is a globe of some size, 64 times larger than the Earth, *Ceres* (as Piazzi had christened his find) was 933 times smaller. Olbers followed it with interest during the few hours he was able to devote to it each night. On 28 March, 1802, while thus engaged, he discerned close to Ceres a star of the seventh magnitude that he had never seen before. Was it a comet, a variable star? After two hours the observer noticed that it had shifted slightly: so it was another planet! Gauss picked up his pen again, and it took him only a few months to establish the intruder's trajectory. It, too, gravitated at a distance of 2.8 and its volume was even less than that of Ceres. The Bremen physician named it *Pallas*.

Astronomers were understandably amazed. How were they to explain the discovery of two planets, both of them tiny and at the same distance from the Sun, at a point where only one had been expected? Olbers suggested that they might be fragments of a large planet that had exploded. If this were so, there might be other fragments whose trajectory was bound, by the laws of mechanics, to pass through certain clearly determined points. The amateur scientist placed these points in the constellations of the Virgin and the Whale.

Events confirmed his prediction. On 1 September, 1804, an astronomer at Lilienthal Observatory named Karl Ludwig Harding (1765–1834) identified a third planet in the Whale; this was *Juno*. On 29 March, 1807, Olbers himself repeated his discovery of 1802 and recorded the appearance of *Vesta* in the Virgin. Here the harvest came to an end, although Johann von Littrow (1781–1840), director of Vienna Observatory, and other astronomers, had expected many more fragments of the 'burst planet'.

Yet Littrow was right. If the hunt did not bring more game, it was simply because the huntsmen lacked good charts that would have enabled them to distinguish the minor planets from the stars. It is not very easy to discriminate between a planet and a star in the most populous constellations of the zodiac, when both appear as minute specks of the eighth or ninth magnitude! This is proved by the fact that as soon as the amateur hunters came into possession of adequate charts their bag showed a notable increase. Planet-hunting became a sport practised by particularly gifted individuals, who feared neither endless watches at the telescope—nor colds in the head.

In 1845 a certain Hencke (1793–1866), postmaster at Driesen, discovered *Astraea*, and in 1847 *Hebe*; between 1847 and 1854 an English professional, John Russel Hind (1822–95), bagged six small planets all on his own; between 1852 and 1861 the German-born Paris painter Goldschmidt catalogued fourteen. But the biggest bags were those obtained by the American C. H. F. Peters, with forty-three items, and the Austrian Johann Palisa (1855–1925) with forty-eight. When these last two began their activities, however, the resources of telescope-hunting were exhausted and the relay had been taken over by hunting with the camera (p. 281).

A profusion of satellites

The power of the new astronomical object-glasses was not brought to bear only on the minor planets: satellite-hunting also yielded excellent returns. It will be remembered that the satellites of Jupiter were discovered by Galileo in 1610 (*Io, Europa, Ganymede* and *Callisto*), while of the five largest satellites of Saturn (*Titan, Japhet, Rhea, Tethys* and *Dione*) the first was found by Huygens in 1655 and the remaining four by G. D. Cassini in 1671, 1672 and 1684.

The conquest of the satellites was resumed a century later. The satellites of Uranus (*Titania* and *Oberon*) fell in 1787 to William Herschel, who likewise took possession of *Mimas* and *Encelade*, two other satellites of Saturn, in 1789. Soon after the discovery of Neptune, a satellite of this planet, *Triton*, was caught by an English amateur named William Lassell (1799–1880). In 1848 it was the turn of a seventh satellite of Jupiter, christened by its discoverer, the American Bond (p. 270), *Hyperion*. Three years later Lassell added two satellites of Uranus to his bag at one blow, *Ariel* and *Umbriel*. After this, astronomers had to wait until 1877 for the American astronomer Asaph Hall (1829–1907) to introduce the two little satellites of Mars, *Phobos* and *Deimos*. In 1892 another American, Barnard (p.283), added a fifth to the four great satellites of Jupiter known since Galileo. In 1898—but this time it was photography that drew out of the blackness the ninth satellite of Saturn, and we shall have a great deal more to say about this method of exploration.

With this unexpected population of minor planets and satellites, the solar system had ceased by the mid-nineteenth century to bear much resemblance to what it had been at the time of the discovery of Uranus, or even in Piazzi's day. Astronomers were now accustomed to seeing a host of turbulent comets performing their evolutions within its limits; and after a meteorite crashed at Laigle (Orne) in 1803, giving scientists an opportunity of analysing its fragments, no one any longer denied the interplanetary origin of these stones, a theory advanced as long ago as 1794 by the German physicist Ernst Chladni (1756–1827).

An abundance of telescopes for the exploration of the heavens

We must bear in mind that this avalanche of new planets was set in motion by the introduction of the new achromatic object-glass. This object-glass was popularized by Dollond, after Guinand had discovered the secret of fusing the glass for it; it was now manufactured industrially by the great optical factory at Munich already referred to briefly on page 238. The Swiss clock- and glass-maker remained with this firm from 1805 to 1813, initiating the manager of the lens-grinding department in his methods.

His departure might have rung the knell of the factory, but as luck would have it the departmental manager who had collaborated with him was also an exceptionally gifted individual. He was at this time a young man of twenty-six, named Joseph Fraunhofer (1787–1826). A glazier's son, he had known in his youth toil, poverty and setbacks of all kinds—including the collapse of his house! He was not destined to enjoy old age, for he died of tuberculosis at thirty-nine; but, although he had only twenty years in which to accomplish his life's work, these two decades weighed particularly heavily in the conquest of the skies. In this short space of time Fraunhofer created the modern astronomical refractor, which is still employed, in this twentieth century, in every observatory.

Fraunhofer's fame dates from 12 December, 1817, the day on which he succeeded in grinding an object-glass such as had never been made before. It had a diameter of $9\frac{1}{2}$ inches and a focus of 14 feet 6 inches. No one had ever seen such a large aperture for such a short focal length. Naturally, these dimensions would make our modern astronomers smile pityingly—leaving the giant reflecting telescopes of Mount Palomar and Mount Wilson out of account, the biggest refracting telescope in the world, at Yerkes Observatory, is over 3 feet in diameter. But in Fraunhofer's day astrophysics was not yet born; what astronomers demanded from objectives was less that they should be large and powerful than that they should be accurate, and in this respect Fraunhofer's new achromatic lens was the last word.

This objective was acquired by Russia, who was then equipping her observatory at Dorpat (now Tartu, in Estonia) under the direction of one of the greatest astronomers of the day, Wilhelm Struve. We shall discuss later, on page 254, the outcome of this meeting between an observer of the first rank and an incomparable instrument, but we must at once stress the interest aroused by the latter. Fraunhofer had striven to embody in it every possible improvement. It was mounted as an *equatorial*, that is to say, like the armillary spheres of antiquity (pp. 65 and 109), so as to follow a star in its diurnal course. The operator did not even have to push the tube in order to keep a particular body in view; this was done by a clockwork mechanism worked by a weight. Man and instrument were sheltered by a moving dome with a look-out slit that could be opened when required. As may be seen, it was in every respect the prototype of today's refracting telescopes.

When death snatched Fraunhofer from the scene in 1826, astronomical optics had begun to make dramatic strides. The firm of Merz & Mahler had taken over in Germany, and a son of Guinand had founded in France a glassworks that is still thriving. This factory broke the record established by the Bavarian pioneer, producing an objective of 13 inches which was ground by the Frenchman Cauchoix (1776–1845) and mounted at Cambridge Observatory in 1835. The road was now wide open and we shall confine ourselves to listing chronologically the largest refractors that marked its principal stages[1].

Year	Diameter of Objective	Optician	Observatory
1825	24 cm.	Fraunhofer	Dorpat (Russia)
1835	32 ,,	Cauchoix	Cambridge (England)
1839	38 ,,	Merz	Pulkovo (Russia)
1866	47 ,,	Alvan Clark	Chicago (U.S.A.)
1871	63·5 ,,	Cook	Cambridge (England)
1873	66 ,,	Alvan Clark	Washington (U.S.A.)
1878	68 ,,	Grubb	Vienna (Austria)
1885	76 ,,	Alvan Clark	Pulkovo (Russia)
1888	91 ,,	Alvan Clark	Lick (U.S.A.)
1897	102 ,,	Alvan Clark	Yerkes (U.S.A.)

Naturally enough, this plethora of achromatic equatorial telescopes caused an abundant growth of observatories. To the venerable establishments at Paris and Greenwich there were added, in particular, that at Berlin in 1700, at Marseilles in 1702, at Milan in 1750, and at Göttingen in 1754. The following century saw the emergence of several more: at Koenigsberg in 1810, at Dorpat in 1813, at Naples in 1817, at Vienna in 1818, at the Cape of Good Hope in 1820, at Harvard College, U.S.A., in 1827, at Helsingfors, Finland, in 1828, at Bonn in 1829, at Pulkovo, Russia, in 1839, and at Toulouse in 1840.

What went on in these observatories? The study of physical

[1] This list is taken from A. Danjon and A. Couder, *op. cit.*

astronomy—of the surface of the Moon and planets, for example—
had almost no place there. Firstly, because this kind of work allowed
too much play for the imagination and was regarded as not quite
serious by 'official' astronomers;[1] and secondly, because it seemed
essential to establish solid foundations before embarking on original
research, and this meant working out measurements for the chart
of the sky that were as strictly accurate as the new techniques
allowed.

Sighting with the micrometer, reading divided circles and spending
nights watching stars travel their courses through the meridian telescope, in order to replace a declination of $40° 42'/24''$ in the catalogues
by one of $40°42'/23·5''$, may seem both terribly boring and supremely
futile. As a matter of fact, if we can praise the patience of the astronomers who forced themselves to carry out this unspectacular and
monotonous task, we must also admire their foresight. Upon this
undigested accumulation of figures was raised the great edifice of
stellar astronomy; from the comparison of these measurements
emerged the image of the universe, and what poem ever attained the
lyrical heights of the one written by this science with its Milky Way
and its myriads of island universes?

We need feel no surprise that astronomers in observatories all over
the world, having been presented by Fraunhofer with these marvellous
equatorial telescopes, should have rushed headlong into the never-
ending tasks of positional astronomy. Their haste is understandable.
The new precision objectives gave them the means of determining the
celestial co-ordinates with unparalleled accuracy—how could they
fail to profit by them? And here, at the head of a section and in italics,
we must inscribe the name of:

Bessel, the man who codified observation of the stars

The author of this book is certainly not the one to deny that
astronomy is the most beautiful, the most thrilling, the most poetic
of the sciences, both by virtue of the picture it presents to the eye
and the fabulous and unending vistas it opens up to the intelligence.

[1] Planetary astronomy was created by amateurs like Schroeter, Beer and Maedler.

But let the reader be under no illusions: if he happens to visit a big modern observatory it will probably strike him as not in the least poetic, nor will he find astronomers to be dreamers given to agreeable meditations on infinite space. Nowadays an astronomer is a mathematician or an engineer; an observatory is a factory. Alert young ladies are to be seen tapping star-keys on a statistical machine, and the astronomer taking a photograph at the focus of a telescope, surrounded by a constellation of control buttons, bears less resemblance to his illustrious predecessor Tycho Brahe than to an electrician controlling a great dam.

This merely confirms that the environment most favourable to the development of enterprising and vigorous astronomical research is one that is intensely realistic and technological. We have already come across several examples of this: the businessmen of navigation encouraging the progress of astronomy for very prosaic ends, Newton's theories receiving an enthusiastic welcome in an England whose ears were generally more attentive to the chink of guineas than to abstract speculations. But no instance is more typical than that of little Bessel, a model clerk in a business house, who acquired a taste for figures through filling up debit and credit columns and finally performed a feat no one had accomplished before him—he measured the distance of the stars.

A boy of fifteen from Minden in Westphalia whose parents had apprenticed him because he took no interest in anything at school, except arithmetic, and made no headway with Latin—such was young Friedrich Wilhelm Bessel (1784–1846) during the latter days of the eighteenth century. His employer was a big Bremen merchant. From the window of his office the new apprentice could see the freighters sailing slowly past on their way to and from India, China or America. At fifteen it is very natural to dream. Bessel did not renounce this pleasure, but his positive turn of mind gave his dreams a solidity which they generally lack. Oh to be a sea-going captain . . . to command a great sailing ship putting out for the Far East. . . . But that required knowledge the young man did not possess. What of it? He set to work to learn English, Spanish, geography, mathematics, the use of the sextant; the latter led him to astronomy . . . and we see him one evening at his window, observing the stars with the aid of a primitive instrument and patiently swotting up Lalande's *Traité d'Astronomie*.

This was in 1802. The papers reported the discovery of the small planet Pallas. And it was a citizen of Bremen, Dr. Olbers, who had discovered it! Who could say that, since they lived in the same town, young Bessel, now eighteen, might not meet him one day at the corner of the street? The miracle happened. The young clerk shyly approached the scientist, presented him with a paper he had written on celestial mechanics—over three hundred pages long—and asked him to read it.

The paper must have been convincing, since Olbers decided to publish it and even suggested to his disciple that he should become an astronomer. There happened to be a vacant post at Lilienthal, which Harding had just left for Göttingen after discovering Juno. The idea of becoming an astronomer appealed to Bessel. But on the other hand he had done very well in his firm. The apprentice of yesterday had grown into an astute businessman; his employers were delighted with him and had made him very attractive propositions, and this vocation, too, was not without its lure for Bessel.

In the end, however, science won the day. Bessel moved to Lilienthal in March 1806, and began to work alongside Schroeter, who was drawing a geodesic skeleton map of the Moon. He brought to his astronomical observations the same qualities of accuracy and rather finicky attention to detail that had served him so well as a book-keeper.

Bessel's achievement is not one of those around which it is easy to weave a romantic fiction. There is nothing frivolous about 'Bessel's formula', which is used daily in meridian observatories. But, as the reader will learn, this formula, which gives the right ascension of the stars, takes account simultaneously of the time when the star passes behind the centre line of the micrometer, of the faults of the telescope and of the aberration. In other words, the co-ordinate is freed from the various approximations which previously vitiated it, so that its accuracy is completely dependable. In fact the probable error of an observation, which reached 25 seconds with Tycho Brahe, 2 seconds with Bradley and 1·5 seconds with Piazzi, fell with Bessel to 0·3 second.

A STEP TOWARDS THE STARS

This meant that in determining the positions of the stars the astronomer was not likely to be more than 0·3 second out—the angle under which a hair would appear at a distance of 3 miles.

There was unquestionably room in astronomy for Bessel's work of rectification. The catalogues in use, that of Lalande (1801) for example, stated the positions of the stars as given by uncorrected observation, taking no account of aberration, precision, atmospheric refraction or the characteristics of the instruments employed. Bradley's catalogue would have been excellent after these corrections had been made. This was precisely what Bessel set about doing. Thus in 1813 he was able to publish Bradley's observations of 3,222 stars with all their 'rough edges' smoothed off. But 3,222 stars is not a very large number. By 1833 Bessel had observed another 75,000, aided by his assistant Argelander—a name to be remembered.

In the process he noted two facts, the importance of which the future was to show. He succeeded in calculating accurately the proper motion of Sirius, and this proper motion intrigued him: Sirius travels through the heavens not along a straight line, but along a wavy one. In 1834 Bessel guessed that this star must be linked to another, invisible, star, and that they revolved around one another. In 1840 he discovered the same irregularity in the case of Procyon, the beautiful star in the Lesser Dog.

Confirmation came in 1862 for Sirius, in 1892 for Procyon. The great American optician Alvan Clark, on the one hand, and his countryman Schaeberle, on the other, perceived that each of these stars really forms part of a *binary* system, the satellite in which was a body of very low luminosity. Paving the way for the discovery of Neptune, Bessel thus founded the *astronomy of the invisible*, and at the same time he discovered the *white dwarfs*, which were to arouse so much discussion at the period of relativity and the atom bomb.

Bessel did not live to see his intuition confirmed. For he passed away in 1846; but fortunately the authorities did not wait till then before recognizing his merits. In 1816 the great astronomer left Lilienthal for Koenigsberg University; two years later he was appointed director of the observatory just set up by King Frederick William III of Prussia. Seventeen years later this institution received a new instrument, a *heliometer*, constructed by Fraunhofer; to this instrument he devoted all his attention until his death. It is because of his achievements with this heliometer that Bessel, the man who codified observation of the skies, is looked upon by posterity as the astronomer who took the first step towards the stars.

The apex of the triangle touches the stars

A heliometer, in principle, was an object-glass divided into two movable segments. When the two halves were in juxtaposition a star gave a single image, as in an ordinary object-glass; when they were separated, by so much as the fraction of a millimetre, the star gave two images. In the case of a double star it was possible to calculate the distance between the two components by measuring the amount of separation imparted to the two halves of the object-glass in order to bring the image of one component against the image of the other.

As we see, the heliometer, which today is little more than a museum piece, furnished a means of measuring exceedingly small angles. As soon as it came into Bessel's possession, he formed the plan of using it to measure the distance of the stars.

The distance of the stars. It is certainly not the first time this question has been raised in these pages. But we have seen time and again how vain were all attempts to answer it.

Since Kepler, the 'fixed' stars were known to be at varying distances from the Earth, and there was no lack of volunteers to try to work out their parallax by the same methods employed to find the parallax of the Moon, the planets or the Sun.

At first sight, be it admitted, the problem seemed in no way fanciful. Herschel had posed it in precise terms when he set himself the task of finding out whether the annual displacement of the Earth on its orbit was not reflected, by the effect of perspective, in the apparent displacement of certain stars. On page 213 this effect of *annual parallax* was compared to the illusion produced by walking from one window to another while looking at a pylon on the horizon. If the two windows are 4 yards apart and the pylon is 4 miles away, it will seem to move 1′ 57″. Why should not a star also appear to move when it is the

Earth that 'walks', not 4 yards, but 200 million miles? The method would consist, basically, in observing a star at an interval of six months, that is to say when our globe is situated at two opposite extremities of its orbit, and checking to see whether its apparent position had changed.

For two centuries, many astronomers had believed they could discern this apparent shift. We now know that the movement their measurements showed them must have been illusory, for the reason that, even in the most favourable instance, it is less than 2 seconds of arc. What they took for movements were no more than errors of observation, which, as remarked just now, amounted to 2 seconds in Bradley's case and 1·5 seconds in Piazzi's. Bessel's good fortune lay precisely in the fact that, with his method, the error was reduced to 0·3 second.

The heliometer made it possible to distinguish, for the first time, between parallax and error. But it was none the less necessary, before embarking on the operation, to make a careful choice of the star upon which to use it. There was no sense in making things difficult for himself; Bessel knew that it would be wasting his time to pick a star in the Milky Way. For his first attempt he must choose a star that was relatively close.

How could he judge this closeness? By the proper motion.

When we watch aeroplanes flying about the sky, the chances are that the one which seems to us to be going fastest will be the one closest to us. Similarly, the varying speed of the proper motion of the stars serves as an indication of their proximity. In this respect, Bessel's attention was quickly drawn to a small star of the fifth to sixth magnitude bearing the number 61 in the constellation of the Swan, which stood out by the fact that it shifted 5·2 seconds a year. A very low velocity, to be sure—it would have taken this star 384 years to traverse an apparent distance equal to the diameter of the Moon—but it nevertheless constituted the speed record for stars at that period.

Beginning in 1837, Bessel periodically checked the position of this star in relation to its neighbours with the aid of his heliometer. He completed the undertaking in 1838 and published the final results in 1840. Comparison of 402 measurements gave him a parallax of 0·3483 second. It meant that, from the star in question, the distance from the Earth to the Sun was subtended by the tiny angle of one-third of a second. A simple sum then showed that the star was 600,000 times farther away than the Sun.[1]

Let us pause a moment and consider this conclusion. It marks one of the major stages in the prodigious conquest of the sky by human intelligence. Until then, this conquest had been limited to the solar system and the reconnaissance operations mounted outside it had regularly failed. For the first time, a 'commando raid' succeeded and brought back a valid figure. This success aroused enthusiasm and spurred on scientists to continue the conquest; but it also confirmed their suspicions and filled them with awe and dread. For this parallax of 0·35 second, this distance of 600,000 times the radius Earth-Sun, demonstrated the terrifying immensity of the stellar universe which had been for so long unknown. If the nearest star was so enormously distant, how immeasurably far away must the rest be?

Six hundred thousand astronomical units—the *astronomical unit* being the distance from the Earth to the Sun—took observers only to the frontier of the empire of the stars, to the edge of the abyss, and Newton's remark sprang to mind: the astronomer who had just measured the distance of his first star was a child playing on the beach with a shell, on the shores of the ocean whose vastness mocks his efforts.

In Bessel's day, however, it was not yet possible to form an idea of the full extent of this vastness, and the acclaim that greeted the great German scientist's achievement was less a call to modesty than a paean of triumph. As a matter of fact it was not only at Koenigsberg that the scientific offensive had pierced nature's front: this had been split at two other points, the Cape of Good Hope and Dorpat.

The Cape Observatory had just been established. In 1831 it was placed under the directorship of a Scot, Thomas Henderson (1798–1844), a former lawyer's clerk, whose work as an amateur had attracted a great deal of attention. This was a particularly favourable position from which to observe the southern half of the sky, and Henderson

[1] According to recent measurements, the annual parallax of 61 Cygni is 0·294 second, which corresponds to a distance of 701,301 astronomical units.

was struck by the brilliance of the three most beautiful stars in this hemisphere, Sirius, Canopus and α Centauri. The positional measurements he made with the meridian telescope showed him that the third of these was subject to a considerable proper motion—though it was less than that of 61 Cygni. For the same reasons as Bessel, the Scottish astronomer felt the desire to find out whether this proper motion corresponded to a measureable parallax, and on his return to his homeland in 1834 he assembled the necessary data. He finished his work in 1839—only two months after Bessel's first epoch-making publication.

It was then seen that, with a parallax of 0·75 second, α Centauri was far closer than 61 Cygni: only 274,332 astronomical units. In other words, the light that took little more than 8 minutes to reach the Earth from the Sun took 4 years and 4 months to get here from α Centauri and 11 years to get here from 61 Cygni. These figures were corroborated by a third piece of evidence, furnished this time by a Russian astronomer.

As a matter of fact this evidence was made public earlier than that brought by either the German or the Scottish astronomer, but it caused far less excitement. This was not because the author, Wilhelm Struve, director of Dorpat Observatory, was not considered reliable, but because the star upon which he carried out his investigations, Vega, was not a very good choice. It was really so far away (six times as far as α Centauri) that the method inevitably lost some of its efficacy. Struve actually attributed to it a parallax of 0·2613 second, whereas it is now assessed at 0·124 second. But the Russian astronomer had other claims to a place of honour in the history of science.

The Struves, as a dynasty of astronomers

In September 1941 the troops of the Germans and their Finnish allies were only twenty miles or so from Leningrad. The investment of the city had begun. Peterhof, the former residence of the Czars, had fallen to the enemy; 120 miles of the Leningrad–Moscow railway had been taken; in the east, Hitler's motorized divisions had reached the Neva. All around, the hills in which the defenders had dug themselves in were reduced to rubble and ashes.

Especially Pulkovo hill, ten miles south-west of the city. The soil here had been churned up as during the worst hours of Verdun. Who would have thought that a great astronomical observatory, the most important in the world after those at Paris and Greenwich, once stood here, boasting a giant refractor with a 30-inch object-glass, backed by a century of tradition, and housing in its library that priceless treasure, Kepler's original manuscripts?

In 1818 the director of Dorpat Observatory died. The Czar appointed to succeed him a young man of twenty-five named Wilhelm Struve (1793–1864). The man who was to become the greatest astronomer of pre-revolutionary Russia was a German, born at Altona, near Hamburg. In 1811, however, he left the Holy Roman Empire for Russia, emigrating to Estonia. He enrolled at the University of Dorpat, took a course in astronomy after a brief incursion into philology, became a professor on completing his studies, began work at the Observatory and finished up as its director—quite an ordinary career, when all is said and done.

But Struve's true career dates from the day on which the Observatory received Fraunhofer's new equatorial (p. 244): a telescope of $9\frac{1}{2}$-inches diameter with a clockwork action and a revolving turret. What subject of study was worthy of this wonderful scientific toy? Struve chose the double stars. Here was new ground Herschel had barely broken and on which the harvest of discoveries promised to be rich. Not only were these double stars curiosities about which it was important to have exact information, but the elliptic motions of their components offered an attractive generalization of Newton's law—and from it could be deduced their mass. To weigh the stars—the prospect of doing so might still be distant, but at least the director of the Observatory did everything in his power to bring it closer.

Thus he set about the useful but thankless task of measuring the angular separation of the binary stars. His $9\frac{1}{2}$-inch refractor was fitted with a micrometer. This served to determine both the space between the components and their *position angle* (the angle their line forms with the meridian). More than 120,000 pairs of stars passed behind its spider-lines. The result of this investigation was the publication, in 1837, of a catalogue of 2,112 double, triple or quadruple stars with their co-ordinates, separation, brightness and colour. On first looking at this work, more than one astronomer lamented that Struve had harvested everything of interest the sky contained, leaving nothing to be gleaned after him. Nevertheless, the discoverer's own son, Otto Struve, was to garner 514 fresh pairs, and an American amateur, S. W. Burnham (1838–1921), a professional shorthand reporter, added another 1,300 towards the end of the century. It is very true that in science the harvest is never finished and that a forgotten sheaf may hide a surprising discovery.

As happened to Wilhelm Struve himself when, in the course of his survey of double stars, he noted the particularly rapid proper motion of Vega. What was hidden behind the sheaf in this case was the measurement of the first stellar parallax.

And also, perhaps, the majestic observatory which Nicholas I had built near his capital, on Pulkovo hill.

The Emperor did not haggle over the outlay. To replace the old observatory built by his predecessor, Peter the Great, on the embankments of the Neva at St. Petersburg in 1725, he chose the most suitable site, allowed fifty-four acres of land, and ordered Struve, one of the most celebrated astronomers of the day, to purchase the instruments without regard to cost. As may be imagined, the astronomer went straight to Munich. He ordered from Merz & Mahler an equatorial telescope bigger than anything seen before—including the 9½-inch instrument at Dorpat and the 13-inch one at Cambridge.

In 1839 the new Pulkovo Observatory was inaugurated. It boasted a telescope with an aperture of 15 inches, a large heliometer and many secondary instruments, housed beneath octagonal turrets rising from a magnificent building. Henceforth Struve had to hand the most perfect instrument with which to continue his investigations of the double stars. Already, like Herschel, he had gone beyond his data, built up on them a theory of the universe whose only fault was to have come a hundred years too soon, and was talking about stellar statistics and the absorption of light in space.

The Dorpat Observatory had been the birthplace of the science of double stars; Pulkovo Observatory was the birthplace of the Struve dynasty. We have already met one of these astronomical dynasties, that of the Cassinis. The Struve dynasty was represented, after the founder, by his own son Otto (1819–1905), who directed the great institution until 1899. His retirement was the signal for dispersal. Only one of his children, Ludwig (1858–1920), remained faithful to Russia and became director of Kharkov Observatory, while the other, Hermann (1854–1920), emigrated first to Koenigsberg Observatory and then to that of Berlin-Babelsberg, which was subsequently directed by his son Georg (1886–1933).

In 1954 the president of the International Astronomical Union, an organization to which the majority of professional astronomers throughout the world belong, was another Otto Struve, born in 1897, the son of Ludwig and great-grandson of the magnificent Wilhelm. This distant descendant had left Europe and become an American, director of Yerkes Observatory and founder of the MacDonald and Leuschner Observatories. That same year Pulkovo Observatory, which had been razed to the ground during the war, rose from the ashes.

Today, as a hundred years ago, the Observatory stands on the hill in a row of buildings bristling with turrets. Nicholas I would recognize its general arrangement, but his astronomer would be struck dumb by the instruments with which it is equipped. In the mind of his successors, the Milky Way has taken the place of the double stars, and they no longer launch their attack at the distance of Vega, but at that of universes ten million times farther away.

Balance-sheet before a fresh start

In astronomy, training is a minor detail; vocation is everything. It may even be said that the greatest discoveries have been made by self-taught men whom an irresistible impulse pushed off the normal track, rather than by scientists brought up inside the seraglio and concerned only with achieving a comfortable career in it. Herschel was a musician, Bessel a book-keeper, Burnham a shorthand reporter, Foucault a handy-man, Pons a *concierge*, and we shall soon make the acquaintance of Barnard, a photographer, Hubble, a lawyer, and Hale —the son of an influential father.

Let us add to this picturesque gallery Friedrich Argelander (1799–1875), born in Memel, who came from the world of banking. Science owes this recruit to Bessel, who took him on as assistant at Koenigsberg Observatory and together with whom Argelander set to work on his star catalogue. Their collaboration lasted only two years, as the young man—he was only twenty-four—was called to Russia in 1823 to direct first the Abo Observatory and then that at Helsingfors (now Helsinki).

In 1837 Argelander presented his first work to the St. Petersburg Academy, who crowned it with a prize. In it he showed that, as Herschel had foreseen, the Sun, a star among other stars, was propelled by a proper motion towards its *apex*.

His second, published from 1859 to 1862, was far wider in scope. It found a place in every observatory library on the shelf for books in everyday use.

This publication was entitled the *Bonner Durchmusterung* because the author had been, since 1837, director of the Bonn Observatory. It was an enormous catalogue of 324,198 stars. All those of the northern hemisphere were listed in it, down to the ninth magnitude. The graphic counterpart to this list was presented in an atlas of forty charts. Complete and reliable, this atlas was destined to become an indispensable working tool for observers. Even today, photographic charts of the sky have not entirely dethroned it. Without it, astronomers would be as lost in the tangle of sidereal topography as an explorer plunging into the wilderness without his map.

When Argelander published his catalogue and atlas great changes were transforming astronomy. Photography and spectrum analysis had just been invented, and telescopes were beginning to assume impressive dimensions. In Britain, Germany and Russia astronomers sensed that the conquest of the sky, hitherto conducted with the sole aid of the meridian telescope and Newton's law, was about to take on a new look. In France the specialists in celestial mechanics regarded their science as pretty well complete, but elsewhere astronomers felt themselves to be in a transition period and on the eve of tremendous scientific upheavals.

In preparation for these upheavals and while waiting for the new means of study with which physics—and no longer mathematics alone—was on the point of supplying astronomical research, it seemed urgently necessary to establish, with the maximum accuracy, the new face of the skies—as it were, to draw up an honest balance-sheet of the gains made.

This had been done by Argelander in respect of the stars of the northern hemisphere. His pupil Eduard Schoenfeld (1828–91) extended his catalogue in 1886 to cover part of the southern hemisphere. But the firmament does not consist exclusively of stars: outside the solar system, we have also to reckon with those peculiar objects, the nebulae. This was territory first penetrated by William Herschel. Only powerful reflecting telescopes such as he constructed were capable of unveiling the pale nebular gleams in the farthest recesses of the sidereal abysses. John Herschel (1792–1871) took over the relay.

John Herschel—another lawyer who found in the firmament his road to Damascus. How could anyone take an interest in petty human disputes and lawsuits over party walls, when he had a father who spent his nights exploring the heavens and who was hailed as the world's leading astronomer? It was under the aegis of the famous veteran that John first took up arms. His inaugural campaign, conducted between 1825 and 1833, yielded a booty of 3,347 new double stars and 525 nebulae. This was too little for his liking. After astronomers had raked the northern sky for centuries, after William had swept it with his huge instruments of 19 to 49 inches, was there any hope of discovering anything new in it with a modest telescope of 18 inches? John Herschel realized that the southern firmament alone, upon which as yet only low-powered telescopes had been trained, could hold the treasures he was seeking.

In 1833 he embarked for the Cape of Good Hope with his family, his furniture and his instruments. He settled in the shelter of Table Mountain. There he mounted his telescope at the spot now marked by an obelisk, and in March 1834 he began to survey the sky.

John Herschel's work in the southern hemisphere was a complement to that accomplished by his father in the north. The 2,500 nebulae noted by the father were balanced by the 1,700 recorded by the son, in addition to 2,102 double stars. The highlight of the picture was the group of the two *Clouds of Magellan*. These clouds were composed not of drops of water, but of stars—in a word, they were *galaxies*, and they were the closest of galaxies, since they lay only 170,000 light-years from the Sun.

Herschel returned to Europe in 1838 to report to the Royal Society. His files were overflowing with celestial riches. In gratitude to the great William, who had opened up the seam, the whole family gathered one day at Slough. They assembled inside the tube that had once been the 4-foot telescope and there, standing upright, intoned a pious psalm of thanksgiving.

Around the same period, an English nobleman who was also an Irish Member of Parliament abandoned his gilded drawing-rooms and ceremonial dress for a handy-man's workshop and the ragged costume of a mechanic. He was William Parsons (1800–67), *alias* Lord Oxmanton, Earl of Rosse, lord of Birr Castle (sixty-four miles from Dublin) and other seats. Being attracted both to mechanics and optics, and entranced by the many discoveries made by the two Herschels, he decided to follow in their tracks.

Lord Rosse spent eighteen years and £73,000 building at Parsonstown, Kings County, Ireland, a telescope that far outstripped the one at Slough. The mirror was 6 feet across and weighed 3½ tons. It rested at the bottom of a 56-foot tube, which moved between two huge parallel walls 50 feet high. In theory, the maximum magnification was 6,000 times. This enormous eye was opened upon the heavens for the first time in February 1845.

In only two months Lord Rosse garnered the first fruits. He observed to his surprise that the nebula in the constellation of the Hunting Dogs (No. 51 in Messier's catalogue) was spiral in shape with two arms branching out from the central nucleus in opposite directions. A year later, he noted a second object of the same type in the constellation of the Virgin (Messier 99). Then others followed—fourteen by 1850. The following year one of the master's assistants, J. P. Nichol, wrote in his book *The Architecture of the Skies* that these spiral nebulae were universes outside our own and similar to it. . . .

8

The Sun, a star in the Milky Way

A setback for the parallaxes—First steps in the photometry of the
stars—The 'climate of astronomy' a hundred years ago—
Photography, a weapon for the conquest of the skies—Photographic raids into the empire of the stars—Stretching out the
stellar surveyor's chain—The latest census of the planets—The
frontiers of the solar kingdom—On the distribution of the stars—
Kapteyn deduces the universe in 1900

IMAGINE the astronomical universe as it had been surveyed by 1800,
that is to say reaching as far as the planet Uranus, represented on
a chart the size of a visiting-card. By 1838, after the first measurements
of the stars, it would have required a chart the size of the Place de la
Concorde. In advancing from Uranus to 61 Cygni, astronomy had
increased its range of action from 19 to 690,988 astronomical units.
Expressed in other terms, if the Sun was symbolized by the Obelisk in
the Place de la Concorde and Uranus placed at the entry to the bridge,
the star 61 Cygni would have been situated . . . at New York.

This fantastic leap forward in the conquest of the skies was
accomplished by Bessel, Henderson and Struve. From now on, the
true relationship of the solar to the sidereal universe was inescapable.
Man could no longer delude himself: the Sun and its suite of planets,
which had previously seemed to him the heart of the cosmos, was now
revealed as an insignificant corner, an atom lost in a cosmic abyss the
depth of which was just beginning to appear from the first soundings.

A setback for the parallaxes

Up to that time it had been possible to reckon celestial distances
in miles or astronomical units. The Sun was 1 astronomical unit
(92,800,000 miles) from the Earth, Uranus 19·2. But now these

standards of measurement proved inadequate for the stellar distances. Those of α Centauri (272,270 ast. un.) and 61 Cygni (690,988 ast. un.) foreshadowed others that might run into millions or thousands of millions. It became essential to create a new unit for the extra-planetary universe, and the *light-year* came into use.

A light-year is the distance travelled by light in one year at the rate of 186,326 miles per second. It is equal to approximately 6 million million miles or 63,290 astronomical units. With this unit the distances of α Centauri and 61 Cygni become respectively 4·3 and 10·9 light-years. Later, astronomers had recourse to a less picturesque unit, the *parsec*. A heavenly body is said to be situated at a distance of one parsec when its annual parallax is one second of arc. In other words, a parsec is the distance of a point from which the interval Earth-Sun would be seen under an angle of one second. It is equal to 206,265 astronomical units or 3·256 light-years.[1]

These various units mean little to the imagination. It would help if we could actually see a light-year or a parsec. This is by no means impossible . . . if we look with the eyes of faith. Let us, for example, seek out the two bright stars Sirius and Procyon on a fine summer's night. They are separated in the sky by 25 degrees, that is to say, to fill the space between them we must hold a halfpenny 2½ inches from our eye. Now, Sirius is 8·73 light-years from the Sun (2·68 parsecs) and Procyon 11·19 light-years (3·33 parsecs). By considering their distance apart in the sky, therefore, we can form some idea of what a parsec and a light-year are.

Naturally enough, as soon as Struve, Bessel and Henderson had obtained the first three stellar distances, other astronomers rushed to follow the trail they had blazed. They selected the stars that seemed most suitable by virtue of their brightness or proper motion, submitted them to detailed observation and tried to work out their parallax.

Unfortunately, results did not generally come up to expectation. The calculation of the first three parallaxes had been a *tour de force*, and it seemed increasingly difficult to repeat it. The smallest parallax

---

[1] Given the parallax of a star, its distance in parsecs is easily worked out: it is exactly the inverse of the parallax. Thus, since the parallax of α Centauri is 0″·758, its distance is 1 : 0·758=1·32 parsecs.

was that of Vega, which Struve estimated, as stated, at 0″·2613. To visualize so small an angle, we must imagine a triangle whose base is the diameter of a halfpenny and whose apex is situated ... 12½ miles up. The slightest error in calculating the base angles was enormously increased in working out the height. If Struve had made a mistake of 1/100 of a second, the distance of Vega would have been altered by nearly 30,000 astronomical units plus or minus. In fact, we now know that he did make a mistake, not of 1/100 of a second, but of 14/100; Vega, which he believed to be 12·5 light-years away, is really 26·2.

That is why it took so long to find the first trigonometrical parallaxes. Every now and then, as the years passed, an astronomer would obtain one by dint of patient observation and calculation; but by 1882 only thirty-seven were known, and after another ten years the number had risen to no more than eighty-seven. Even the smallest parallaxes were extremely dubious, for they were often confused with errors of observation.

This state of affairs was a great disappointment to scientists. They had hoped that the trigonometrical method, coupled with the use of the heliometer, would provide an inexhaustible means of sounding the skies, and now it was out of breath after the first few steps and quite useless beyond a few dozen light-years. The conquest of the skies, upon which Bessel, Henderson and Struve had set out at such a spanking pace now hung in the balance, and astronomers asked themselves whether there might not be some other way of calculating the distances of the stars.

First steps in the photometry of the stars

There was indeed, and the suggestion came from physics.

The stars appeared as luminous points of varying brightness. Was this because they were at varying distances? Were the most brilliant stars—Canopus, Sirius, Vega—also the closest? It was at least probable. In that case, physics could offer a very simple method of ascertaining their distances, the method of *photometry*. The basic law of photometry is as follows: the luminous intensity of a source of light is inversely proportional to the square of its distance. If you place your lamp two times farther away, it will give you four times less light. It can therefore be assumed, *a priori*, that if one of two stars shines four times less brightly than the other, the first one is twice as far away. A new line of approach was thus provided to the problem of celestial distances.

It was a very attractive line of approach on which a good deal of preliminary work had already been done. Assessment of the relative brightness of the stars had been one of the matters to which astronomers of the past had given their attention. Ptolemy first conceived the idea of arranging them in six magnitudes—a term that did not imply any assumption regarding their real dimensions. Al Sufi, Tycho Brahe and Flamsteed did their best to render this classification more accurate, while John Herschel sought to place it on less subjective foundations. He created an 'artificial star' by the reflection of moonlight on a prism, and employed this as a standard to which he compared the brightness of the stars.

In his first catalogue, published in 1843, Argelander utilized this method of comparison, but went further than his predecessor, classifying the stars not only by magnitudes, but to tenths of a magnitude. For example, while he attributed the magnitude 1 to α Centauri, as John Herschel had done, he classified the polar star as 2·12. This excessive precision proved to be something of an illusion, since Argelander was unable to establish the point at which the first magnitude gave place to the second or to state the relationship between one magnitude and another.

As Lord Kelvin declared later, 'Nothing is scientific except that which can be measured,' and it is impossible to measure the unmeasureable. The magnitude of the stars was certainly unmeasurable: it was really a matter of personal judgement. The margin of variation as between one observer and another was not too great in respect of stars visible to the naked eye, but in the case of stars only visible through the telescope it was disastrous. The term 'magnitude of a source of light' is unknown to physics, which speaks only of the *intensity* of the source. This is generally measured in candle-power with a photometer. But it is impossible to assess the brightness of a star in candle-power. On the other hand, unless all the gains derived from the work of the old astronomers were to be jettisoned, this inadequate term 'magnitude' must be retained. The only way of giving it an exact meaning was to try and link it up with the term *luminous intensity*. If the two terms could be amalgamated, it would be possible to give a strict mathematical definition of magnitude and grade the brightness of the stars according to an unambiguous scale.

The sought-for link was found in 1854 by Norman Pogson (1829–91) of Radcliffe Observatory, Oxford. Taking John Herschel's work as his starting-point, he submitted stars of different magnitudes to the photometer. He then noticed that when he moved from one magnitude to the one above, the luminous intensity was 2·5 times as great. For example, a star of the fifth magnitude showed itself on the photometer 2·5 times as brilliant as one of the sixth; a star of the fourth magnitude 2·5 times as brilliant as one of the fifth, and so on.

This constant proportion of 2·5 allowed a relationship to be established between luminous intensity and magnitude. In other words, the latter ceased to be an imaginary value depending upon the eyesight of the observer and became a measurable scientific factor. Pogson evolved a formula linking the magnitude of a star with its intensity, which acquired a fundamental importance in astrophysics.[1] The German psychologist Fechner also took this formula as his starting-point when he established, in 1861, his famous law: a sensation increases as the logarithm of the stimulus that induces it.

Pogson's formula, which introduced order where chaos had formerly reigned, was undoubtedly a great step forward. It provided a means of drawing up catalogues in which stars were classified according to magnitudes that now had an exact meaning—for example, the catalogue of B. A. Gould (1824–96) which appeared in 1879 and gave the magnitude of 8,000 stars of the southern hemisphere, C. E.

[1] Let I and I' be the intensity of two stars whose respective magnitudes are m and m'. Pogson's formula is written:

$$\frac{I}{I'} = 2·5^{m'-m}.$$

It may also be written: $\log \frac{I}{I'} = (m'-m) \times \log 2·5$.

As the logarithm of 2·5 is 0·4, we come to the expression generally used today: $0·4(m'-m) = \log I - \log I'$.

Pickering's of 1884, covering 4,260 stars of the northern hemisphere, and that of C. Pritchard (1808–93), containing 2,784 such stars. Yes, Pogson's formula was a great step forward . . . but it cast no light on the original problem—the problem of the distance of the stars. True, astronomers could now say that when a star seemed four times less brilliant than another, it was probably twice as far away—but only on condition that both of them were of the same absolute brightness (p. 221). Only comparables can be compared: it would be ludicrous to attempt to calculate the distance of a lighthouse by comparing its light with that of a pocket torch. It would be no less absurd to indulge in photometric deductions concerning stars without being sure that they were of the same luminosity.

If all the stars were built on the same model, if, for instance, they were all exactly equal to the Sun, it would be sufficient for one of them to appear 100 times, 10,000 times or 1,000,000 times less bright to be able to state that it was 10 times, 100 times or 1,000 times farther away than the Sun. Unfortunately we have no guarantee that all stars are alike. Even in the time of Napoleon and Queen Victoria astronomers guessed that they must vary enormously, and therefore that some other way of calculating their distance would have to be found.

The 'climate of astronomy' a hundred years ago

It is now 1850. Let us try to get a bird's-eye view of the situation. Let us copy the general of days gone by, who, the battle over, surveyed from a hilltop or a clock-tower the ground captured by his troops.

There is no denying that a mental survey of the astronomical universe conquered by 1850 gave little cause for satisfaction. True, Le Verrier had just added the feather of Neptune to the planetary cap; true, the distances of three stars had just been determined. But these were only timid reconnaissance expeditions that scarcely scratched the frontiers of the vast empire of the stars. The avowed aim of astronomers, official observatories, all astronomical investigation, remained wearisome positional astronomy. In 1840 Bessel asserted that the sole purpose of astronomy was 'to find the rules governing the motion of every heavenly body and to deduce from these its position at any moment'. William Herschel's discoveries were admired, but rather as a solid citizen admires Picasso while feeling that his work is not to be taken seriously and that there are more useful ways of painting. For most astronomers, their science had undergone no fundamental change since the days of Hipparchus; it had merely improved its instruments and perfected its techniques. The meridian telescope was nothing but the descendant of the Alexandrine plinth and the equatorial no more than an improved armilla.

Was this due to intellectual timidity? Lack of curiosity? Poverty of imagination? Habit? All these certainly played their part in the path taken by astronomy at the period of the siege of Sebastopol, the war in Italy, Gounod's *Faust* and *The Origin of Species*. 'She is a very beautiful woman,' wrote Charles Fabry wittily of astronomy at this time, 'but her charms are already those of maturity. She has enjoyed great successes and asks nothing better than to start all over again. In short, she is inclined to keep on repeating herself.' A pretty poor conqueror of celestial space, to be sure!

As a matter of fact the drab grey of astronomy stands out in startling contrast to the violently colourful background of the century. A few lines above, a number of symbolic events were listed, wars, the creation of an opera, the publication of a book. But of far greater significance was the general 'spirit of the age', the process of industrialization that was sweeping the countries of Europe into a more rapid rhythm of life, the epidemic of inventions, the proliferation of machines that were upsetting the traditional scale of values. If Britain was the first nation of the world, she owed it less to her navy or her diplomacy than to her coal and her engineers. And the growing prestige of Germany sprang from her astounding industrial transformation, from her ability to extract from her soil, and especially from her coal, both power and chemical products.

In this upsurge of technology, science was taking an increasingly important part. The German universities and engineering institutes were attracting students from every country. In Germany in particular, and to a lesser extent in Britain, engineers and capitalists had grasped the significance of scientific research, realizing that it was the source of their success or fortune. In these countries it was considered, not a useless pastime as in France, but an essential element in economic life. Research laboratories began to be set up in factories. Remember that it was in the two countries where the link between science and industry was closest, Germany and Britain, that the greatest scientific discoveries of the century germinated—electrodynamics (Faraday), spectrum analysis (Kirchhoff and Bunsen), thermodynamics (Helmholtz and Clausius), electromagnetism (Maxwell and Hertz) and the kinetic theory of the gases (Boltzmann).

And alongside these two powers there arose a third, the young giant who was growing up on the other side of the Atlantic. The end of the War of Secession in 1865 marked the starting-point of the United States' sweeping progress. A civilization was born whose sole aim, in the words of Robert Schnerb, was 'material comfort obtained by the most efficient means', and which was dominated by 'self-made men' and 'big business', and where the caution of European businessmen gave place to a violent alternation of booms and slumps.

Here, too, the importance of scientific research was grasped. Nothing proves this more convincingly than the fact that it was American businessmen, the most realistic and profit-seeking in the world, who gave the decisive impulse to the most disinterested of sciences, the exploration of the heavens.

It was now, in the middle of the nineteenth century, that the Americans began to take part in the conquest of the skies. They brought to it their capital, their methodical intelligence, their enthusiasm, their youth, their urge to break records. They wanted everything they did to be the finest, the biggest, the best in the world. They gave a second wind to the old science of the Mesopotamians. And when their immense material achievements were combined with the inventive genius of European scientists an entirely new astronomy was born.

Harvard College Observatory was founded in 1839. In 1847 it received a refracting telescope of the same power as the one that had been mounted in 1839 at Pulkovo, with its 15-inch aperture the largest in the world. A few years later the English amateur astronomer

Dawes came across a miniature-painter in the depths of Massachusetts who spent his leisure moments grinding lenses. The name of this artist was Alvan Clark (1804–87), and Dawes had no hesitation in ranking him among the greatest opticians in the world, alongside Fraunhofer, Cauchoix and Merz.

The future showed that Clark was superior to all of them. In 1862 he produced a 19-inch object-glass that was mounted at Chicago Observatory; in 1873 another one of 26 inches that was acquired by the U.S. Naval Observatory, Washington; in 1884 yet another of 30 inches, ordered by Pulkovo Observatory. All these objectives, the glass for which was supplied by the French successors of Guinand, cost fantastic sums. But there were always Maecenases willing to earn forgiveness for having got rich quick by ostentatiously subsidizing the servants of Urania. To have captains of industry, who had made a fortune in skins, soap or scrap-iron, fighting for the honour of lavishing dollars upon them was a stroke of luck astronomers had certainly never enjoyed before.

One of these nabobs, James Lick, the piano king, died in 1876 leaving $700,000 to construct the largest telescope in the world—and an observatory to house it. The building of the latter began in 1879 on a Californian mountain-top, and Alvan Clark ground for it an object-glass of 36 inches.

In 1895, at the request of G. E. Hale, another nabob, Charles T. Yerkes, the railway king, built the observatory that now bears his name near Chicago. Clark had just disappeared from the scene, but his sons succeeded him. It is to them that astronomy owes the biggest telescope objective ever seen. It has an aperture of 40 inches; the convex lens of crown glass weighs 204 lb., the concave lens of flint glass 308 lb.

Many other benefactors subsequently manifested an unexpected benevolence towards the science of the skies, such as the industrialist Hooker who paid for the 100-inch telescope on Mount Wilson, the banker McDonald who bought one of 82 inches for the observatory of that name in Texas, and even a charming Canadian lady, Mrs. J. D. Dunlap, who built at Toronto in 1932 the largest observatory then to be found anywhere in the British Empire.

Nineteen thirty-two! We have jumped almost to the present and we must quickly take a few paces back to the years 1840–60 at which we halted just now. We contemplated the astronomical panorama of those days and deplored the fact that, entangled as he was in the mummy-wrappings of his outmoded methods, the astronomer was incapable of bringing his science up to date and pushing forward with the conquest of the skies.

At this period the two most powerful telescopes in the world were those of 15 inches at Pulkovo and Harvard. But possession of a large telescope is not a necessary and sufficient precondition for making discoveries. This calls for that combination of skill, aptitude for constructive hypothesis and fertility of imagination controlled by intelligence which has always been, and still remains, the monopoly of Europe, and which is perhaps identical with genius.

There can be no doubt that the quinquagenarian who rang the bell at the entrance gate of the Paris Observatory one morning in 1838 was very small beer by comparison with the great Arago he had come to see.

This quinquagenarian was known to everyone in Paris as the inventor of a popular diorama. His name was Louis Daguerre (1787–1851). Inheriting the results obtained by his associate Nicéphore Niepce (1765–1833), he had succeeded in fixing the images drawn in his dark room. Not, however, without prolonged research, not without a single-minded passion that led his wife to ask the famous chemist Jean-Baptiste Dumas whether her husband would not be better locked up. . . . But Daguerre unpacked his equipment in Arago's study, developed his plate of silvered copper after a quarter of an hour's exposure, and the astounded director of the observatory saw a shimmering but miraculous picture appear.

Everyone knows the sequel to this story. Arago, an inspired busybody, was wildly enthusiastic about Niepce and Daguerre's discovery and proclaimed it to the four corners of the world. Within a few weeks photography had spread all over the earth; then it was improved by the invention of the negative (1841), the wet collodion plate (1851), the dry plate (1861), and the silver bromide emulsion (1871). . . .

Arago had made himself the champion of the daguerreotype, and he was, among many other things, an astronomer. What more natural than that he should try to utilize the daguerreotype in astronomy? He expressed this intention the first time he presented the invention to the public, on 7 January, 1839. 'Already,' he declared, 'Monsieur Daguerre has cast the image of the Moon formed at the focus of a medium lens on to one of his "screens", where it left a manifest white imprint.'

A manifest white imprint. . . . The result was not inspiring, but it was up to astronomers to realize the tremendous future of this pallid image. They needed only imagination and audacity and the conviction that the daguerreotype could be useful to astronomy. But French astronomers, though at the birthplace of the great discovery, were not in the least convinced of its utility. Astronomy to them was celestial mechanics—it was only seven years since the discovery of Neptune—and none of them could see what use photography could be to this austere science. Thus, in spite of the efforts of Arago and a few unofficial workers, like Fizeau and Foucault,[1] they treated it with utter disdain.

Imagination, audacity, enthusiasm, the will to do something new —these were qualities which the Americans, by contrast, possessed in plenty. Hence it is not surprising that as soon as Daguerre's process had been made public, transatlantic scientists went all out to profit by it. The pioneer was the professor of chemistry in the medical faculty at the University of New York, an English-born American named John William Draper (1811–82). In 1840 he obtained the first photograph of the Moon, at the focus of a reflecting telescope of 5 inches aperture and with twenty minutes' exposure. It took another ten years, however, before the technique reached a stage of practical efficiency. That this stage had been reached was demonstrated by a new series of proofs of the Moon shown, to the admiration of visitors, at the Great Exhibition of 1851 in London.

These pictures were the work of another American, William Cranch Bond (1789–1859), a former clockmaker who had been drawn

[1] It was these two physicists who, in 1845, obtained the first photographs of sunspots.

to astronomy. Bond founded Harvard College Observatory in 1839 and it was with this observatory's 15-inch refractor that he obtained his superb records. With the same instrument, in 1850, he took the first photograph of a star. This historic event occurred during the night of 16 to 17 July. Bond, assisted by J. A. Whipple, took a photograph of Vega, a star of the first magnitude, in 100 seconds. One of the second magnitude left no impression on the plate.

This was really the prehistory of celestial photography. From now on, the advantages of this type of observation were clearly evident. Not only did it save the astronomer from all risk of error or subjective interpretation, but it also enabled him to see stars that would otherwise have remained for ever invisible to him. At the eyepiece of the most powerful instrument a few seconds of ocular observation are enough to see everything the telescope is capable of revealing; the photographic plate, on the contrary, registers more details the longer the exposure. At the focus of the great reflecting telescopes of today it often takes hours, sometimes dozens of hours. The operator photographs spiral nebulae which he cannot see and perhaps will never see.

After the American pioneers, the second half of the nineteenth century saw competition spread to Britain, where a whole pleiad of astrophotographers rivalled one another in capturing images of the stars. Along with the American lawyer Rutherford (1816–92) we must mention the Englishmen Warren de la Rue (1815–89), the author of some fine photographs of the Sun, and William Huggins (p. 299), the first to use dry plates and co-founder, with Secchi, of stellar spectroscopy.

But since our purpose is to follow, step by step, the conquest of the sky, we must draw special attention to another American, by name Benjamin Apthorp Gould (1824–96), (p. 264.) He was a geodesist who, in his youth and after studying at Harvard, had attended the European observatories, Greenwich, Paris, Berlin, Altona, Gotha. The main, indeed almost the sole, concern of these great centres was positional astronomy. Hence, Gould was deeply imbued with this approach. Since he was an American and immersed in a hectic world hungry for novelty, it is no surprise that he tried to adapt to positional astronomy the most promising of novelties, photography.

An important date is the year 1866, when Gould took a series of shots of the Pleiades. He estimated the distance between the stars at the microscope and compared his figure with that obtained by Bessel at the telescope. This was the first time an astronomer had taken micrometric measurements from a photograph. Gould's measurements agreed with Bessel's, which showed the extent to which classical astronomy could benefit from Daguerre's process. When, therefore, the astronomer was invited to set up an observatory in Argentina, he seized the opportunity to put into effect a project of broader scope.

Córdoba Observatory, opened on 24 October, 1871, by President Sarmiento and himself, has become one of the most important in the world. It was here that Gould, between 1875 and 1882, made the first photographic maps of the sky. Since the experiment carried out on the Pleiades showed that such images were reliable, there was every reason to photograph the starry sky and then do the required measuring at leisure and in the peace and comfort of the laboratory, and with all the proper instruments, on the photographic plates.

The 1,400 fine shots obtained by Gould set the ball rolling. Between 1885 and 1889 the director of the Cape Observatory, David Gill (1843–1914), produced photographic charts of the southern celestial hemisphere showing stars down to the tenth magnitude. At the Paris Observatory the brothers Paul Henry (1848–1905) and Prosper Henry (1849–1903) went down to the sixteenth magnitude in 1885. One of their plates contained nearly 5,000 stars, only 170 of which had been seen with the eye. In 1887 an international congress of astronomers met in Paris and decided to prepare a photographic map of all the skies. Eighteen observatories in the five continents, from Helsingfors to Melbourne, were selected to take part in this project. All were equipped with identical instruments, so that the photographs should be comparable, and the aim was to reach stars of the fourteenth magnitude.

Photographic raids into the empire of the stars

Faced with the task of registering millions of stars and covering 22,000 plates, the photographic chart of the heavens languished and dragged on to an indecisive end. Indispensable though the undertaking seemed, it had the misfortune to be born at a moment when astrophysics was developing at a spectacular rate and opening up totally fresh vistas. Understandably, young astronomers preferred these to the stern satisfactions of positional astronomy—even when carried out by photography.

The greatest benefit the latter derived from the new techniques was increased accuracy. The reader will recall that the average error of observations, which had been 2 seconds in Bradley's day, was diminished to 0·3 by Bessel. Photography reduced it still farther. On David Gill's photographic charts the position of the stars was guaranteed to within about 0.1 second, then photographs taken with the aid of instruments with a very long focus attained an approximation of 0·03 second. Such a level of accuracy inspired astronomers with the wish to tackle once more the old problem of the stellar parallaxes, which the heliocentric method had only broached.

Gill was delighted with the possibilities offered to him by photography. Since micrometric measurements made on photographs were so exact and so easy, why not use them to determine the slight shift imparted to the stars by the parallactic effect? The backward and forward motion of the Earth on its orbit is revealed in the slight apparent swing to and fro of the near stars against the background of the more distant stars. A series of exposures made in the course of the year brought this swing out very clearly. If in January, for example, a Centauri is seen to be $1'$ $35''\cdot422$ from a certain very remote star, while in June it is $1'$ $36''\cdot938$, an elementary process of reasoning showed that the parallax of a Centauri was

$$\frac{1'\ 36''\cdot938 - 1'\ 35''\cdot422}{2} = 0''\cdot758$$

It was in this way, by measuring the angular separation on photographs with a micrometric microscope, that Gill calculated the parallaxes of a Centauri, Sirius and seven other stars between 1882 and 1883. He found, in particular, 0·38 second for that of the splendid star in the Greater Dog. This gave a distance of 8·56 light-years, rather below the correct figure, which is now taken to be 8·95 light-years, corresponding to a parallax of 0·36 second.

The enlargement of the universe by photographic parallaxes was the work of an Englishman and an American. The Englishman was Pritchard (p. 265), professor of astronomy at Oxford; the American, Frank Schlesinger (1871–1943), director of Yale Observatory. The first from 1886, the second from 1910, devised methods enabling several parallaxes to be obtained at once. After this, parallaxes were no longer the result of an exhausting feat of mental acrobatics, and in consequence the thirty-seven parallaxes known in 1882 had become a hundred by 1900, two hundred by 1915, two thousand by 1925 and nearly ten thousand of recent years.

Unfortunately, it is no easy matter to work out these increasingly small distances of separation on a photographic plate. A moment comes when the distance measured is no larger than the possible error. At this point a halt must be called, since beyond it the figures found will be quite unreliable. This limit has been reached when the average error exceeds 0·012 second, which means that the trigonometrical method of measurement is not valid beyond a hundred or so parsecs, say 300 light-years.

Obtained first with the heliometer and then with the camera, this limit defines a sphere of some 300 light-years radius centred on our Sun. Within this sphere astronomers have, for a hundred years, stretched their surveyor's chain in all directions, and the measurements they have arrived at are no less trustworthy than those made within the confines of the solar system. Both groups rest on the principles of triangulation. This, like all mathematical operations, is absolutely accurate—apart from any errors due to the instruments employed. At the centre of this microcosm 300 light-years in radius, we are like a colonist looking round his domain. Within it he feels at home; he knows every stick and stone; he has measured it up without much difficulty. Beyond is the wilderness, the mysterious and terrifying unknown.

The borders of this domain of 300 light-years are marked by a few splendid stars, the Corn-Ear of the Virgin, Antares, Bellatrix and α Cassiopeia, with a common parallax of 0·014 second. The majority of the most brilliant stars are inside this: α Centauri (0″·758), Sirius (0″·363), Procyon (0″·304), Altair (0″·204), Fomalhaut (0″·137),

THE SUN, A STAR IN THE MILKY WAY

Vega (0″·124), Pollux (0″·101), Arcturus (0″·080), Capella (0″·069), Regulus (0″·058), Aldebaran (0″·057), Betelgeuse (0″·017). The surveyed universe, which the astronomers of 1800 were able to represent on a visiting-card and for which their successors of 1838 would have required the Place de la Concorde, covered by 1910 an area 900 times larger; instead of the Place de la Concorde, it would have taken just about the whole area of Paris.

Stretching out the stellar surveyor's chain

In proportion as their ambitions grew, as they strove to measure the distance of more and more remote stars and so to enlarge the explored universe, the nineteenth century astronomers realized more and more clearly the capital importance of one thing: the distance Earth to Sun.

Whether the distance of the stars was expressed by their parallax or by its equivalent in astronomical units or light-years, the ultimate basis was always the line Earth-Sun. It was both the base of the triangle drawn by trigonometry, and the unit of length of the sidereal universe. It alone provided the scale for the empire of the stars; it constituted the sole link between this empire and the humble terrestrial world, between a globe on which dimensions are measured in miles and the cosmos in which they are reckoned in light-years. Confronted by the stellar universe which he intended to map out, the astronomer was in the position of the geographer who sets about mapping an unknown country; he selects reference points and measures their distance by means, for example, of a surveyor's chain. But naturally his map will be accurate only if his chain is. He will therefore have it carefully checked at the Department of Weights and Measures before setting out. He will not forget that if his chain is too short, say by 1 centimetre, this will introduce into his work an error of 1 metre per kilometre, or a whole chain every 10 kilometres.

The astronomer, the geographer of the skies, was understandably worried, during all his triangulations, by the fear that his 'chain'—the base of his triangles—might not be dead right. An error of 1 centimetre every 10 metres, that is to say an error of 1/1,000, was for him an error of 1 astronomical unit in 1,000. With this error of 1/1,000 in his base line he would have placed the nearest star, α Centauri (272,270 astr. un.), 272 astronomical units closer or farther away.

In short, the distance of the Sun had long been regarded as a fundamental 'constant' in astronomy, and the reader will recall the efforts made to render it accurate. By the end of the eighteenth century, after Cassini's endeavours in connexion with the parallax of Mars,[1] and similar attempts connected with the transit of Venus in 1761 and 1769, after the expenditure of much talent, toil, time and money, the figure of 92,200,000 miles was reached, corresponding to a solar parallax of 8·91 seconds (p. 180).

This figure was far from being universally accepted. In vain the director of Gotha Observatory, the celebrated German astronomer Johann-Franz Encke (1791–1865) went over all the data relating to the last transits of Venus and published in 1824 a parallax of 8·58 seconds; he did not succeed in gaining unanimity for long.

This was because the method of the transits of Venus was no longer the only way of obtaining the desired measurement. Laplace had already outlined a 'gravitational' method in his *Mécanique céleste*. It was applied in 1854 by the Danish mathematician Hansen, who has been mentioned here before: he discovered that the apparent monthly variation in the motion of the Sun sprang from a real displacement of the Earth round the centre of gravity of the system Earth-Moon. As this displacement depended, in turn, upon the mass of the Moon and the distance of the Sun, it was possible to deduce the latter from solar observations. In this way Hansen found a distance of 95,900,000 miles.

That was not all. The phenomenon of aberration provided another means of dealing with the same problem. The solution stemmed from a common observation: that of drops of rain streaking the windows of a carriage. When the train is stationary the streaks are vertical; as it gathers speed the streaks become more and more oblique, because the speed of the drops is combined with the speed of the train. The degree

[1] It must be borne in mind that the parallax of the Sun or of a planet (called the *horizontal* parallax) is the angle under which the equatorial radius of the Earth would be seen from the Sun or planet, while the parallax of a star (*annual* parallax) is the angle under which the interval Earth-Sun would be seen from this star.

of obliquity reveals the relation between the two speeds. Similarly, the speed of the light that reaches us from the stars combines with the speed of the Earth on its orbit—this is the phenomenon of aberration. After this has given the speed of the Earth, a very simple geometrical operation makes it possible to deduce from it the radius of its orbit— that is to say its distance from the Sun. By this method the great physicist Léon Foucault (1819–68) arrived in 1862 at a distance Earth to Sun of 95,600,000 miles, which was confirmed in 1872 by his compatriot Alfred Cornu (1841–1902).

In spite of these original efforts, the method of the transits of Venus remained the most favoured. Perhaps the rarity of these phenomena and the necessity of observing them from far-away places contributed to their being looked upon as great astronomical events. Thus, when the time approached for the transit of 8 December, 1874, every great observatory made serious preparations. Even more than in the preceding century, national pride was at stake. France and Germany each organized six expeditions, Britain twelve, the United States eight, Italy three and Russia twenty-six. The Académie des Sciences, Paris, struck a medal showing Venus eclipsing Apollo and bearing a Latin inscription meaning: 'By their meeting, the heavenly bodies make known the distance that separates them.'

Once again, sad to say, the outcome was almost total failure. Various phenomena prevented men and instruments from registering the precise moment at which the little circular disc of the planet entered or left the solar disc. As a result the British deduced from it a parallax of 8·75 seconds, and the French one of 8·88 seconds. Harkness, an American, estimated that uncertainty regarding the distance still remained 1,600,000 miles.

Hence enthusiasm was a great deal less when the transit of 6 December, 1882, drew near. Russia and Austria refused to make any observation at all, Italy declared that she would not leave her peninsula, and America that she would play a lone hand. Nevertheless, France set eleven expeditions on foot and shared the task with Britain, Belgium and Germany.

The results were slightly better than on the previous occasion. The distance was narrowed down to between 92,250,000 and 93,000,000 miles. Would the figure have been closer to the truth if astronomers had turned to the planet Mars, instead of Venus, as Cassini had done? Gill thought so in 1877 and profited by the opposition of this planet, which took place that year, to put his plan into execution. There was no need for him to send an observer to Cayenne, like Cassini. He confined himself to taking up a position on Ascension Island and sighting Mars with the heliometer among its company of stars at the beginning and end of the night. The rotation of the Earth on itself gave him the base of 6,000 to 8,000 miles which he needed. The result was a parallax of 8·78 seconds, corresponding to a distance of 93,000,000 miles. This time, he was very close to the correct figure.

After the indifferent Venusian campaign of 1882, astronomers were now convinced that the 'method of Mars' was the best. The only drawback lay in the fact that, seen through the telescope, the orb presented a perceptible disc and not a point, so that readings lacked precision. What was needed was a planet made to measure, at about the same distance as Mars, but small enough to be sighted as a point.

Now, there were plenty of such planets made to measure. The minor planets that gravitated very little farther off than Mars filled the bill, as had been noted in 1872 by Galle, the former observer of Neptune. The following year he compared various observations of the minor planet *Flora*, discovered by Hind in 1847, and arrived at a good solar parallax of 8·87 seconds. Gill, who enthusiastically adopted every novelty, schooled himself in the new technique and, in 1874, derived 8·77 seconds from observation of Juno.

It was only after the admitted failure of the transits of Venus, however, that use of the minor planets became an officially accepted method in the science. *Iris* in 1888, *Victoria* and *Sappho* in 1889 enabled Gill to reduce the uncertainty, bringing the parallax to 8·802 seconds.

In 1898 the German astronomer Karl Gustav Witt (b. 1866) discovered a new unit in this vast army, the 433rd, which he christened *Eros*. It offered the singular advantage of coming closer to the Earth at times than Mars. In other words, apart from the Moon, Eros proved to be the closest of the heavenly bodies. Hence it afforded an unhoped-for opportunity of applying the method. Scientists seized this opportunity in 1901, the year of its passage at perihelion, 30,000,000 miles from the Earth, and organized international co-operation in determining the parallax. On the initiative of the director of the Paris Observatory, Maurice Loewy (1833–1907), fifty-eight observatories agreed to take part. Their best photographs were assembled and examined by the English astronomer Hinks (1873–1945). After eight years of study the latter obtained a solar parallax of 8·806 seconds, giving a distance of 93,437,000 miles.

Thirty years later, the return of Eros to its perihelion enabled the accuracy of this figure to be improved upon. This time it was only 16 million miles away. Thanks to progress in the instruments, improvement in photographic processes and the skill of the operators, an unparalleled approximation was achieved. Twenty-eight observatories participated and took 2,487 photographs. All this material was placed in the hands of the English astronomer Harold Spencer-Jones (b. 1890). It took ten years for this scientist to arrive at the figure of 8·790 seconds, corresponding to a distance of 93,527,000 miles. Spencer-Jones, who later became Astronomer Royal and hence director of Greenwich Observatory, from 1933 to 1955, commented thus on the result: 'A hundred years ago the distance of the Sun was only known to within 1/20; little by little, the uncertainty was reduced to 1/100, then to 1/1,000; now it is only 1/10,000.'

1/10,000—astronomers, so hard to please in matters of accuracy, nevertheless declared themselves satisfied with this very small margin of error. In 93,527,000 miles it meant, in fact, an uncertainty of less than 10,000 miles—the equivalent of measuring the distance from Paris to Marseilles (485 miles) with a possible error of ± 70 yards.

The latest census of the planets

Once again we have done violence to chronology and come to a halt on the very threshold of the present. Considering that we without scruple skipped a century, by-passed tremendous upheavals in science and the world, and jumped from minor planet No. 6 (Hebe, p. 242) to minor planet No. 433 (Eros), the reader may be inclined to feel that we have rushed our fences and should now return to the beginning of the nineteenth century and discuss the origins of spectral analysis.

In fact, less has been overlooked than might seem. The whole conquest of the stellar trigonometrical parallaxes and the solar parallax is merely the outcome of progress in astronomical photography. To this technique alone is due the immense chain of discoveries since the middle of the last century which now enable us to regard our inventory of the solar system as practically complete.

This inventory, first sketched out by Galileo, was pursued for more than three centuries, and it might almost be said to have remained the exclusive aim of the conquest of the heavens until towards the dawn of the twentieth century. Then, from 1838 onwards, at first timidly and sporadically, then more and more systematically and with more and more powerful instruments, exploration extended to the stars. After the first world war the shape of astronomy was moulded by new conditions, till today it looks quite different from the traditional picture of Urania held in Le Verrier's day. It has become a vast factory in which, with magnificent equipment undreamed of fifty years ago, a study is made of stars millions of times farther away than α Centauri, of galaxies, of whole universes. Amidst this hum of activity one small corner alone remains silent, containing a few scattered workers looked upon by their colleagues with a touch of ironic pity—the corner devoted to the solar system. Here there is no need for giant reflecting telescopes, spectrographs of aperture ratio f/0·3 and laboratories in which teams of physicists, chemists and engineers rub shoulders. Occasionally, no doubt, an expert in the spectrography of spirals or the expanding universe is kind enough to loan his exploring apparatus, but for the most part the 'planetary' astronomer works with medium-range telescopes, and simple visual or photographic observations. Thus, line by line, like a draughtsman finicking away at his work while a great industry is roaring next-door to him, he puts the finishing touches to the plan and inventory of our solar universe.

Scarcely a year passes in which this inventory does not undergo some slight modification with the addition of a few asteroids or comets; it is not even impossible that it may one day surprise us with a tenth major planet, gravitating obscurely the other side of

Pluto. But this would scarcely alter the appearance of the whole. Apart from a few units, the microcosm of the planets is known in detail and an almost final statement of its contents can be drawn up.

It will be opportune to set down this statement of contents here, before we leave the well-beaten tracks of the solar domain for the virgin and exhilarating solitudes of galactic astronomy. The contents may be grouped under three heads: the minor planets, the satellites, the major planets.

The minor planets. . . . Well, it will be remembered from p. 242 that after 1846 the hunt for them became almost a sport. The hunter moved round the ecliptic with his telescope, degree by degree, comparing each section of the sky with the chart. Any star that did not appear on the latter might be the coveted prey. A dreadfully long-winded method which did not, however, prevent the bag from amounting to several items every year. By 1870 the total was 110; by 1885, 250; by 1891, 320.

In this year, on 22 December, a Heidelberg amateur astronomer named Max Wolf (1863–1932) was developing a photograph of the sky that he had taken with a telescope with a wide field when he discovered, in the midst of the black dots formed by the stars, a short line. The young man thought at once that this was a star which had moved. His supposition was confirmed. This star, whose movement was sufficiently rapid to have made an impression on the plate in a few hours of exposure, was a minor planet already registered under the number 323. The importance of his rediscovery lay less in the asteroid itself than in the way in which it had been detected. For other hunters at once imitated Max Wolf. Aim a telescope with a wide field capable of embracing a large section of the firmament at the region bordering the ecliptic (the path of all the planets), expose it for a few hours and then scrutinize the negative for a little dark line—the task was infinitely easier than formerly. Consequently, from this time on, an avalanche of 'planeticules' descended upon the transactions of scientific societies. Certain investigators exhibited a marked talent for finding them. By the end of the century C. H. F. Peters had bagged over fifty items, Palisa more than eighty, and Auguste Charlois (1864–1910) of Nice Observatory one hundred and twelve ! But all records were broken by Wolf himself, who, after becoming director of Koenigstuhl Observatory, Heidelberg, specialized in this occupation and discovered several hundred asteroids on his own.

The terminology of hunting, it must be admitted, is inadequate to describe the work involved. For it was not enough to spot a thin streak on the plate; the observer had also to be able to discern whether it was really made by a minor planet and, if so, whether this planet was genuinely new or whether it had already been found and then lost again. At this point the experts in celestial mechanics went into action and calculated the orbit. On condition, of course, that they were supplied with a sufficient number of observations or photographs. When this was not the case, the asteroid that had been spotted disappeared once more on its mysterious path into the depths of space —until another seeker caught sight of it in his turn and the whole question was reopened.

It was thus that, like hundreds of others, the minor planet Athalia, which appeared to the eyes of Max Wolf in 1903, was found again fifty years later—in 1954—by the Cincinnati Observatory in America.

By 1940 some 1,500 of these worlds were numbered and duly identified by their orbits; fifteen years later the number had risen to 1,600. Few indeed by comparison with those that remain to be extracted from their obscurity. According to the traces distinguished on the 100-inch reflector at Mount Wilson, Hubble estimated that there must be more than 30,000 of them.

Naturally, the ones known are the largest. Only some thirty of them exceed sixty miles in diameter. Most of the others are blocks of rock without definite shape, whose dimensions vary from a few miles to a few yards.

The whole of this teeming mass of planets is situated between Mars and Jupiter, between 2·17 and 2·45 astronomical units from the Sun, apart from a few eccentric individuals that have deliberately wandered away from the flock. From among them let us mention two discoveries of the German-American astronomer Walter Baade (b. 1893): *Hidalgo*, found in 1924, which carries its anti-conformity to the point of going as far away as Saturn; and *Icarus* (1949), which, on the contrary, comes closer to the Sun than Mercury.

But perhaps the most interesting discoveries for us inhabitants of the Earth, apart from Eros, of which we have already heard, are *Apollo, Hermes* and *Adonis*. The first two were discovered by the German astronomer Karl Reinmuth (b. 1892), Max Wolf's successor at Heidelberg Observatory, and date respectively from 1932 and 1937; the third was detected in 1936 by Eugène Delporte (1882–1955) while director of the Belgian Royal Observatory at Uccle, Brussels. Apollo may pass at only 2½ million miles from our globe, which spells 'proximity' in the language of astronomers; in the case of Adonis, this proximity may go down to 1¼ million miles, and in that of Hermes to 375,000 miles. Such close approaches have, from time to time, set the pens of journalists scribbling at high speed, but the likelihood of their ever developing into collisions is too slight for us reasonably to advise the most pessimistic of our readers to drop everything and make their wills.

The frontiers of the solar kingdom

The use of photography, which forced a whole swarm of planetoids to emerge from their obscurity, also brought to light a crowd of unsuspected satellites. In 1898, seven years after Max Wolf's first discovery, the main centre of activity in this field was transferred from Europe to America, or rather to Jamaica, where a former Harvard astronomer named William Pickering (1858–1938) had just founded an observatory. Here, one August evening, he recognized on a series of shots of Saturn a moving point. This was a new satellite of the splendid planet. It was christened *Phoebe*.

This was the beginning of a succession of finds that may still be far from ended. After Saturn, it was Jupiter's turn to yield up another secret. At the same great telescope of the Lick Observatory with which Barnard had previously found a fifth satellite of Jupiter, his colleague Charles Perrine (1867–1951), who became director of Córdoba Observatory in 1909, detected photographically a sixth in 1904 and a seventh in 1905. The latter is only 25 miles in diameter. It appears as a mere dot of the seventeenth magnitude. The eighth, discovered by Melotte of Greenwich Observatory in 1908, is smaller still, with a diameter of no more than 19 miles. In fact it is so small and so dim—of the eighteenth magnitude—that it was lost for forty years! Although its period of revolution (739 days) should have rendered it periodically visible, it was not found again until 1941. American scientists had to bring their big guns to bear in order to get their hands on it again. The astronomer Paul Herget, of Cincinnati Observatory, got in touch with John Mauchly, one of the designers of the famous electronic machine E.N.I.A.C., who had one of his assistants work out the future position of the missing satellite every ten days from 1940 to 1980. In this way the situation of the body among the stars at the end of 1954 was determined, and the astronomer Seth B. Nicholson did in fact track down the fugitive on 25 January, 1955, on a photograph taken through the great Mount Wilson reflector.

The name of Nicholson (b. 1891) deserves to be inscribed four times over in the annals of Jovian satellites. It was he who disclosed a ninth in 1914, then, after an interval of a quarter of a century, a tenth and eleventh in 1938, and a twelfth in 1951. The happy moon-hunter celebrated his sixtieth birthday in the year of his last discovery. Let us wish him long life in which to complete the picture, so well sketched in by him, of a Jovian system richer than the solar system.

The harvest of satellites is, however, by no means the prerogative of astronomers grown grey in the service. This is shown by the case of a young scientist who combines with youth the merit of having applied his talents as an investigator in many different directions. The scientist in question is Gerard Peter Kuiper (b. 1905), a Dutch-American astronomer who, after working at Leyden Observatory, now directs the McDonald Observatory referred to on p. 268. At the 82-inch reflector of this establishment he obtained, in 1948, a photograph of Uranus that revealed the existence of a fifth satellite. This distant body of 125 miles diameter and nineteenth magnitude received the name *Miranda*. The discoverer repeated his exploit the following year, when he detected a second satellite of Neptune, *Nereid*. The latter is so small that it would fit in between Paris and Rennes, and it gives no more light in the depths of space than a candle at 2,800 miles.

But the most important discovery in this field was, of course, that of *Pluto*, the last major planet, the 'trans-Neptunian' planet so long sought by those whom the fame of William Herschel and Le Verrier kept awake at nights.

After Saturn, which had always been regarded as demarcating the frontiers of the solar kingdom, the Bath organist discovered Uranus; after Uranus, the ex-engineer from the Tobacco Department discovered Neptune. The boundaries of the kingdom moved back in proportion as instruments were improved. Was there not reason to believe that, with even more powerful means, another planet more remote than Neptune might be brought to light? Might it not be possible to make sure of the existence of such a globe by the very method employed by Le Verrier, that is to say by computing the perturbations of Uranus and Neptune?

The problem attracted the American astronomer Percival Lowell (1855–1916). Lowell was a former diplomat who, having a comfortable private income, had abandoned his career in order to devote himself to the study of the planet Mars. In 1894 he erected at Flagstaff, Arizona, an observatory equipped first with a refracting telescope of 18 inches aperture, then with another of 2 feet 4 inches, and finally a 3-foot reflecting telescope. Here he made those observations of the 'canals' of Mars that gave rise to so much argument.[1]

Lowell tackled the problem of the perturbations of Uranus as Le Verrier had done. After eliminating those attributable to Neptune, he showed the presence of a residue which he supposed to be due to the hypothetical planet he was seeking. In 1915 he published the result of his calculations and indicated the point in the sky at which, in his view, it must be situated. Unfortunately, the beautiful unknown failed to turn up at the rendezvous.

The scientist's death the following year brought these investigations to a close. They were not resumed until thirteen years later. Lowell Observatory had acquired a photographic telescope of 13 inches aperture and exceptional performance. With this instrument the whole ecliptic was photographed, in such a way that the suspected planet, of the twelfth or thirteenth magnitude, must inevitably be caught as it passed.

[1] Pierre Rousseau, *Mars, terre mystérieuse* (Hachette).

Confronted by a negative spattered with thousands of black dots, the layman may wonder what mysterious process of divination enables the astronomer to say, 'That one is a planet,' though it looks exactly like the rest. In fact it involves neither miraculous intuition nor even a prodigy of arithmetic. The astronomer simply works on the basis that, by its very etymology, a planet is a 'wandering orb'. Today close to one star, tomorrow it will be near another. It is, of course, humanly impossible to examine thousands of black dots one by one to see if any of them have moved; so recourse is had to an instrument known as the *blink microscope*.

This blink microscope is fundamentally a stereoscope. Two photographs of the same zone of the sky, taken at an interval of, say, one month, are inserted in it. A mechanical device lights up each of these plates alternately in a very rapid rhythm, so that only one of them is visible at a time. If they are both exactly the same, the operator will see no difference. But if a star has moved between the one and the other, its image will seem to jump and the change will be immediately noticeable. Thus, on 18 February, 1930, the Flagstaff astronomer in charge of this review put aside two negatives, taken at an interval of six days, which looked to him suspicious.

The astronomer was Clyde W. Tombaugh (b. 1906), a former Kansas cowboy, who had been admitted to the Observatory in January 1929 and whose work consisted in systematically photographing the whole path of the ecliptic. It was therefore about a year after taking up his duties that he spotted, in the vicinity of the star δ Geminorum, a dot that jumped slightly from one plate to the other. From the next day on, this object was kept under surveillance. At the end of a month they were certain: on 13 March, 1930, the Lowell Observatory announced the discovery of a new planet.

Calculation of the orbit of *Pluto*, as it was called, showed it to be very near the one predicted by Lowell. Its semi-major axis is 3,600 million miles (or 39·6 astronomical units) for a period of revolution of 248 years. The founder of Flagstaff's claim to being a second Le Verrier might be disputed, but there could be no denying that, if he had not discovered Pluto himself, he had at least pointed out the existence of a planet in the region of the sky in which it was actually found and had ascribed to it approximately the true path. He was mistaken about its mass, but twenty-five years later astronomers have got no farther, since even today they are undecided as to whether it is equal in size to the Earth or only one-tenth of this.

In any case, there is nothing majestic about the latest planet. According to Kuiper its diameter is less than half that of our own planet. Its brightness, of the fourteenth magnitude, makes it barely visible except to instruments of over 1 foot diameter. For the time being—and with the exception of certain comets—it marks the farthest boundary of our planetary district. A circular district 7,000 million miles in diameter—an expanse that is beyond the power of human imagination, but only an insignificant speck in the empire of the stars.

On the distribution of the stars

Pluto, Neptune, Uranus—the name of the planet that marks the confines of our domain matters little: there is no need of figures to bring out the crushing magnitude of the universe by comparison with this domain. The vastness of the former in relation to the latter was no discovery of yesterday; realization of this vastness has been typical of men of genius throughout the ages. But the universe proved more and more overwhelmingly immense in proportion as science progressed. The stellar empire as pictured in Napoleon III's day had little in common with the cosmos conceived a hundred years later by the relativists, a cosmos that is finite though unbounded and isolated in a hyper-space inaccessible to the senses.

At the beginning of the nineteenth century only a few rare thinkers asked themselves whether the apparently random distribution of the stars did not, in reality, obey some well-defined law. No one doubted now that the Sun was one of these stars, but great astronomers like William Herschel went further and considered the problem of their over-all distribution in space. We have seen his answer to this question: starting from the postulate that they all possessed more or less the same luminous intensity, he came to the conclusion that they formed a flat agglomeration in the shape of a girdle-cake, which extended indefinitely in its plane and appeared to observers on Earth as the Milky Way.

Obviously this theory, to which first John Herschel and then Wilhelm Struve added further detail, could be no more than pure supposition, since the distance of the stars was a problem that had scarcely been tackled. Nothing could be established regarding the way in which they were distributed until it was known whether the brightness of each star was due to its own luminous intensity or merely to its degree of proximity.

In other words, astronomers could not begin to form any idea of the structure of the universe until they were in possession of a sufficient number of stellar distances, which was not until the second half of the century. Then this problem seemed grandiose but simple. Just as earthly power was divided among a few powerful, highly organized and hierarchical states—such as the British, French and Russian Empires—so it seemed natural to suppose that the world of the stars, rather than an anarchical mass of orbs wandering at will, should be subject to a strict order, a degree of subordination fixed once and for all by nature.

A variety of conceptions were formed of this galactic assemblage. Thus, to the mind of the English astronomer Richard Proctor (1837–88), the universe was shaped not like a girdle-cake, but like a snake coiled several times round itself with the Sun at the centre. The German Heinrich von Seeliger (1849–1924) returned to Herschel's *gauges* and agreed with Herschel that the universe had the shape of a rather convex girdle-cake, to which Seeliger attributed a diameter of 23,000 light-years. The Dutchman Cornelis Easton (1864–1929) imagined an agglomeration in the shape of a spiral with two branches, the Sun being situated near the centre. The Frenchman Charles André (1842–1912) preferred to suppose the Sun and all the stars gravitating round a monstrous orb, the pivot of the universe.

The fancifulness and variety of such theories is enough to tell us that they were entirely products of the imagination without any firm basis in fact. The only point on which everyone was agreed was that, in order to form a rational idea of the distribution of the stars, the real brightness of each star must be taken into account. For if such and such a star appeared dim, this might be because it was very remote, but it might also be because its luminosity was less than that of other stars.

Towards the end of the nineteenth century, astronomers were no longer totally ignorant of relative luminosity. The discoveries of spectroscopy had made it possible to detect inequalities between stars as pronounced as those between human beings. Stars with a high absolute brightness were known to exist alongside stars of inconsiderable brightness. For example, it was known that, if placed at the same distance as the Sun, Sirius would shine 26 times more brightly than the Sun, and its satellite—for Sirius is a double star—333 times less brightly. The importance of taking these inequalities into account in forming a valid picture of the distribution of the stars was obvious.

The task was none the less delicate. There could naturally be no question of examining one by one all the stars in the sky, or even the hundreds of thousands in Argelander's catalogue. But the difficult is not the impossible: the physicist is also unable to examine one by one all the innumerable molecules that make up a gas; this does not prevent him from calculating exactly the gas's characteristics, its density, pressure and temperature. For this purpose he applies the principles of statistics, which, in this particular case, becomes the kinetic theory of gases. Of course it appeared possible to apply the same treatment to the stars, by regarding each of them as a molecule, but such a method was seriously at variance with classical astronomy, and to venture to put it into practice called for a tendency to originality bordering on eccentricity.

Kapteyn deduces the universe in 1900

Now, in 1878, a professor of astronomy and theoretical physics was appointed to the University of Groningen, Holland—Professor Jacobus Cornelius Kapteyn (1851–1922). The teaching was indeed very theoretical, since the chair did not carry any laboratory, any instrument or any prospect of ever acquiring any. Kapteyn was twenty-seven and an enthusiastic astronomer; he would have liked to measure himself against his colleagues who, at Kensington, Berlin, Vienna, Meudon and Harvard, were adding storey after storey to the magnificent edifice of astrophysics. But as all his equipment consisted of a blackboard and a piece of chalk, he had to direct his ambitions towards mathematical astronomy. It occurred to him to write to the director of the Cape Observatory, David Gill, whom we have already met, and suggest that as Gill was fully occupied with the material aspects of his celestial photography he might like to entrust to him, Kapteyn, the work of analysis and measurement. Gill accepted his offer, and a collaboration was born that was to be both long and fruitful.

From this collaboration the director of the Groningen Astronomical Laboratory benefited no less than the director of the Cape Observatory: from the negatives and data with which the latter supplied him, Kapteyn was able to create *stellar statistics.*

The Dutch scientist's first finding was this: the galactic mass, taken as a whole, was undoubtedly of the shape ascribed to it by Herschel. It was like a highly convex girdle-cake, almost an egg— what we should call an ellipsoid—in which the stars were increasingly dense the closer they lay to the centre. The Sun was situated in the vicinity of this centre.

A second finding, obtained in 1904, was the existence in the heart of this mass of stars of two 'currents'. To understand the nature of this discovery, we must recall that, ever since Halley noted in 1718 that the stars moved (p. 215), a growing number of these 'proper motions' had been observed and measured. They had regularly appeared in the catalogues, and by 1870 several thousands were known. In this year Proctor noticed that five of the stars in the Great Bear had the same proper motion: they moved towards the same spot in the sky at the same speed. This was neither an appearance of motion due to the translation of the solar system, nor an effect of chance, since Proctor found an analogous phenomenon in the constellation of the Bull. From this he concluded that there existed 'currents' of stars.

In 1904 Kapteyn greatly widened the scope of this observation. He discovered that all the stars—or at least all those whose movement was perceptible—were swept along by one or other of two enormous and opposing currents. Imagine two trains travelling in opposite directions along parallel tracks. In each of these trains the travellers are walking up and down the corridors; in other words, they are moving about at random while at the same time being carried along by the train in a general common movement. Similarly, Kapteyn asked his colleagues to picture the stars as being transported *en bloc* by two immense currents while at the same time moving at random inside each of them.

There is no denying that this discovery was both vitally important and strange. Of vital importance, because it showed without a doubt that the myriads of stars grouped in the Milky Way were by no means an anarchic horde, but that they formed, on the contrary, a disciplined society subject to the rule of these two currents; strange, because there was no apparent explanation of the latter. Why should half the stars travel in one direction, and half in the other? What mysterious force carried them along?

When Kapteyn died in 1922 he was still struggling to get to the bottom of this riddle. He was an old man of seventy-one, whose mentality, studies and tastes tied him to the nineteenth century. But the era of relativity and giant reflecting telescopes had dawned. In America, at Harvard Observatory, an astronomer of thirty-seven named Shapley had already glimpsed the true nature of Kapteyn's currents and the true structure of the universe.

*   *   *

We may regard the great Dutch astronomer's work as marking the close of a stage in the history of the conquest of the skies. A stage which the astronomers of the whole world had spent all the nineteenth century in travelling, which began in 1838 with the first stellar parallax and ended in 1922 when Kapteyn, combining the findings of all his forerunners, strove to comprehend the whole universe in a homogeneous image.

At this end of a stage, how far we are from the imaginative constructions of William Herschel! The fashion is for realism; astronomers are no longer satisfied with words and smile at the memory of the island universes. Island universes? There is only one—our own.

The universe is occupied by a single stellar formation. Our *Galaxy*, that is to say the group of stars which we see as the Milky Way, is the whole of the universe, with its thousands of millions of stars, its stellar conglomerations, its nebulae. Yes, these nebulae themselves, far from being exterior universes, have turned out to be integral parts of the Galaxy: their intimate connexion with it is revealed by the increasing abundance of their distribution the farther they are from the median plane of the Milky Way. The whole of creation is contained within this ellipsoidal frame, beyond which there is nothing. The dimensions of this cosmos? Seeliger estimated it at 23,000 light-years, Kapteyn at 40,000. These are huge numbers before which the mind reels.

Yet the day is drawing near when these numbers will appear ludicrously small, when they will have to be multiplied by 1,000, 10,000 or 100,000, when the island universes will be reborn and proliferate, when our universe, our Galaxy, ceasing to fill the whole universe, will gradually lose its pre-eminence, then its importance and finally be reduced to the level of a wretched little agglomeration of heavenly bodies, lost in indefinite space along with thousands of millions of other agglomerations.

What is Galileo's revelation beside this?

9

The universe through which we are travelling

Spectrum analysis, the key to the secret of things—The chemistry
of the stars—The mystery of the stars unveiled by their spectra—
The spectrum gives the distances of the stars—New instruments
for a new science—The new astronomy, a daughter of wealthy
America—The cepheids: sounding the extra-galactic depths—
Shapley reveals the Galaxy—The problem of the spiral nebulae—
Hubble, the Christopher Columbus of the nebulae—The realm
of the nebulae—Hubble discovers the recession of the galaxies—
A magnitude and a half for £2 million—An arithmetical error in
cosmic surveying—An outline of the universe 1958

THE most important date in the conquest of the skies, after the
invention of the telescope (1609), is the invention of spectrum
analysis (1859).

The telescope, after all, is no more than an extension of the human
eye. It never shows us more than the external appearance of things.
Spectrum analysis, on the other hand, enables us to penetrate to their
very heart and reveals the intimate secrets of their age and constitution. If spectrum analysis had not yet been invented we should
certainly possess giant telescopes and photographs of stars, nebulae
and galaxies, but we should be unable to say what these objects were.
The assumption that stars are suns like our own would be pure
hypothesis. If we kept strictly to the data of observation we should
have to regard them as mere points of light. Trigonometry would
certainly have allowed us to calculate the distances of those nearest to
us, but the rest of the universe would have remained an enigma and we
should have been unable to tell whether the spirals scattered over the
Mount Palomar negatives were hundreds or hundreds of millions of
light-years away. We should not even have been able to decide
whether they were colossal agglomerations of stars or merely
vaguely luminescent clouds.

The most astonishing thing about this great invention is not that it was made, but that it should have been made so belatedly. How many experimenters had come within a hair's breadth of it since Newton showed, in 1666, that white light was a mixture of various coloured lights? He learnt how to break it up by passing it through a glass prism, and how to spread out its components in a band, a *spectrum*, in which the traditional colours of the rainbow were regularly found side by side. Similarly, in 1752, the young Scot Thomas Melvill, who died at twenty-seven, studied a flame into which he had introduced a packet of sea salt, potassium, alum or saltpetre and noted that the spectrum was almost always reduced to a magnificent orange line. In 1802 it occurred to the Norfolk physicist William Hyde Wollaston (1766–1828) to receive on a prism not a random bundle of solar rays, but one coming from a very narrow crack. Not only did he observe a purer spectrum, in which the colours overlapped less, but he distinguished five dark transverse lines. Wollaston was not at all curious by nature, an unfortunate thing in a scientist: he regarded these lines as merely separating the different colours and left it at that.

Fraunhofer came even closer to the great discovery. The reader will recall the fine practical achievements of this Munich optician, his object-glasses and equatorial. It was while studying the refrangibility of lenses in 1814 that he was led to repeat Wollaston's experiment, that is, to examine the spectrum of solar light passing through a narrow crack. He naturally found the five lines already known, but, being more inquiring than his predecessor, he inspected them through a small telescope. He then saw not merely five, but multitudes of lines. They covered the solar spectrum like the meshes of a net, some fine and in a few cases barely perceptible, others massive and inescapable. Fraunhofer measured the separation between the more important ones with a theodolite, and in this way established the position of 324 lines out of more than 600.

The puzzle confronting Fraunhofer grew more complicated when he directed his prism towards the Moon, Venus and Mars: the light of these orbs showed the same lines, far less intense, but situated in the same positions. By contrast, the light of Sirius and Castor revealed, instead of innumerable lines, only three broad black bands, while that of Pollux gave a spectrum of the same type as the Sun.

What did these divergent facts imply? Where did these lines come from? Why did those of solar light differ from those of certain stars?

Fraunhofer came within an ace of the solution one day in 1815, when he noticed that the orange line discerned by Melvill in 1752 occupied exactly the same position as a very distinct line, line D, in the solar spectrum. The sagacious optician sensed that the bright line and the dark line were one and the same thing, but he did not pursue his investigations any further either. As an optician, his job was to manufacture optical instruments, not to try and unravel mysteries that were the prerogative of the physicists. He left the matter to the experts.

But the experts continued on the wrong track. The situation was rather like the game in which a player looks for a hidden object while the onlookers call out 'You're getting hot . . . you're burning' as he approaches the hiding-place. Physicists were hot for nearly half a century and occasionally burning, but without ever putting their hands on the treasure. They noted, for example, that the dark line D in the solar spectrum or Melvill's orange line appeared whenever the flame being studied contained sodium, but unfortunately these lines also turned up on many occasions when there was no proof that sodium was involved.

To avoid being lost in a maze of contradictions, to extract something useful from such varied experiments, to get at the truth obscured by so many particular cases, demanded an eminently critical mind. This was not a matter for imagination or hypothesis, but for cold logic. The Theseus of this labyrinth had less need of an impetuous brain capable of flashes of insight, than of the ability to pursue imperturbably the more prosaic path indicated by facts. It was no Newton or Herschel who was destined to accomplish this piece of detective work; it was a Descartes.

Or let us say a Kant, since Kirchhoff, the man in question, was born in Koenigsberg like the father of Pure Reason. The possibility that something more than coincidence linked his place of birth and the unfailing positivism he applied to his investigations is a point we shall not venture to discuss. We shall confine ourselves to noting that Kirchhoff belonged to that school of pure mechanists exemplified by Helmholtz in Germany, Kelvin in Britain and Berthelot in France. For the benefit of those readers who are not too clear about this philosophical attitude, we will exemplify it by a story once told by the chemist Camille Matignon in the *Revue de Paris*.

One day Matignon, who was at that time laboratory assistant to Berthelot, laid before his superior a scientific memoir. From the bare result of his experiments—a few lines of facts and figures—the young man had drawn some interesting and original deductions, upon which he expected that the great scientist would compliment him. Instead, Berthelot picked up a pencil, drew a square round the simple result and crossed out the rest.

Gustav Kirchhoff (1824–87) was a man of this stamp: nothing counted for him but the bare experimental fact. In 1859 he was professor of physics at Heidelberg University, where he had sought a chair in order to be with his friend Robert Bunsen (1811–99), who taught chemistry there.

It is not surprising that spectrum analysis should have been invented by this man who accepted the dominion of facts without risking an interpretation of them. We can picture him, for example, studying the spectrum of a Bunsen burner, in whose flame he had placed a pinch of salt (sodium chloride) and seeing Melvill's beautiful orange band flare up.

He then proceeded to the experiment of passing the Sun's light through the flame of a Bunsen burner before it reached the prism. The brilliant band vanished and was replaced by the rainbow of the solar spectrum. Through the middle ran the dark line D, unusually broad and intense.

After this he carried out a final experiment in which it was not the Sun's light that he passed through the flame, but that of an oxy-hydrogen lamp.[1] This latter normally gives a continuous spectrum, that is to say a rainbow band devoid of lines. But interposition of the sodium flame immediately caused the appearance of the dark line D.

[1] Oxy-hydrogen light is given by the incandescence of a stick of lime, induced by the combustion of hydrogen in oxygen.

The conclusion Kirchhoff came to was dictated exclusively by the facts.

When the sodium flame is examined by itself, its spectrum is limited to a brilliant orange band, the *emission line* of sodium.

When the sodium flame is superimposed upon another stronger light (that of the Sun or an oxy-hydrogen lamp), the spectrum is that of this second source and the formerly brilliant band stands out as dark (the *absorption line* of sodium).

In other words, line D is the sign of sodium. It appears either light or dark according to whether the light comes from the sodium flame alone or from another, more intense source.

Together with his friend Bunsen, Kirchhoff extended his experiments, considering sources of light that contained not only sodium, but potassium, lithium, calcium. . . . He confirmed that each of these elements possessed its characteristic spectrum, a red and violet band for potassium, a red and a yellow one for lithium, one orange, two yellow and one violet for calcium, and so on.

The truth blazed forth. Spectrum bands are a hieroglyph written by nature that contains the secret of the composition of bodies. This was the discovery which Kirchhoff, a Champollion of light,[1] laid before the Academy of Sciences, Berlin, on 15 December 1859. The first result was to cause the collapse of the mystery of the Sun, along with all the groundless hypotheses advanced by Arago and the Herschels. The Sun is nothing but an incandescent globe in which spectrum bands reveal the presence of sodium, iron, magnesium, calcium, chromium, copper and many other bodies, and if these bands appear dark it is because the solar atmosphere is interposed between the dazzling orb and the Earth.

The chemistry of the stars

Eighteen fifty-nine. Physical laboratories had long been in possession of spectroscopes. Physicists were even able to calculate the wavelengths of the various colours of the spectrum and of the spectrum lines —without knowing what these lines were. Since Fraunhofer, the clue to

[1] Jean-François Champollion, the first decipherer of the Egyptian hieroglyphics.

the riddle had been within easy reach, but prior to Kirchhoff no one had picked it up. We must suppose that there was no practical need present to provide scientists with a spur, for we have seen that once scientists are given a definite task they master it in no time: the invention of the atomic bomb was accomplished in four years, whereas a century might not have been long enough if atomic scientists had not been prodded by military necessity.

The discovery of spectrum analysis hung fire from 1802 (Wollaston) to 1859, and after this date developed at breakneck speed. Perhaps we may see here too the effect of the accumulated pressure of external circumstances. Perhaps realistically-minded people, technologists, industrialists, economists, realized the practical progress which this invention might bring about—chemical analysis and the manufacture of products of ever-increasing purity, the metallurgy of alloys, the measurement of temperatures in iron-smelting, the improvement of optical glass pursuant on the spread of photography. In any case, the impetus was given, spectrum analysis was elevated to the status of a new science, which spread through the laboratories and led to a ramification of practical applications.

We shall not spend long with the spectroscopists as they follow their special path; we shall merely accompany them to the end of the road they pursued while working on the conquest of the skies. It is no exaggeration to say that the astronomical, and even philosophical, importance of the discovery was incalculable. What Kirchhoff had brought into being was a chemistry of the universe that preluded the foundation of a new astronomy. Alongside the astronomy described by Bessel—a science concerned solely with determining the motion of the heavenly bodies and predicting their future positions—there arose a new one devoted to the unlikely task of making a chemical analysis of the stars. On the human plane, the undertaking was heavy with consequences, since from it stemmed a great part of atomic physics. On the philosophical plane the implications were no less sweeping: it showed that the laws of chemistry were the same everywhere and applied on the boundaries of the universe with the same rigour as in the laboratory. In short, it constituted a supplement to Newton's work: whether it was a question of the structure of bodies or of gravitation, man had wrested from nature the knowledge of universally valid fundamental laws.

The fruitfulness of the new method was not, of course, overlooked by astronomers. Only three months after Kirchhoff had expounded it to the Berlin Academy, one of them attempted to decipher the message of the stars transmitted in their spectra. This was the director of the Florence Observatory, Giambattista Donati—a man of thirty-four destined to die of cholera at forty-seven. But the spectrum of a star, even of the first magnitude, is incomparably less legible than that of the Sun, and this forerunner achieved a tremendous feat in distinguishing the most pronounced bands in some of them. The true meaning of the hieroglyph was not grasped until some years later, by the English astronomer Sir William Huggins (1824–1910), who may be regarded as the chief founder of the science of astrophysics or spectroscopic astronomy.

Huggins presents the almost perfect picture of a sage whose happy and long life passed without conflict between love of science and conjugal love. He enjoyed a small private income and pursued astronomy as an enthusiastic amateur. He equipped a laboratory in his house at Tulse Hill, South London, and his friends took pleasure in visiting this peaceful household in which an affectionately united couple devoted their evenings to star-gazing. His orderly and regular mode of life gained him sixty years of scientific activity.

Huggins's first communication to the Royal Society, in 1864, was also the most momentous. What are the stars made of? he asked himself. Then he spent months and months patiently examining the spectra of certain brilliant stars, such as Betelgeuse, Aldebaran and Sirius, recording their lines and comparing them with the emission lines of known bodies. The word 'patiently' is apt, since instead of taking photographs of spectra and then studying them at leisure, as modern astronomers do, Huggins was obliged to study them visually. Some idea of the strain he imposed on his eyes by so doing may be gained by imagining the feeble gleam of a star after it has been spread out in a spectrum.

Nevertheless, it was by working thus that the diligent astronomer identified in the stellar spectra the lines of sodium, iron, calcium, magnesium, bismuth and sometimes hydrogen and other metalloids. This was work of great precision, the major drawback to which was that it would have taken more than a thousand years to analyse one by one all the visible stars! As luck would have it, at the very period when Huggins was devoting himself to this rigorous dissection, another scientist was undertaking a less detailed but more rapid review of the sky.

When geographers set about drawing a map they have recourse, according to their needs, to aerial photography or direct observation of the terrain. The first gives them the general physiognomy of the region and permits them to link it up with the rest of the country; the second furnishes them with the details of the topography and relief. One is certainly no less indispensable than the other.

The same comparison might be made between Huggins's work and that of his Italian colleague, the Jesuit father Angelo Secchi (1818–78). While the former was the observer on the ground, who misses no feature of the terrain, the latter resembled the aerial observer, who flies over the whole countryside in order to form a general picture of it. Secchi was director of the observatory of the Roman College, set up on the church of St. Ignatius. If he managed to give the spectrum characteristics of 4,000 stars in only four years, it was clearly because he was satisfied with a less detailed study of each of them.

Father Secchi brought this review to a close in 1867. The importance of the catalogue he published will be evident from the fact that it constituted the first classification of the stars by their spectra. He had noticed that in some of them the lines of hydrogen were most in evidence, while in others it was the lines of the metals. For example, white or bluish stars like Sirius and Vega showed only four very visible lines, those of hydrogen. In the case of less white or even yellowish stars, such as Arcturus and Capella (and our Sun), the lines were fewer but representative of the metals. In the case of orange stars like Betelgeuse and Antares these rays were so intense as scarcely to allow the light to filter through. Finally, there were some stars so red that their spectrum was reduced to a few rays of ruby light filtering through between massive black bands.

Secchi therefore divided the stars into four main classes: white, yellow, bright-red and dark-red. This inevitably raised the question of why the stars were not all the same colour. Hermann Karl Vogel (1841–1907), who became director of the Potsdam Observatory in 1882, thought in 1874 that these variations were due to differences of temperature. Just as a heated poker becomes first dark-red, then light-red and finally white, was it not probable that a dark-red star like Antares was less hot than a light-red star like Betelgeuse or a white star like Sirius?

The mystery of the stars unveiled by their spectra

The idea was ingenious, but the only way of testing it was by a really thorough study of the stars. This could not be made until it became possible to photograph them.

The first step along this path was taken in 1871 by J. W. Draper, the American pioneer who, as we saw on page 270, obtained the first daguerreotype of the Moon. In this year he recorded on a wet collodion plate a spectrum of Vega showing the four hydrogen lines. Huggins carried on from here. Armed with his 18-inch reflecting telescope, he set about taking stellar spectrograms going right down to ultra-violet. At this point it became reasonable to wonder whether it would be advantageous to replace Secchi's spectrum catalogue, drawn up by eye, by a photographic catalogue. The answer was given by a Harvard astronomer named Edward Pickering (1846–1919), elder brother of the man who discovered the satellites Themis and Phoebe.

Up to that time, astro-spectroscopists had always placed the prism at the focus of their telescope, in place of the eye-piece, and had always used it in conjunction with a slit. Pickering had the original idea of placing it in front of the object-glass and doing away with the slit. As the prism was of large dimensions it covered a relatively extensive field, so that the plate, instead of receiving the spectrogram of a single star, received those of several. This was almost mass-production, as the astronomer proved in 1886 when he obtained the spectra of all the stars in the Pleiades with one shot.

This technique was very well suited to the preparation of a

catalogue of spectra, and the Harvard Observatory immediately embarked on such a project. The catalogue was published in 1890. It bore the title *Draper Catalogue*, because Draper's widow had generously put up the money. It contained no less than 19,000 spectra, going down to the eighth magnitude. It had proved impossible to retain Secchi's rudimentary classification in four types: Pickering had distinguished as many as fifteen classes, which he designated by the letters of the alphabet A to O. He had been a trifle over-hasty, and together with his team of astrophysicists had gradually to modify his classification as the years passed. The last edition of the *Draper Catalogue*, which appeared in 1924, contained the spectra of 225,000 stars divided into only nine classes, from the whitest and hottest to the reddest and coolest, designated by the letters W, O, B, A, F, G, K, M, N.

The spectrum analysis of the stars and the classification of the latter according to their spectra really founded astrophysics. The consequences of this development were tremendous. This branch of astronomy, which might, to begin with, have been thought purely speculative, has proved, on the contrary, susceptible of ever wider and more spectacular application. Let us not forget that if our epoch may be called the atomic age, it owes this just as much to the astrophysicists as to the nuclear experts.[1] This lies outside our province, however, and if the spectrography of the heavens weighs singularly heavily in the present phase of technology and civilization, let us also recall what an inspiring chapter it opened in the epic of celestial conquest.

We left this conquest on page 262 when it had extended over an area approximately 300 light-years in radius. This was not much. Indeed, astronomers suspected that it was only the edge of an inconceivable abyss, but how were they to extend their soundings? When applied to a star situated at this distance, trigonometry had to work with angles of around one-hundredth of a second, and even the photographic method invented by Schlesinger failed to improve the situation. Of the 600 parallaxes given by this scientist, over half were subject to a margin of error of at least 50 per cent!

[1] See on this subject the present author's *L'Astronomie nouvelle* (Fayard) and *Notre Soleil* (Hachette).

No one foresaw that when trigonometry reached the limits of its resources the task would be taken over by astrophysics, that the spectrum analysis of the stars would provide a means of passing beyond this island of 300 light-years and plunging right into the sidereal ocean.

At bottom, astronomers had never ceased to regret that the photometric procedure explained on page 262 was not utilizable. If all stars possessed the same luminosity, if, for example, they all had the same absolute brightness as the Sun, it would be sufficient for one of them to appear four times less brilliant than another for us to say that it was twice as far away.

But not only were astronomers convinced that stars were of very varying brightness, they also had no means of measuring this brightness. How could they tell whether a star shining at a distance of hundreds or thousands of light-years would shine more, less or equally brightly by comparison with the Sun if situated at the same distance from us as this luminary?

Out of this blind alley astrophysics opened a path—a path that led towards the sought-for solution and furnished the key to the sidereal distances.

The spectrum gives the distances of the stars

The first blow was struck in 1905, in the shape of an article in a scientific review. It caused little commotion because the review was as unknown as the signatory of the article. This was a Danish chemical engineer of thirty-two named Ejnar Hertzsprung, who practised astronomy as a hobby. In his article he came out in opposition to the stellar theories of Harvard College, then universally accepted. Harvard took the classification of the stars in nine groups as being indisputably related to temperature. According to this view, the white (or verging on blue) stars must be the hottest and therefore the most fiercely burning, the youngest, the most voluminous, the ones with the highest absolute brightness; while the red ones were seen as the coolest and therefore the oldest, the most worn out, the most shrunken, those with the lowest absolute brightness.

Now an unknown amateur slashed recklessly at this closely woven fabric of theory. There was no real proof, said Hertzsprung, that the red stars were the old orbs whose luminosity was dying away. It appeared, on the contrary, that they included two very distinct types: on the one hand, dwarf stars that really were of low luminosity, and on the other, giant stars of considerable absolute brightness, whose apparent dimness was only to be explained by their greater distance.

It was not immediately evident, firstly whether Hertzsprung's assertion was correct, and secondly where it would lead. Nevertheless, it appears to have been considered plausible, since in 1909 its author was appointed assistant at Goettingen Observatory, moving to Leyden Observatory in 1919. In any case, it attracted the attention of an American astronomer, Henry Norris Russell (1877–1957), director of Princeton Observatory.

Anxious to check Hertzsprung's statements, Russell drew up a list of those stars regarding which both the distance and the spectrum class was known. From this he deduced their absolute brightness.[1] He then entered these stars on a diagram that took account of both their spectrum class and absolute brightness. The result, shown in Fig. 9, is known as *Russell's diagram*.

This diagram is highly instructive. It shows that in classes B and A the stars are not scattered; they are all concentrated round an absolute brightness 100 to 10,000 times greater than the Sun's. From class F to class M, on the contrary, they are split into two groups: at the top of the diagram, stars of very high absolute brightness, and at the bottom, stars of very low absolute brightness. In other words, Russell's diagram proved that stars might be of every absolute brightness, from the highest (Canopus, 80,000 times that of the Sun) to the lowest (Krueger 60, 15/10,000 of the Sun's). So there must exist *giant*, and even *super-giant* stars, and *dwarf* stars, with every possible intermediate size.

Russell's conclusions were published in 1913. They aroused great curiosity—and also, it must be admitted, some incredulity: all this

---

[1] It is easy to calculate the absolute brightness of a star when its apparent brightness and distance are known. Take Arcturus as an example. Its apparent brightness is $1/608 \times 10^8$ that of the Sun; its distance, 2,578,312 times that from the Earth to the Sun. From this its absolute brightness is inferred to be 100 times that of the Sun.

was pure theory. Since no telescope was sufficiently powerful to show stars otherwise than as points without dimension, it was impossible to decide by direct observation whether there really were giants and

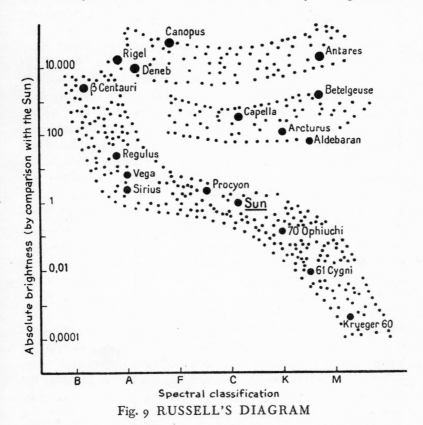

Fig. 9 RUSSELL'S DIAGRAM

The stars are here arranged in terms of their spectral classification (on the abscissa) and absolute brightness. It may be seen that in classes B and A they remain concentrated round absolute brightnesses 100 to 10,000, whereas from class F to class M they are divided into three very distinct groups: at the top the *super-giants*, in the middle the *giants*, at the bottom the stars of the *main series* and the *dwarfs*.

dwarfs. But was there perhaps an indirect means of finding out? A very voluminous, giant star must resemble an enormous bubble of gas of low density and low pressure, while a dwarf star was probably a shrunken globe in which the matter was much compressed and very dense. This difference of density and pressure between the giant and the dwarf must appear in certain characteristics of the spectrum, the intensity of the lines of absorption, for example.

This was how an astronomer at the Mount Wilson Observatory named Walter Sidney Adams (1876–1956), born at Antioch in Syria of American parents, reasoned in 1914. As a first experiment he chose the two stars Aldebaran and 61 Cygni. These stars gave the same spectrum. So they belonged to the same spectrum class, class K. They were therefore of approximately the same temperature, 7,000 degrees F. Yet according to Russell's diagram (Fig. 9), one was a dwarf and the other a giant. Together with his co-worker Kohlschuetter, Adams examined their spectra to see whether this difference in volume was revealed in any anomaly. He found, in fact, that a calcium line was very strong in the spectrum of 61 Cygni and faint in Aldebaran, whereas a strontium line was faint in 61 Cygni and very strong in Aldebaran. This was proof that the size of stars, and therefore their luminous intensity, could be discovered from their spectra. In other words, it was possible to learn the value of their absolute brightness from a study of the relative intensity of certain rays.

No one could fail to see the importance of this discovery. Now that a means had been found of calculating the absolute brightness of the stars it was at last possible to make use of the famous photometric method. All that was needed in order to find out the distance of a star, by applying the basic law of the inverse square, was to determine the absolute brightness as revealed by the spectrum and then to measure the apparent brightness on the photometer.

The fact that the apparent brightness of the stars was an inexact criterion which was replaced, for preference, by the magnitude has been explained on page 263. A few words were also said on the subject of certain catalogues, those of Gould, Pickering and Pritchard, which had as their aim to establish the magnitude of the greatest possible number of stars.

As the reader may have guessed, the widespread introduction of photography into observatories led to these catalogues, drawn up from visual comparisons made at the photometer, being replaced by photographic catalogues. It is clear that, with the same exposure, stars must impress upon the negative black spots that increase in size according to the brightness of the star. This technique was devised in 1910 by the German Karl Schwarzchild (1873–1916), an astronomer at Goettingen. It formed the basis of several catalogues published during the ensuing years.

The apparent magnitude was one of the factors upon which the law of photometry operated; the other factor was the absolute brightness. It goes without saying that the criterion 'absolute brightness' suffered from the same lack of precision as the criterion 'apparent brightness'. The latter had been replaced by the *apparent magnitude*; the former had similarly to be replaced by the *absolute magnitude*. This absolute magnitude was defined in exactly the same way, in relation to the absolute brightness, as the apparent magnitude in relation to the apparent brightness.[1] Thus, once the astronomer was in possession of these two magnitudes, absolute and apparent, it became absurdly easy to obtain either the distance of a star or its parallax. This was called the method of 'spectroscopic parallaxes'.

New instruments for a new science

Adams himself set about applying his method in 1916 and published a preliminary list of 1,646 stellar distances in 1921. The relay had now been taken over from the trigonometrical parallaxes, and the measurers of the universe were no longer condemned to helplessness once they passed beyond 300 light-years. Adams placed in their hands a technique that remained valid whatever the distance—so long as the spectrum was still sufficiently legible to estimate the intensity of its lines. This condition was itself dependent upon the star: obviously, a giant star, which shines far more brightly than a dwarf star, produces a spectrum that can be deciphered at a far greater distance. Astronomers could reckon that the surveyed universe, formerly 300 light-years in radius, now extended to about 3,000, while the margin of error was less than

[1] By convention, the absolute brightness (and absolute magnitude) of a heavenly body is the one it would have at a distance of 10 parsecs (32·5 light-years).

20 per cent. It was even possible to read the spectrum and calculate the distance of stars of the tenth magnitude, which give no more light than a candle at 10 miles. A map of the explored universe, which a century earlier would have gone on a visiting-card and around 1910 would have covered an area equal to that of Paris, would now have spread over 100 square miles. This was a tremendous leap, which carried the span of investigations ten times as far as before and increased the volume of the 'observable sphere' a thousandfold.

Figures speak for themselves—to those with sufficient imagination to visualize what lies behind them. When we speak of stars of the tenth magnitude the reader must picture the astronomer, in the silence of his dome, focusing his telescope upon a tiny glimmer—the light of a candle burning at Nogent as seen from St. Cloud. This light is broken up by the spectrograph and spreads out into a spectrum on the photographic plate, and the wonder is that the scientist can count and identify its lines with a degree of accuracy not very much less than in the case of the solar spectrum. Only when he is dealing with stars of the sixteenth magnitude or below does the degree of detail drop, so that the astronomer has to be content with identifying two or three major lines. A star of the sixteenth magnitude—this is as though the candle we spoke of just now was situated not at Nogent, but at Berlin, 700 miles away. Its spectrum is about $\frac{1}{10}$ inch long.

To measure the intensity of spectrum lines, deduce from them the star's absolute magnitude and calculate its distance was a thrilling task for the astrophysicist. Not only did it open up an ever-widening path to the discovery of the skies, but it also caught the attention of laymen. Practical men, and even governments, began to look with a spark of interest at this daughter of physics that was enriching its mother with ever more numerous applications. This growing interest in the young science is attested by the creation of new observatories, in which the old instruments of classical astronomy, the mural circle, meridian telescope and heliometer, were supplanted by the *astrograph*[1] and the spectrograph, in which the venerable refracting telescope itself made way for the triumphant reflecting telescope. The Meudon astrophysical observatory was completed in 1877, that at Potsdam in 1879.

[1] A refracting telescope adapted to photographic observation.

In 1891 the transfer of the Brussels Observatory to Uccle was finished. The great American establishments rose up one after the other, Lick in 1888, Yerkes in 1897, Mount Wilson in 1908—Mount Palomar in 1949.

The giant refractor at Yerkes Observatory, in which all the light collected by an object-glass over a yard across is concentrated in an eye-piece of $\frac{1}{5}$ inch, remains a unique monster of its kind. In order to obtain the spectra of more and more distant stars, astrophysicists demanded instruments that were more and more powerful, in other words instruments with wider and wider apertures. How did refracting telescopes satisfy this demand? In the first place, the manufacturers of optical glass found themselves unable to produce larger lenses than the famous Yerkes objective; in the second, the physical properties of light were changed by its passage through these two lenses of flint and crown glass, an intolerable situation since the whole purpose of spectroscopy was the study of these properties.

Hence the reflecting telescope gradually gained favour. This instrument does not interfere with the properties of light, since the light does not pass through any piece of glass; chromatic and spherical aberration are unknown, and glassmakers declared themselves able to cast discs of unparalleled dimensions. Glassmakers? Yes, indeed! For the mirrors were no longer made of metal, like Herschel's and Lord Rosse's, but of glass. This material was incomparably easier to work. Léon Foucault had invented a method enabling glass to be given a parabolic curve of extreme precision, and in 1857, one year after his Munich colleague C. A. Steinheil (1832–93), he discovered how to silver its surface.

From this moment on, the advantages of the reflector became so obvious that it replaced the refractor in all astrophysical research. In 1867 Foucault himself built a 32-inch reflector for the Marseilles Observatory. Eight years later the record was broken by his pupil Adolphe Martin (1824–96), who mounted a 48-inch reflector at the Paris Observatory. In 1891 a London amateur A. A. Common (1841–1902), equipped his observatory at Ealing with one of 60 inches. In 1918 Mount Wilson Observatory installed its famous 100-inch reflecting telescope with a mirror ground by George Willis Ritchey (1864–1945).

The spread of spectroscopy, the setting up of observatories devoted exclusively to it, the abandonment of refractors in favour of reflectors, marked a turning point in the history of celestial discovery. Up to that time, this discovery had been above all a matter of reasoning and theory based on observations of position calling for relatively inexpensive instruments. But now the simple measurement of the co-ordinates of the stars gave place to the analysis of their light. The instruments of precision astronomy made way for spectrographs capable of making the fullest use of the dim light of the stars. Of the two factors that condition scientific discovery, the accumulation of observations and the elaboration of theories to explain them, the first acquired growing importance. Because of this, and in order to penetrate farther and farther into the firmament, astronomers were compelled to erect more and more powerful, and hence more and more expensive telescopes. Astronomy, which was gradually changing into astrophysics, became increasingly a science for wealthy countries, and as time passed Europe, willy-nilly, abandoned the sceptre to the United States.

It may almost be said that there are two astronomies, one prior to the giant reflecting telescopes and one subsequent to them. The first told us all there is to know about the solar system and ventured upon preliminary reconnaissance into the empire of the stars. The second disclosed the structure of this empire, the Galaxy, the swarms of spiral nebulae and the inconceivable Einsteinian Great Universe curved back upon itself in space-time. The whole of this astronomy was built up on the information gained through the reflecting telescopes on the other side of the Atlantic.

After Europe had been impoverished and torn by war America alone was capable of building centres of scientific research as luxurious as those at Mount Wilson and Mount Palomar. The time was past when she had to call in the aid of European technology, when the glass for the great objectives had to be ordered from Parra-Mantois or Saint-Gobain. Not only had she trained engineers able to cope with the problems of astronomical optics, but she had even given birth to scientists capable of posing these problems. We will cite here the names of three American physicists who helped their country to achieve its special destiny in this field: Samuel Langley (1834–1906), explorer of the solar spectrum and infra-red light; Henry Rowland (1848–1901), designer of the *diffraction grating* that replaced the prism in spectrum analysis; and above all the great Albert Michelson (1852–1931), whose measurements of the speed of light were at the source of the vast current of relativity.

No, the United States certainly had no further need of experts from the Old World. They even produced born organizers, rather on the pattern of Arago, with the knack of obtaining grants and distributing them to the best advantage for astronomy—men like Edward Pickering, Newcomb and Hale.

Such grants were very important, for in order to erect monster telescopes it was not enough to raise men capable of drafting plans, other men capable of putting them into effect and yet others capable of using them. The necessary money had also to be found.

By the end of the nineteenth century the United States was wealthy. In 1895 her capital amounted to £47 million as against £21 million in the case of Great Britain, £17 million in the case of Germany and £14 million in that of France. Solidly based on her deposits of coal and iron and strong in her heavy industry, she had by now already pushed Britain out of first place. Colossal monopolies held the production of steel, petrol and electricity, the manufacture of preserves, textiles and chemical products in their tentacle-like grip. Such phenomena as the millionaires Carnegie, Rockefeller, Pierpoint Morgan or Vanderbilt existed nowhere else.

Yes, the United States was rich, but it did not follow that her great capitalists would necessarily spend their money on satisfying the needs of scientific research and in particular of astronomy.

We will once more draw the reader's attention to the paradox of rich American businessmen lavishing dollars on observatories from which they could not hope to derive the slightest profit. The time has come to try and explain this paradox. For since, in Europe, the major part of scientific training and research is carried out at the expense of the state, it is at least surprising that in the United States it should have been paid for out of the pockets of philanthropic millionaires. Peabody founded the Yale University Museum of Palaeontology, Hopkins founded a university at Baltimore, Vanderbilt founded another at Nashville, Rockefeller and Carnegie created scientific institutes—each of these is an example of the general fact that, in 1930, of the 166 million dollars spent on research, 116 were gifts from industry; in 1940 it was 234 out of 345.

This solicitude on the part of industrial magnates towards disinterested knowledge is no doubt largely to be explained by the conviction that 'research pays'.[1] More far-seeing than many of their opposite numbers in Western Europe, the directors of General Electric, Bell Telephones and Du Pont de Nemours had long ago realized the practical benefits to be derived from adding to their factory a laboratory equipped with first-class instruments and paying research workers to study the subjects of their choice. Even in astronomy this practical benefit was clearly perceived. The photographic industry, radio, television and electronics were all to derive growing advantages from work carried out in connexion with the spectrography of spiral nebulae, from the study of the solar corona and new techniques of photo-electric observation.

To this utilitarian aspect we should perhaps add a certain naïve pride, which impelled Americans to strive after the biggest, the best, the most splendid in the world. Science can only rejoice in this spirit of record-breaking when it is applied to the achievement of such undertakings as the Mount Palomar reflector or the Berkeley cosmotron!

As a final explanation of the surprising favour shown to the conquerors of the heavens by Maecenases, we must not forget to mention the piety of these men. This combination of religious enthusiasm with profit-seeking is a peculiarly American characteristic. An American humorist declared that the progress of astronomy was linked with the progress of the religious spirit and the bacon trade. This witticism contains a truth that scarcely needs demonstrating. It is only to be expected that in a country where Protestant sects proliferate,

[1] 'There is no better national investment than well-conducted scientific research' (R. G. Casey, Australian minister, 1955).

where religious associations—the Salvation Army, the Christian Science Church and so on—do highly profitable business, the starry heavens should appear as the finest of God's works and to assist their study be considered an act of piety. Moreover, the aid granted it by business men was only the result of its growing popularity among the general public. Today no people, with the possible exception of those of Soviet Russia, possess more observatories and planetariums, belong in greater numbers to astronomical societies or show greater enthusiasm for amateur observation.

Religious zeal or utilitarian considerations—it matters little in what proportion the two elements combined to produce establishments like the Mount Wilson Observatory, in which first Carnegie and then Hooker invested hundreds of thousands of dollars. It is enough for us to note the immense leap forward which such concrete encouragement led celestial discovery to make. This is one more example of the salutary interaction between astronomy and civilization. The first had received a great deal from the second; it now began to give even more than it had received.

The cepheids—sounding the extra-galactic depths

In 1636—the year of Corneille's *Cid*, three years after Galileo's trial—an American named John Harvard founded a college near Boston, at the little town of Cambridge. Some two hundred years later the astronomer W. C. Bond added to this college, which had grown into a powerful university, an observatory of which he became director. Two-thirds of a century later still, in 1902 to be exact, the observatory engaged as assistant a spinster of thirty-four named Henrietta Leavitt (1868–1921).

The daughter of a clergyman, Miss Leavitt was a shy, reserved person, attached to her church and her work. Under the direction of Edward Pickering she specialized in the problems of photographic magnitude. We should have seen her engaged in this task one day in 1912, examining negatives of the Lesser Magellanic Cloud and counting its variable stars.

We have already spoken of the two Magellanic Clouds, those

concentrations of stars which inhabitants of the southern hemisphere see above their heads like a whitish haze. The variable stars are not new to us either, but we must now consider the fact that they are of more than one type. When a star is described as 'variable', it immediately suggests either a light that goes on and off at regular intervals, or else an occulting lighthouse in which the focus is periodically eclipsed by a screen. There are variable stars of both these kinds. The first are torches that really change in brightness—the star δ Cephei, for example, which expands and contracts and simultaneously changes in luminosity. The second are occulting lighthouses, like Algol, round which gravitates a dark satellite that masks it at each revolution.

They were variables of the δ Cephei type, that is to say *cepheids*, that Miss Leavitt was counting on her negatives of the Lesser Magellanic Cloud. In view of the part these stars play in our story, it may be as well to get to know them a little better. Today nearly 1,500 have been identified. Each has an absolutely fixed period of variation. The period of δ Cephei is 5 days 8 hours 47 minutes 27 seconds; that of the pole star, a cepheid of very modest amplitude, 3 days 23 hours 16 minutes 14 seconds; that of L Carinae, 35 days 12 hours 46 minutes 30 seconds, and so on. In the course of its period δ Cephei passes from an apparent magnitude of 3·78 to an apparent magnitude of 4·63, following the curve in Fig. 10; in the course of their periods, the pole

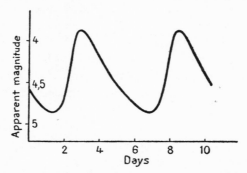

Fig. 10 THE LUMINOSITY CURVE OF A CEPHEID

This curve represents the variable luminosity of a cepheid (δ Cephei). In approximately 5 days 8 hours this star passes from minimum brightness (at 4.86 apparent magnitude) through maximum (at 3.89) to minimum again.

star passes from 2·48 to 2·62, and L Carinae from 4·97 to 5·99. These figures show that period and variation have been measured with a degree of exactitude that leaves nothing to be desired.

Let us return to Miss Leavitt busily engaged in checking off the cepheids in the Lesser Magellanic Cloud. Her attention, as she later recounted, was caught by the fact that the cepheids with the longest period were also the brightest. She studied a number of these variable stars and was left in no doubt that a relation did indeed exist between a cepheid's period and its apparent magnitude.

This phenomenon is explained, as was subsequently shown by Shapley and Eddington, by the structure of this type of heavenly body. When it contracts, its heat rises and it therefore shines more brightly; this is the moment of its maximum brilliance. When it expands, its temperature drops and its brilliance falls to a minimum.

Whatever the explanation, however, the fact was that, since the apparent magnitude was bound up with the period, the former could be deduced from the latter. The importance of this fact was proved by its immediate application.

The Lesser Magellanic Cloud is an agglomeration of stars situated at a certain distance from the Earth. All its cepheids are, therefore, at roughly this same distance. Consequently, it is those which possess the greatest *absolute* brightness which appear to us the most brilliant. In other words, the apparent brightness of all these stars is proportional to their absolute brightness. Thus their period indicates not merely their apparent brightness, but also their absolute brightness.

Let us take as an example two of them whose periods are respectively 1 day and 10 days. The curve in Fig. 11, which is the graphic translation of the relation found by Miss Leavitt, shows that the absolute luminosity of the two stars is in the ratio of 3 to 16.

This can also be stated inversely. Photograph two cepheids having the same period, but one of which has an apparent brightness four times that of the other. The identity of their periods indicates the equality of their absolute brightness. Since the two stars possess the same absolute brightness, one must be twice as close as the other in order to appear four times brighter. The period-luminosity relationship therefore gives an idea of the distance.

But only an idea. For if it tells us that such and such a cepheid is *n* times farther away than such and such another one, it gives us no information as to its distance in light-years or parsecs. Suppose that we detect on a photograph a cepheid having exactly the same period as δ Cephei, but whose apparent brightness is four times fainter. We conclude from this that the distance of this star is twice that of δ Cephei. Hence all that is required to find the distance of any cepheid is to know the distance of δ Cephei.

Of δ Cephei, or, naturally, of any other cepheid. Given the distance of any one of them all the rest would follow from it.

To calculate the distance of a cepheid by the classical method of triangulation, Adams's method or any other, was a problem first tackled by Hertzsprung in 1913. Unfortunately, no cepheid was close enough for the trigonometrical method to be applied. Nor was any of them amenable to the spectroscopic method. Hertzsprung then approached the matter statistically, starting from the fact that the closer a star is to us, the more rapid appears its motion. Estimation of this proper motion makes possible an estimation of its distance.

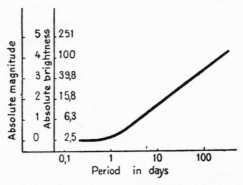

Fig. 11 THE PERIOD-LUMINOSITY RELATION
OF THE CEPHEIDS

The curve shows that the longer a cepheid's period, the higher is its absolute brightness. Since 1952 it has been known that this curve has to be corrected to take account of Baade's discovery (p. 337).

Hertzsprung's endeavour was resumed in 1918 by a young American beginner working at Mount Wilson, by name Harlow

Shapley (b. 1885). He was a former amateur who tried his hand first at journalism and then at zoology before becoming a professional astronomer. To achieve maximum accuracy, Shapley turned to the nearest cepheids, that is to say those which, according to Miss Leavitt's table, exhibited the shortest period. In this way he succeeded in determining the distance of some whose period was less than 1 day. Stars like RR Lyrae, for instance, which varies in 13 hours 40 minutes 48 seconds from the magnitude 7·2 to the magnitude 8, were found at a distance of 30 parsecs. From these figures there followed the whole scale. L Carinae proved to be situated at 45 parsecs, the pole star at 143, δ Cephei at 200 and so on.

The discovery of the period-luminosity relation and its scale must be regarded as a major victory in the conquest of the skies. The resulting procedure for measuring distances in no way duplicated existing methods. The triangulation method was only valid as far as 300 light-years, that of spectroscopic parallaxes as far as 3,000; now, all the cepheids are stars classed by Russell's diagram among the giants, and even the super-giants, whose absolute brightness is equal to 10,000 times the Sun's. They are therefore visible from very much farther away, much farther than those upon which Adams's method was used. It was actually thanks to them that it became possible to sound the extra-galactic depths. Shapley immediately provided an example of what they could do by studying those found by Miss Leavitt in the Lesser Magellanic Cloud and calculating their distance,[1] which he made 32,540 parsecs or 106,000 light-years. At the first stroke, he arrived at a figure vastly higher than those to which astronomers were accustomed.

Shapley reveals the Galaxy

By 1918 Shapley had been working at the Mount Wilson Observatory for four years. The new buildings were enlivened by a gay and dynamic team, spurred on by Hale. The workers queued up to observe at the 60-inch telescope introduced in 1908, the 100-inch one being still in production.

[1] This distance is now estimated to be 170,000 light-years.

Shapley's activities were centred entirely upon the *globular clusters*. These, of which there are about a hundred, are splendid agglomerations of stars so concentrated towards the centre as to form a uniform luminous cloud. When the scale of the period-luminosity relation supplied a new means of calculating distances, Shapley resolved to apply it to these heavenly objects. Among them he discovered cepheids, which enabled him to situate the clusters at distances of 20,000 to 150,000 light-years.

One fact that struck him as odd was the distribution of these clusters in the sky: they were almost all grouped in the southern hemisphere. When we are at the theatre and most of the audience is behind us, this can only mean that we are not sitting in the middle of the auditorium, but near the front. The distribution of the globular clusters could only be explained by supposing that the Earth—that is to say, the solar system—was not in the middle of them, but far to one side. As they seemed, on the other hand, to be equally distributed on both sides of the plane of the Milky Way, Shapley inferred from this that they must form a spherical system 150,000 light-years in diameter, but that the Sun must be situated a very long way from the centre of this system, at some 65,000 light-years.

Shapley localized this centre in the direction of Sagittarius, the densest region of the Milky Way and the one richest in star-clusters and novae. Then he had a brilliant idea: if this region of Sagittarius was the densest in the Milky Way, was this not because the centre of the latter was just about here? And if the centre of the system of globular clusters coincided with that of the Milky Way, was this not because the Galaxy and the system of globular clusters were one and the same thing?

This conclusion of Shapley's, propounded in 1918, marks an important stage in the history of the discovery of the sky. Until Galileo, the Earth had been supposed to be at the centre of the universe. Then this place had been withdrawn from it and ascribed to the Sun. Now, in the vast whole that had been revealed, the Sun itself was dislodged from its privileged position and relegated to a situation of no importance, like any one of the myriad stars of the Galaxy. At one stroke the Sun lost all the eminence attributed to it by man. The universe ceased to have been made for it. Astronomy sketched out the main lines of an overall plan comprising both the globular clusters and the stars of the Milky Way, to the whole of which the name Galaxy was extended and in which the role of the Sun dropped to zero.

Thus, following Shapley's investigations, the universe was regarded as being occupied by an enormous quantity of stars, agglomerated in the shape of a girdle-cake 300,000 light-years in diameter and 10,000 thick. Round this girdle-cake a hundred or so globular clusters traced the outline of a flattened sphere.

This was the moment (1921) when Shapley left Mount Wilson to take over the direction of Harvard Observatory. This was also the moment when, in Europe, Kapteyn published his first papers. He persisted in adhering to the hypothesis of a universe only 60,000 light-years in extent with the Sun in the centre. Too much theoretical speculation had gradually divorced him from the data of observation. The work of his transatlantic rival, who followed the facts step by step, showed that the only way to arrive at a valid hypothesis concerning the structure of the universe was to found it upon irrefutable evidence and that more or less reckless speculation led nowhere. As this evidence could only consist of photographs and as the great American reflecting telescopes were alone capable of obtaining them, European astronomy was henceforth out of the running and it was up to her young and powerful sister in the United States to carry on the conquest.

Today, when we reconstruct this phase in the history of the science, when we picture ourselves confronted by the conclusions of the young Shapley and the old Kapteyn, we cannot easily imagine how the astronomers of that day—which is not so far-off, after all—could have hesitated. Yet Kapteyn supported his thesis on the authority of Herschel and the whole line of scientists who had graced stellar astronomy in Britain and Germany during the nineteenth century. Although Europe brandished theories and America wielded observations, the dispute was not so very unequal. It nevertheless ceased in 1927—and it was brought to an end by two Europeans, the Swede Bertil Lindblad and the Dutchman Jan Hendrik Oort.

Lindblad (b. 1895), a future director of Stockholm Observatory, was thirty-one when the idea that the universe was shaped like a girdle-cake led him to think that this girdle-cake must revolve. Mechanics teaches that no system of this kind is stable unless the elements are held apart by a centrifugal force born of their joint rotation. Observation also showed that if many celestial bodies have the appearance of a flattened sphere (the Earth, the Sun, Jupiter, and so on) it is because they rotate upon themselves. The lenticular aspect of the Galaxy suggested to Lindblad that it, too, must rotate upon itself. And was it not possible that this rotation would explain Kapteyn's famous 'currents'?

The rotation of the Galaxy was really demonstrated the following year (1927) by Oort (b. 1900) at Leyden Observatory. While studying the proper motion of certain stars, the young scientist found that it indicated a motion of the whole system—not, however, like a rigid block or a wheel, but, in conformity with Kepler's laws, at a greater and greater speed the closer the stars were to the centre. Near the Sun this speed approached 170 miles per second, and the centre of rotation lay in the direction of Sagittarius, 30,000 light-years away from us.

Sagittarius, which was already the centre of the Galaxy and the system of globular clusters! Its pivotal role left no further doubt about the reality of the Galaxy and finally settled the Shapley-Kapteyn dispute. Shapley had won the day.

Thus, towards the end of the first quarter of this century, the notion of the Galaxy imposed itself upon astronomers. The Galaxy was just about everything we can see in the sky. First, of course, it was the stars. An attempt was made to count these stars by modern means. Hipparchus's catalogue listed 1,026; Ulugh Beigh's 1,018; Tycho Brahe's 1,277; Hevelius's 1,553; Flamsteed's 2,934; La Caille's 9,766; Lalande's and Piazzi's 47,000; Bessel's and Argelander's 100,000; the *Bonner Durchmusterung* 500,000.

During the first decades of the present century photographic catalogues extended the inventory down to the tenth magnitude—adding some 270,000 stars. When astronomers came to push it farther they ran into difficulties: the great reflecting telescopes went down to the twenty-first magnitude (and even the twenty-third, in the case of Mount Palomar), and the negatives were so thickly strewn with tiny stars that at the rate of one per second it took as much as a week to count those on a single plate! A star-by-star inventory was impossible. It had already occurred to Kapteyn in 1905 to return to Herschel's gauges, that is to say to limit the counting to a certain number of selected areas, and from the number of stars contained in an area of so many square degrees to work out the total number in the whole sky. The Dutch astronomer proposed 206 such areas. The stars in these areas were counted in 1917 by van Rhijn at Harvard, and in 1925 by Seares at Mount Wilson.

We shall not dwell upon the results of this census, which have already been dealt with elsewhere.[1] Let us say only that stars brighter than the twenty-first magnitude number 1,890 million, and the total of all the stars in the Galaxy has been estimated by van Rhijn and Seares at 30 thousand million.

Nor shall we dwell upon the other celestial objects that co-exist in this swarm of suns, star-clusters (not globular, but more or less 'open', like that of the Pleiades), nebulae like that of Orion, and even the clouds of obscuring matter that hide the most distant stars and to which attention was first drawn by the American Edward Emerson Barnard (1857–1923).

The problem of the spiral nebulae

As a matter of fact, the problem of the nature of the nebulae was far from having been solved. In Herschel's day it had been accepted that some of them must be colossal agglomerations of stars fused together by distance, while others were mere clouds of phosphorescent matter. But Lord Rosse had discovered nebulae that were spiral in shape and had detected recognizable clusters of stars in their midst. This observation added weight to the conviction that, given a sufficient magnification, all the nebulae would resolve themselves into stars.

Then, in 1864, Huggins noted a decisive fact. Directing his refractor equipped with a spectroscope upon a nebulae in the Dragon,

---

[1] Particularly in the present author's books, *Exploration du Ciel* (Hachette), *Le Monde des Étoiles* (Hachette) and *L'Astronomie nouvelle* (Fayard), and in the fine *Astronomie populaire Camille Flammarion* (Flammarion), which gives the most up-to-date outline of astronomy.

he observed that its spectrum was virtually limited to one green line. According to the laws of spectrum analysis, just established by Kirchhoff and Bunsen, the source of this greenish luminescence could only be gas. Herschel's hypothesis was therefore confirmed: there were indeed nebulae consisting of simple gaseous masses. In 1868 Huggins found that this was also the case with the Orion nebula and some twenty others of the sixty-six he had studied.

At the beginning of the twentieth century, when America began to aim her giant instruments at the sky, the question was at roughly the same point. No doubt photography had obtained precise pictures of these odd formations, and in particular had enabled the English astronomer Isaac Roberts (1829–1903) to discover in 1888 that the Andromeda nebula was a spiral when seen from the side; no doubt the Irishman J. L. Dreyer (1852–1926) had published the same year a catalogue of 7,840 nebulae and clusters, with a supplement in 1894; no doubt, too, the American James Keeler (1857–1900) had estimated that, of the 120,000 nebulae accessible to the 36-inch reflector at Lick Observatory, half must be spiral in shape; but the difficulty had merely shifted.

Everyone agreed that there were 'resolvable' and 'unresolvable' nebulae. Of the latter, Huggins had proved that some were purely gaseous, and Scheiner, a German, showed in 1900 that others were composed of stars (their spectra, that of the Andromeda nebula for example, being exactly similar to the solar spectrum). What did this mean? The Orion nebula was undoubtedly a cloud of gas belonging to the Galaxy; but what about the Andromeda nebula, the stellar nature of which had been proved by spectroscopy? Fundamentally, whether they were resolvable or not, the majority of astronomers tended to think of them as simple clusters situated on the boundaries of the Galaxy. There seemed no doubt that all the nebulae, and in particular the spiral nebulae, formed part of the Milky Way: there were none in the milky band of the Galaxy, whereas they abounded towards each of its poles. This certainly proved that they obeyed a symmetry of distribution in relation to this vast system. Only the contemporary writers of science fiction regarded them as independent systems, as island universes, following the example of their great forerunner at Slough!

Nevertheless, in 1920, a serious scientist, a former astronomer at Yerkes Observatory, stated plainly in his doctorate thesis: 'If these spiral nebulae form part of the Galaxy, their nature is a mystery; if, on the contrary, they lie outside the Galaxy, we must regard them as agglomerations similar to the Galaxy itself.'

These lines were signed with the name of an American, Edwin Hubble.

Hubble, the Christopher Columbus of the nebulae

In the history of celestial conquest there are not many conquerors of the same calibre as Hubble. Apart from Newton and Laplace, whose work was quite different, it is difficult to name any besides Galileo and Herschel. The first of these opened up to mankind the horizon of the solar system, which till then had been hidden by the smoke of so much wild speculation; the second put the solar system in its proper place and revealed the vast panorama of the stars that surrounded it. With Hubble, the universe of the stars was itself reduced to a dot, while the fabulous ocean of the extra-galactic nebulae spread in all directions.

It is no exaggeration to say that Hubble revolutionized the classical conception of the universe almost to the same extent as Einstein. After the discoveries of these two men, it is impossible to feel anything but surprise and pity for those who believe that humanity is more than an ephemeral and puny insect, linked to an insignificant star belonging to a very modest spiral nebula, in the midst of a universe peopled with myriads of galaxies.

Hubble himself is a typical illustration of a remark that has repeatedly been made in these pages: where astronomy is concerned vocation is everything. We are about to see the career of a man who felt himself pulled by astronomy but tried to resist, who yielded, drew back and finally gave in, like a watercourse that eventually finds its line of greatest fall.

Edwin Hubble's youth was the commonplace one of any good scholar. He was born at Marshfield, Missouri, on 20 November, 1889, but soon moved with his parents to Chicago. Among the teaching staff at Chicago University, which he attended after completing his secondary education, were two scientists of the first rank, Millikan and Hale.

Robert Millikan (1868–1953), a brilliant physicist and future Nobel prizewinner, was engaged in preparation for an epoch-making experiment: the measurement of the charge of an atom. George Ellery Hale (1868–1938) was a devotee of astronomy who had placed at the service of this science his gifts as an engineer and organizer. He had already invented the *spectroheliograph*,[1] created the Yerkes and Mount Wilson observatories, and was now encouraging Ritchey in his work on the 60-inch reflector. In short, it is very understandable that contact with Millikan and Hale should have inspired in young Hubble a lively interest in science and particularly in astronomy, which he felt inclined to adopt as a profession.

But Mr. Hubble Senior had a good position in insurance. He wanted his son to follow in his footsteps and had no wish to see him wandering off into a career that seemed to him preposterous. Edwin obeyed his father, and in 1910 left America to read law at Oxford. On his return three years later he was admitted to the bar and began to practise at Louisville, Kentucky.

Happily for science, his earlier vocation was not suffocated beneath briefs and rubber-stamped documents. It reawoke in 1914. As others escape for a month to the seaside or into a Trappist monastery, Hubble, who was then twenty-five, wrote to Edwin Frost (1866–1935), the blind director of Yerkes Observatory, asking to be taken on as an assistant. It seems that his taste for astronomy had no difficulty in getting the better of his taste for law: the Louisville offices were closed down and the lawyer set out upon the road marked out for him by destiny. With less difficulty still he parted from another career for which he was fitted by his physique. Hubble was and remained a strapping fellow of six feet two inches, and if he had felt like it, he could have confronted the world heavyweight boxing champion, Jack Johnson, with good chances of success.

We cannot say whether sport and jurisprudence ever recovered from the defection of this brilliant recruit, but we must state that as

[1] An instrument for photographing the Sun with monochromatic light.

soon as he made up his mind to follow his true vocation Hubble went from success to success—successes that later became triumphs. In 1917, when the United States entered the war on the side of the Allies he had just published his first paper. It is good to think of Hubble enrolling as an infantry private and fighting on the French front. It is also good to learn that many years later he put all his prestige as an eminent scientist behind the demand that his country should declare war on Germany—long before Pearl Harbour. Once hostilities had broken out, he abandoned his beloved nebulae for three years and devoted himself to the problems of ballistics, a matter of more immediate urgency.

The epithet 'beloved' as applied to the nebulae is no literary exaggeration. The galaxies were really dear to Hubble. His affection for the hundred objects in Messier's catalogue was like that of a father. Just as a father can instantly give the age, height, weight, and date of the first tooth of his offspring, so Hubble knew through long intimacy the distance, dimensions, structure and whereabouts of hundreds of galaxies.

This intimacy dated from the year 1919 when, after taking part in the war and the occupation of Germany, the young astronomer accepted Hale's invitation to join him at the Mount Wilson Observatory.

This observatory had been in existence since 1904. It was animated by a dynamic team that included Hale, Adams, Shapley and Pease. They had initially confined themselves to the study of the Sun, and two *solar towers* were erected, in 1907 and 1911. Then investigations were extended to the stars and the 60-inch reflector, with a mirror marvellously ground by Ritchey, was completed in 1908. Finally, Hale's overwhelming enthusiasm led to the construction of a gigantic instrument of 100 inches, which was paid for by Hooker and the Carnegie Institute and first reflected the sky on 1 November, 1917.

It was with this Hooker telescope that Hubble achieved practically all his successes. As in Herschel's case, a conjunction had taken place between an outstanding observer and an exceptional instrument. The resulting harvest was likewise exceptional. Hubble had already taken an interest in the nebulae during his pre-war period at Yerkes. Once he had joined the Mount Wilson team he devoted his whole life to them.

It would be a great exaggeration to say that Hubble had a philosophy: it is the strength of contemporary scientists that they have no preconceived philosophy. Nevertheless, perhaps instinctively, Hubble allowed himself to be guided by an observation which he had erected into a principle, what we might call 'the principle of the uniformity of nature'. We do, in fact, constantly observe that the laws of the universe everywhere conform to what we expect of them. This really goes without saying, since otherwise the world would be unknowable. The rules of spectrum analysis are the same in the heart of the molecule and in the most distant galaxy, and Newtonian gravitation determines the revolutions of our planets as well as of a double star lost in the midst of some spiral nebula 500 million light-years away. Applied to the nebulae, this principle works out something like this: the most accessible nebula, astronomically speaking, is that of Andromeda (M 31); its spectrum indicates a stellar nature; therefore this nebula is 'resolvable', it is composed of stars.

A first argument in favour of this proposition was the appearance, in 1885, of a nova right inside this nebula. A nova was an old friend. It put astronomers back on familiar ground. Then, from 1922 onwards, after he had been studying photographs taken with the Hooker reflector for several years, Hubble distinguished within the outline of the beautiful nebula a number of equally identifiable minor figures, globular clusters, open clusters (like the Pleiades) and even individual stars. However cold-blooded and master of himself this American may have been, we cannot imagine that he showed no emotion when he afterwards noted on the blink microscope that some of these stars seemed regularly to change their brightness; for these stars might be cepheids, and by virtue of the principle of the uniformity of nature those on Andromeda must conform to the same period-luminosity relation as those in the Galaxy.

Remember that a cepheid is a giant or super-giant star. Even as far off as the boundaries of the Galaxy, where a star like the Sun would be totally invisible, it does not fall much below the eighth apparent magnitude. Now, the cepheids Hubble laboriously made out in the Andromeda nebula at the end of 1923 were less bright than the eighteenth magnitude. Since it was nevertheless perfectly possible to follow their variations of brightness, the astronomer did not have too much difficulty in measuring their period and deducing from it their absolute brightness and distance. These cepheids, and hence the nebula in which they were situated, were 900,000 light-years away.

Hubble lost no time. He immediately turned his attention to the nebula in the Triangle (M 33). He identified its cepheids and in 1924 deduced from them a distance of 700,000 light-years. Five years later, the distances of eighteen nebulae were known in all, apart from four others forming part of a cluster in Virgo. Enormous figures, verging on a million light-years, had been obtained and confirmed by observation of many cepheids. Decisive proof had finally been found: as all these distances far exceeded the dimensions of the Galaxy, it became manifest that the spiral nebulae were systems outside the latter. They were other galaxies, the island universes suspected by Kant and William Herschel.

This revelation burst upon the astronomical world in 1925. Immediately, the prestige of the Galaxy faded; it was no longer alone in the universe, although it remained the masterpiece. The negatives at Mount Wilson showed clouds of spiral nebulae stretching out of sight into the indeterminate depths of space.

The realm of the nebulae

Hubble continued his investigations. His assistant in the photographic part of the work was Milton Humason (b. 1891), whose career had been somewhat unconventional. The son of a wealthy banker, he left school, which he detested, at fourteen, and went to work at the Mount Wilson Hotel, near the observatory. He groomed the mules, took the astronomers their food and helped them with odd jobs . . . until one day in 1922, when he fell in love with the daughter of one of them, married her and finally cast in his lot with his new friends.

To the Hubble–Humason team we owe a great many magnificent pictures of M 31, M 33 and all those nebulae henceforth known as *galaxies.* Like a general taking advantage of an initial success to push as far forward as possible by throwing in all his troops, Hubble took the maximum advantage of his 100-inch reflector by driving on to the limit of penetration and at the same time moving all his pawns forward on the chessboard.

His pawns were not merely the cepheids, but also other means of taking soundings which he had invented himself. For the cepheids were no longer enough for him. Brilliant as they are, they cease to be visible at around one million light-years. This was quite a figure, but Hubble was pretty sure it represented only the edge of a chasm that must be counted in hundreds of millions of light-years.

Even after the elimination of the cepheids, the photographic method remained applicable, provided that it could be used on stars that were not only individually identifiable but also had a known absolute brightness. In galaxies too far away to show cepheids, Hubble therefore looked for novae. Those observed in our Galaxy often attain an absolute brightness 100,000 times greater than that of the Sun. Sometimes, even, they are *super-novae*, 1,000 times brighter still. It occurred to Hubble that extra-galactic novae and super-novae would also exhibit these characteristics and that the law of photometry would therefore operate. For example, a nova of apparent magnitude 14·5 appearing in an extra-galactic nebula may be compared to a galactic nova of an absolute brightness equal to 100,000 suns, which corresponds to an absolute magnitude of 11·5. The absolute and apparent magnitude then give a distance of 614,000 parsecs, or 2 million light-years.

Unhappily, at 7 million light-years the novae drop to the twenty-first apparent magnitude. At this distance the weapon of conquest fell from Hubble's hand. But he had the good luck to find, at exactly 7 million light-years, a positive nest of galaxies, the group in the Virgin which was referred to a little earlier. It is a cluster containing 2,500 visible nebulae, not to mention the others. Some of them, in which stars of known brightness could be seen—novae or blue giant stars— were estimated to be 100 million times as bright as the Sun. Thereafter, the supposition that all the galaxies were, on an average, of an absolute brightness 100 million times greater than the Sun's provided a new key to the extra-galactic distances. This was effective up to 250 million light-years. These 250 million light-years, incident-ally, were by no means the limit of the 100-inch reflector's range: on the most sensitive taken with the longest exposures a multitude of tiny dots were visible. Each of these dots was a galaxy, the most remote of which lay some 500 million light-years away.

The book in which Hubble told the story of his discoveries, *The Realm of the Nebulae*, published in 1936, has not been supplanted by Shapley's more recent *Galaxies*, which came out in 1945. The first is a tale of discovery. The author, an intrepid pioneer, plunges into a totally unknown universe. No sooner has he entered it than he is assailed by strange creatures. He has to improvise techniques of investigation on the spot, to introduce classifications extempore, to describe and measure the beings he meets, to pay attention to new and, at first sight, disconcerting phenomena.

Once the distance of the galaxies was known, it became possible to work out their real dimensions from their apparent diameter. In this way a diameter of 40,000 light-years was attributed to the Andromeda nebula, with a thickness of 9,000, while Hubble assigned to the rest diameters ranging from 6,000 to 10,000 light-years.

There seemed nothing surprising about the fact that the Andro-meda galaxy measured only 40,000 light-years, whereas our own, according to Shapley, reached 300,000. In 1925 it still seemed likely that our Galaxy was the most important in the universe. Even so, this *galactocentrism* aroused some suspicions. To these doubts was added another: if the spiral nebulae were really universes totally alien to the Galaxy, how did they come to be so neatly distributed in relation to it (p. 321)?

The solution to this dual riddle was found in 1930 by an astronomer at the Lick Observatory, the Swiss-American Robert Trumpler (1886–1956). Trumpler studied the open clusters. He managed to calculate the distance of some of them and found their dimensions to be of about the same order of magnitude. He was then very surprised to see that, contrary to what he had expected, a cluster situated at 2,000 light-years did not seem to be twice as small as a cluster situated at 1,000 light-years. Where did the error lie? Undoubtedly in the fact that the first cluster was not as far away as it seemed and, in any case, that it was less than 1,000 light-years from the second. How was it possible that a celestial object at, say, 1,500 light-years, had an apparent brightness as faint as though it was at 2,000? This could only be explained by supposing that part of the brightness was lost on the way, that is to say that a fraction of the cluster's light was absorbed by *something* between it and the Earth. Trumpler concluded from this that inter-stellar space could not be absolutely limpid, that drifting about in it there must be clouds of dust or gas capable of intercepting some of the starlight.

This conclusion corroborated other earlier investigations. Hence it was accepted by astronomers with good grace. It showed that the stars were less distant than had been thought. For example, the frontiers of the Galaxy, believed to lie 300,000 light-years away (Shapley), shrank to 100,000; the centre of the Galaxy, which observation placed at 65,000 light-years (Shapley), while the laws of dynamics put it at 30,000 (Lindblad and Oort), proved actually to be at this latter distance; and the explanation of the curious symmetrical distribution of the spiral nebulae in relation to the Milky Way became clearly apparent: these objects were spread equally over the whole sky, but they were not seen in the plane of the Milky Way because they were hidden by the layer of absorbent matter, which lay precisely in this plane.

Naturally, the distance of extra-galactic objects must also be affected in a certain proportion. Thus the Andromeda nebula (900,000 light-years according to Hubble) moved in to 750,000.

Trumpler's discovery reduced our Galaxy to a size more or less comparable to that of the Andromeda nebula, but it left astronomers free to indulge their persistent anthropomorphism by considering that this Galaxy was still the most important in the universe, because it had the honour of housing mankind.

Hubble discovers the recession of the galaxies

In 1925, while Hubble was deeply involved with the cepheids and the spiral nebulae, his attention was caught by an article in the *Astrophysical Journal*. The article dealt with the *radial velocity* of galaxies.

Its author, Vesto Melvin Slipher (b. 1875), director of Lowell Observatory, had been studying them since 1912. The article listed forty-five of these radial velocities.

Hubble was not, of course, unaware of Slipher's researches, but he had not previously paid a great deal of attention to them. Slipher has more than one claim to a position of honour in contemporary astronomy. Lowell took him on at Flagstaff in 1901, and he succeeded Lowell as director in 1916. After this date he made a name for himself by fine observations of the planets and by organizing researches that culminated in the discovery of Pluto. Parallel with this, he had been patiently working since 1912 to determine the radial velocity of the spiral nebulae.

At this point a few words of explanation are no doubt called for.

Suppose that, while sitting at the roadside at the dead of night, we see the headlights of a car coming towards us. The closer the car approaches, the more the light-waves given out by the headlamps are compressed; that is to say, they have to occupy a continually shortening space; in order to do so, they must decrease in length. The expression 'decrease in length' means that they pass, for example, from a wavelength of 0·00058 millimetres to one of 0·00047. As the former corresponds to yellow light and the latter to blue light, we should expect the light to change from yellow to blue. This phenomenon could be observed by directing a spectroscope upon one of the headlamps; we should see its spectrum rays moving from yellow to blue, the faster the car was travelling. This is the *Doppler-Fizeau effect*, noted by the Austrian physicist Christian Doppler (1803–53) in 1842, and given its correct explanation in 1848 by the French physicist Hippolyte Fizeau (1819–96).

Let us hasten to add that the experiment quoted can only be imaginary. In order for the spectrum of a source of light to pass from yellow to blue it would have to travel at a velocity of 35,600 miles per second, and our cars have not yet reached this speed. Even the stars, carried along by their proper motion, do not move as fast as this. However, as some of them do travel towards us exactly like a car, it is possible to compute on the spectroscope the slight shift of their rays towards blue and to deduce from this their velocity. The same is true of the stars that are moving away from us. In this case the light-waves grow longer instead of shorter and the shift is towards red.

The radial velocity of the stars was first measured in 1868 by Huggins. Aiming his refractor fitted with a spectroscope at Sirius, he noted that the dark line F had shifted slightly towards red, as compared with a parallel spectrum. Application of Fizeau's law indicated that the star was moving away at a velocity of 29 miles/second. Vogel, then Keeler and Frost, and their countryman William Campbell (1862–1938), later attached their names to the calculations of these radial velocities. By 1920 some 2,000 were known, the highest of which was no more than 250 miles/second.

We can therefore understand Hubble's astonishment on reading the *Astrophysical Journal*. With the exception of the Andromeda nebula, which was approaching the Earth at the rate of 187 miles/second, all the other spiral nebulae were moving away at speeds of up to 1,130 miles/second, much faster than the fastest stars.

Slipher had at his disposal only a 24-inch refractor. Hubble immediately brought the whole power of the 100-inch reflector to bear on the same problem. With the aid of an exceptionally powerful spectrograph Humason obtained the spectra of more and more distant spiral nebulae—up to 240 million light years—and in 1929 was able to publish a preliminary paper on the subject.

On drawing up a list of the radial velocities obtained, the two astronomers noticed first that, apart from a few nearby spiral nebulae, like that of Andromeda, all the galaxies were moving away; and second that the farther away they were, the faster they were moving. Thus spiral nebula N.G.C. 4473 (that is to say, spiral nebula No. 4473 of Dreyer's *New General Catalogue*), at a distance of 7 million light-years, was making off at 1,400 miles/second; spiral nebula 379 (23 million light-years) at 3,400 miles/second; a spiral nebula in a cluster in the Great Bear (85 million light-years) at 9,600; another in a cluster in the Heavenly Twins at 14,300.

In a general way, the velocity of *recession* was proportional to the distance; the former increased by 105 miles/second to every additional million light-years in the latter. The merest schoolboy could have deduced from this that at 240 million light-years (the limit reached by

Humason) the velocity must go up to 25,000 miles/second; at 500 million light-years (the limit of penetration of the Hooker reflector), to 52,500 miles/second; and if an instrument were ever constructed that would 'carry' 1,785 million light-years, nebulae would be found fleeing at the speed of light. . . . Even if the Earth, or rather our Galaxy, were not the special object of this general repulsion, even if it were all the galaxies that repelled one another, this phenomenon would be stupefying by its magnitude.

Those readers who took an interest in science at the time will certainly recall the bombshell that burst when Hubble published his distance-velocity relation in 1929, and the second bombshell thrown in 1930 by the great English astrophysicist Sir Arthur Eddington (1882–1944), when he declared that the recession of the galaxies was a sign that the whole universe was expanding.

Eddington took as his starting-point the work of a brilliant Belgian mathematician, Abbé Georges Lemaître (b. 1894), a young professor at Louvain University. Utilizing the framework offered by the general theory of relativity, Lemaître regarded the universe as a kind of four dimensional bubble, the fourth dimension being time. He showed that this bubble was not stable but condemned to swell, like a dilating balloon. We can understand Eddington's cry of triumph. Was not the recession of the galaxies observed by Hubble the material proof of this expansion of the universe?

Let us be quite objective about it. A quarter of a century later, at the moment of this book's publication, the question has not yet been definitely answered (p. 344). Although the shift of spectrum lines towards red is an undeniable observed fact, it still remains to be proved that astronomers are not on the wrong track in ascribing it to a Doppler-Fizeau effect. Who knows whether it may not be the result of some other phenomenon, such as the *Compton effect*, or even of some phenomenon as yet unknown but simpler? This thought has occurred to many astronomers since the ideas of Abbé Lemaître and Eddington spread. Even those who supported them admitted that the expanding universe raised enormous and fantastic problems. This did not discourage them—what is science if not a limitless succession of problems in which the solution of one provides the data for the next? And

333

could men be filled with enthusiasm for science if they were not haunted by an ever-present question mark?

The giant 100-inch reflecting telescope, intended to solve puzzles, had raised a fresh one, the greatest of all. And everyone could see that it was not capable of providing the answer. It already appeared necessary to have recourse to a more powerful instrument which, by plunging deeper into space, would give a clear answer to the question: Is the universe expanding, or isn't it? Will it, in a few million years, leave the Galaxy all alone in empty space?

A magnitude and a half for £2 million

Thanks to the growing size and complexity of the instrument, the cost of an astronomical telescope had increased somewhere in the region of two thousand times between 1845, when Lord Rosse constructed his reflecting telescope, and 1917, when the 100-inch Mount Wilson reflector was manufactured.

Nevertheless, the president of the New York General Education Board subscribed to Hale's views and declared in 1928 that the construction of a 200-inch reflector was indispensable; whereupon the California Institute of Technology received a grant enabling it to build the most powerful observatory in the world on Mount Palomar.

It would be mistaken to suppose that astronomy would have been the recipient of such a lavish gift if it had been a totally disinterested science, like the study of Sanskrit or archaeology. As a matter of fact, the link between astronomy and civilization, which we have seen grow closer with the passage of the ages, was already very apparent. Navigational bearings were only a minor application, and it was astrophysics itself that led the way in many fields of industrial technique.

Today a very little inside knowledge is enough to show the part astrophysics has played in the most important discoveries of the age. There is no need to remind readers of the hydrogen bomb, which would never have seen the light of day without the discoveries of solar physics, but we must point out that short-wave telecommunication depends upon daily study of the solar corona; that the Schmidt camera[1] furnished the essential device for large-screen television; that the electronic telescope[2] was the starting-point for research on electron multiplying devices, the commonest application of which is in television cameras; let us remember the technical problems astronomers had to solve in order to construct radio-telescopes and radio-interferometers and the benefits accruing from their achievements to the radio and radar industries; in a very different sphere, let us recollect the information which the Soviet astronomer G. A. Tikhov obtained from a study of the vegetation on Mars and applied to agriculture in the Arctic; finally, let us not forget the crack of the whip with which the demands of spectrography urged on the optical and photographic industries.

More than ever, the discovery of the sky proceeds hand in hand with the advance of civilization. It is not surprising that highly materialistically-minded industrialists should subsidize certain astronomical investigations, nor that governments should fit out observatories, since they stand at the spearhead of progress. The scientists who watch the Sun through the Lyot instruments at the Pic-du-Midi Observatory have been entrusted with a very concrete task, and the British Government was less disinterested than might have appeared when it financed the erection of a giant radio-telescope at Jodrell Bank.

The astronomer of today has his feet planted firmly on the ground. He wields a power that is second to none, and is understandably more concerned with political and social events than with the hair-splitting philosophical exegeses and religious controversies in which his predecessors delighted. Understandably, too, the dispensers of funds made no bones about it when Hale, regarding the 100-inch reflector as inadequate, called for the construction of one twice that size.

The Mount Palomar reflector involved an outlay of $6 million— some £2 million—to which must, of course, be added the cost of other appliances (notably a Schmidt camera with a 48-inch aperture), the buildings, staff accommodation and so on. The advantages of this super-giant over its elder brother at Mount Wilson? A gain of 1·5

[1] This instrument, invented in 1930 by the German Bernhard Schmidt (1879–1935), gives a large field of observation free from the drawbacks of spherical aberration.
[2] Invented in 1938 by the Frenchman André Lallemand (b. 1904).

in magnitude, that is to say the former can register the image of stars down to the twenty-third magnitude, whereas the latter stops short at magnitude 21·5.

At first sight, this gain of 1·5 in magnitude seems hardly to justify the expenditure of six million dollars, the twenty years' work, the mobilization of so many gifted experts and the most varied industrial resources. Nevertheless, to reach magnitude 23 instead of magnitude 21·5 means to attain stars of four times fainter apparent brightness and hence twice as far away; in other words, if the range of the Hooker reflector was estimated at 500 million light-years, that of the Hale reflector runs to 1,000 million. This implies that the radius of the known universe has been doubled, its volume increased eight times. And after all, are $6 million too high a price to pay for the revelation which Baade presented to the dumbfounded astronomical world in 1952? A revelation, or revolution, of which Hubble, who set this flood of discoveries in motion, was destined to know only the prelude, since he was carried off by cerebral thrombosis on 28 September, 1953.

An arithmetical error in cosmic surveying

Baade is the German-American astronomer who was referred to briefly on page 282. He entered Hamburg Observatory in 1919, at the age of twenty-six, and there carried out research on the comets, minor planets and variable stars. He left Germany in 1931 and took a post first at the Mount Wilson Observatory and then at Mount Palomar, where he changed his interests and switched from the stars to the galaxies. In 1950 he was given the job of completing, at the 200-inch reflector, the inventory of the Andromeda nebula begun by Hubble at the 100-inch reflector.

He started this inventory by taking stock of the cepheids, which were so valuable in working out celestial distances. Those discovered by Hubble showed periods of several dozen days. As we know, it was from these periods that the great astronomer had deduced their absolute magnitude and had then, after measuring their apparent magnitude, worked out the distance of the nebula by applying the period-luminosity relation.

No one dreamed, at that time, of questioning the correctness of this relation. Yet there were some astronomers who felt a certain uneasiness when they employed it. This relation had been established on stars of the type RR Lyrae with a very short period (a few days). Could they be sure that it was still valid for the cepheids, some of whose periods extended over months? The only means of finding out was to discover in the Andromeda nebula variables of the RR Lyrae type and to compare them with cepheids of long variation. Unfortunately, as the reader will recall, the shorter the period, the less bright the star. The RR Lyrae are therefore much less luminous than the classical cepheids. Considering that the latter appeared on the Mount Wilson negatives only as tiny dots of the eighteenth or nineteenth magnitude, it is not surprising that the search for RR Lyrae was entirely fruitless. In fact, their apparent magnitude at the distance of the Andromeda nebula must be around 22·4. No wonder they were invisible, since the instrument did not go beyond magnitude 21·5.

The significance of the work undertaken by Baade is manifest: these RR Lyrae variables of magnitude 22·4, which the Hooker reflector was incapable of detecting, must inevitably appear at the Hale reflector since the latter went down to magnitude 23.

Baade took shot after shot, on plates which, with an exposure of half an hour, registered down to magnitude 22·8. The harvest was some 700 variables, including a good number of cepheids. But those with the shortest period did not fall below three days, that is to say the RR Lyrae persisted in remaining invisible.

This stubborn game of hide-and-seek intrigued the astronomer. The situation was rather like that of a man going for a walk at night, who knows that in such and such a direction he ought to see the light of a house. If he does not see it, that may be because the house is not sufficiently brightly lit; but it may also be because he is still too far away.

In the case of RR Lyrae, was it possible that their brightness was not sufficient to render them visible, in other words that their magnitude was lower than the predicted value of 22·4? No, this value had been checked time and again by the globular clusters.

Must it be assumed that the Andromeda nebula was farther away than had been supposed?

Baade sensed that this was the correct answer. In fact, if his negatives showed no traces of RR Lyrae, they did reveal certain red stars whose brightness was four times as great. This meant that the RR Lyrae must be four times too faint to appear. And if they were four times less bright than had been expected, it was because they were twice as far away. That is to say, the Andromeda nebula must be not 750,000 light-years away, but 1,500,000.

This was the sensational revelation that Baade made to the Congress of the International Astronomical Union meeting at Rome in September 1952. Under the presidency of Lindblad, 350 astronomers from 35 countries were holding their deliberations in the halls of the University. To visualize the 'atomic' effect which Baade's bomb had on this gathering, we must imagine a congress of geographers which has just been told that a mistake has been made in calculating the width of the Atlantic and that the distance from Paris to New York is twice as great as had been thought. . . . No doubt the first reaction of the participants would be to demand proof.

Now, no sooner had Baade finished speaking than one of the audience sprang to his feet, the astronomer A. D. Thackeray of Pretoria Observatory, South Africa. He announced that he, too, had looked for RR Lyrae, not in the Andromeda nebula, but in the Lesser Cloud of Magellan. More fortunate than his colleague, he had found them. But their brightness was four times fainter than anticipated. This meant that the Lesser Magellanic Cloud must be two times farther away than had been thought.

The astronomers' first feeling in the face of these incredible declarations must certainly have been stupefaction—and perhaps also humiliation. For thirty years all their extra-galactic measurements had been based on the distance of the Lesser Magellanic Cloud and the Andromeda nebula; all their celestial surveying had been built on this foundation; and now, at a thunderclap, the whole edifice collapsed.

Their second thought was to ask themselves how such a mistake— double the correct figure—could possibly have been made.

Precisely, as some of them had suspected, through applying the same period-luminosity relation to variables like the cepheids, whose period is counted in weeks or months, as to variables like RR Lyrae, whose period is counted in hours. They had audaciously applied to the cepheids of Magellan and Andromeda the same law as to those of the Galaxy. Facts showed how wrong they had been, since the Andromeda nebula was twice as far away as had been thought—that is to say, in order to exhibit the brightness they were known to show, when they ought to have been almost invisible, the cepheids of the Andromeda nebula must be four times more luminous than had been thought.

Let us try to survey the flood of consequences. The Andromeda nebula was twice as far away, so the absolute brightness of its cepheids was four times as great (400,000 suns instead of 100,000), therefore all photometric measurements based on them were wrong and must be doubled; the distance of the Magellanic Clouds had to be increased to 170,000 light-years, that of the Andromeda nebula to 1,500,000, the limit of penetration of the 100-inch reflector to 1 thousand million light-years and that of the 200-inch reflector to 2 thousand million. This meant doubling the diameter of all the spiral nebulae, except, of course, our own, multiplying the volume of the accessible universe by 8 and halving the velocity of the recession of the galaxies.

Today, six years after Baade's communication, no astronomer has any doubt about its accuracy. The universe is really twice as large as was thought. Our own Galaxy alone retains its old dimensions since all its measurements, made on RR Lyrae stars, are homogeneous. The diameter originally attributed to the Andromeda galaxy, 40,000 light-years, then doubled to take account of the reduction of brightness due to the interposition of interstellar matter, has had to be doubled again and calculated at some 150,000 light years, say 50,000 more than our galactic agglomeration.

This dealt the death-blow to whatever was left of our invincible anthropocentrism. Not only was the Sun not the pivot of the universe, any more than the Earth, but the Galaxy itself lost all the pre-eminence that had been ascribed to it since the beginning of the century. Galacto-centrism proved just as illusory as Ptolemy's geocentrism. The Galaxy fell to the status of a very modest and very commonplace unit in an army that counted thousands of millions of such units.

Baade's discovery undermined the scale of extra-galactic distances laboriously established by Hubble. But that is not all. Just as a single blow with a pickaxe may bring a whole dilapidated building tumbling down, so it is to be feared that the blow struck by the eminent Palomar astronomer may cause all the rest of the edifice to totter dangerously.

According to Baade, the cepheids are brighter than was expected by a magnitude and a half, which means multiplying their distance by 1·9. This correction led one of his colleagues, Allan R. Sandage, to check the list of apparent magnitudes of the spiral nebulae drawn up by Hubble. To tell the truth, Hubble himself felt that these apparent magnitudes should be treated with caution, and he began to revise them on the Hale reflector. This revision Sandage now resumed, with the aid, this time, of photo-electric procedures. His first findings, published in 1953, showed that the factor by which the distances had to be multiplied was not necessarily 1·9, but was often higher. For example, the distance of the nebula in the Great Bear, M 81, was estimated by Hubble at 1,700,000 light years; according to Sandage it was at least 7,000,000 light-years, that is to say four times as great. The cluster in the Virgin, placed at 7,000,000 light-years, was situated at 22,000,000. In short, the photo-electric revision of the apparent magnitudes begun by Sandage and covering, by 1954, 800 galaxies, already gives reason to think that the scale of distances established by Baade was itself only a very rough approximation.

Perhaps we are not at the end of our surprises.

Outline of the universe 1958

To form a simplified picture of our Galactic homeland according to the most recent information, we must visualize it not as the simple girdle-cake shown by the earliest investigations, but as a spiral nebula like those of Andromeda, the Triangle, the Great Bear or the Hunting Dogs popularized by photography. It measures 100,000 light years in diameter and 16,000 at its maximum thickness. Around it, the systems of globular clusters form something like a ring of sentinels (Fig. 12). The centre lies 30,000 light-years from the Sun and from it sprout two whorls swarming with stars. We ourselves lie somewhat between the two whorls and are involved in the rotation of the whole which occupies a period of 220 million years. The total mass is approximately

200 thousand million times that of the Sun, a figure in which interstellar matter accounts for about half. If the whole system were pulverized and the resulting powder spread through the whole volume of the Galaxy, the mean density would be 7 grammes per 1,000 cubic kilo-metres: a volume the size of the Earth would contain 7,507 tons of 'galactic powder', or slightly more than the mass of the Eiffel Tower.

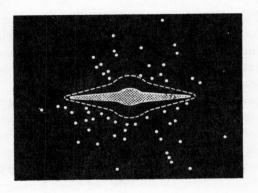

Fig. 12 HOW THE GALAXY IS NOW PICTURED

The main part of the Galaxy is shown by the stippled area, but stars are scattered as far as the limits indicated by the dotted line. The position of the Sun is marked by a cross. The large dots are globular clusters. (After *Sky and Telescope*, 1955, p. 327.)

Once again, we must guard against the mistake of supposing that our Galaxy possesses a particular importance in the cosmos. It is only an insignificant object, and to visualize the position it occupies we need only cast our eyes over one of the photographs taken at Mount Wilson or Mount Palomar and tell ourselves that any one of the thousands of spiral nebulae dotted all over it is just like our own. One would have to be affected by incurable anthropocentrism to persist in thinking that because there is, in this ridiculous little heavenly body one star, more ludicrously small still, around which revolves a planet bearing thinking beings, this constituted a unique case or a pheno-menon having the slightest cosmic significance. There is, on the contrary, every reason to suppose that human thought, born on this globe as the result of an unlikely physico-chemical reaction, is only an unimportant incident, due to 'faulty asepsis', as Eddington called it, of which nature will quickly rid itself.

Taking stock of the spiral nebulae at the 100-inch reflector, Hubble counted up to 1,450 per square degree—which means that our hand at the end of our outstretched arm will cover 350,000 galaxies in the sky. Yet his instrument penetrated only a hundred thousand light-years and scarcely went below magnitude 21. It is reasonable to suppose that the Mount Palomar instrument, having twice the range, must disclose eight times as many nebulae. This is an extrapolation whose accuracy depends, it must be admitted, upon certain ideas as to the shape and dimensions of the universe and upon the truth of the theory that it is expanding.

In any case, just as astronomy owes an entirely new cosmology to the Hooker reflector, so it seems also to have been completely revised by the Hale reflector. This instrument has been in use only a few years, and already it has not merely overthrown accepted views concerning the radius of the observable sphere, but also afforded a picture of this sphere that differs appreciably from the one which prevailed yesterday.

The name to be cited here is Fritz Zwicky (b. 1898). Zwicky is a Swiss citizen born in Bulgaria, who made his way to the United States in 1925 as a young physicist and remained as a professor at the California Institute of Technology (to which are attached the observatories at Mount Wilson and Mount Palomar). During the last war he made a study of reaction motors for the American Navy. He was so successful that in 1949 President Truman presented him with the Medal of Freedom. This did not stop the Navy expelling him from the laboratories he had himself created, on the grounds that he was an alien. . . .

In the story told in this book, Zwicky plays the part of a Galileo or Hubble of the final phase. The findings we are about to detail were obtained by him with the 200-inch reflector of Mount Palomar and with this observatory's Schmidt camera. The findings were staggering and even reversed part of Hubble's newest discoveries, which shows better than anything what a tremendous turmoil is at present agitating astronomy. Less than a hundred years ago astronomy looked like a finished science; now we know how terribly mistaken this belief was, since discoveries continue to come in an ever vaster and more rapid flood.

From his census of the spiral nebulae Hubble concluded that they were scattered at random in space. It appears from Zwicky's, on the contrary, that they are concentrated in clusters. In the world of the nebulae, isolated, bachelor galaxies are rare. The general rule is a family group, sometimes numbering thousands of members.

We must not imagine, however, that all these galaxies are systems as majestic as that of Andromeda or even our own. Dwarfs are in a majority and it may be, if Zwicky is to be believed, that there is no sudden jump from the great galaxies to the simple star-clusters or even from these to the grains of dust.

These latter are no figments of the imagination. It seems that in the intergalactic expanses grains of dust (and gases) play a role of some importance. The total emptiness, the transparency, the limpidity of this space are illusions which it seems necessary to abandon. Bridges of light have have been discerned, for example, bands of matter interlinking neighbouring galaxies in all directions. Who can tell whether these filaments, which appear to be drawn out like glue, may not have arisen through the contact, or even the collision, of galaxies? Did not Baade record the existence of two spiral nebulae in the process of interpenetrating one another? Incredible though it may seem, radio-astronomers have picked up in their radio-telescopes the 'sound', the radio-electric radiation, emitted by the hydrogen clouds of these swarms of worlds, which impinge upon one another at a distance of millions of millions of light-years.

To these staggering secrets wrested from nature by the Palomar giant, to the prodigious questions that now confront us, we must add that of the expanding universe. One more discovery made with the Hooker reflector which astronomers demand to have corroborated with the Hale reflector.

As soon as he had this latter instrument at his disposal, Humason set about verifying the velocities of recession recorded at Mount Wilson. His spectrograms were more detailed, but they confirmed the shift of the lines towards red. Humason even succeeded in obtaining the spectrogram of a galaxy of the nineteenth magnitude, whose rays almost disappeared under the luminosity of the night sky. The red-shift indicated a velocity of recession of 38,000 miles/second, which was increased to 56,000 miles/second in 1956 thanks to the photon counter of Dr. W. A. Baum.

The distance-velocity relation—taking Baade's correction into account—seemed, therefore, to have been confirmed in respect of a far larger sample of the universe than that on which Hubble had worked. The increase in velocity of 105 miles/second for every additional million light-years in distance had to be corrected to 34·4 miles/second. But it remains to be proved whether this really means that the universe is expanding.

There is, of course, no question of denying the red-shift of the spectrum lines, which is an indisputable experimental fact; but the interpretation of this shift as a Doppler-Fizeau effect, and its generalization, was perhaps over-bold. All the distance between fact and theory separates this red-shift from the expansion of the universe. But it is still too soon to express an opinion, and Mount Palomar will have to garner many more observations before being in a position to answer the question asked on page 333: Is the universe expanding or isn't it?

*   *   *

Only yesterday, on the strength of Hubble's investigations, the universe was regarded as a finite volume possibly spheroid in shape—and of four dimensions. This hyper-sphere was thought to have a radius of 5 thousand million light-years and a mean density of $1/10^{29}$, which makes 1 gramme per 1 million kilometres cube. Today no one dares to be positive, and when Zwicky suggests increasing the density a thousand times nobody can contradict him.

Fundamentally, as we see, the farther science progresses, the more powerful become its means of exploration, the more complicated and obscure becomes the universe. The planetary world appeared very simple to Galileo and Newton; as seen by Laplace and Le Verrier it was no more than a theorem in mechanics. The discovery of the world of stars and the world of nebulae, following the introduction of the great reflecting telescopes, swept away these splendid certainties. As was proved at the same period by the irruption of atomic physics, nature was decidedly more complex than had been supposed, and a simple extrapolation was no longer sufficient to enable astronomers to explore the confines of the universe.

The incorrigible scientist has no sooner assembled a few facts than he hastens to generalize them and build up on them an explanatory theory (as Hubble constructed his distance-velocity relation in 1929 on the study of twenty-two galaxies). He then perceives that his generalization was erroneous and hence that his theory is unfounded. Since the Mount Palomar dome opened to the sky, many hypotheses have been abandoned, many generalizations revised, many contradictory facts recorded. The universe appears a much darker and deeper chasm than it was judged yesterday, and the light cast upon it by the 200-inch reflector is only a tremulous glimmer that is very far from reaching the bottom. To augment the mystery, when we listen to space we hear a curious sound. Our radio-telescopes interpret it as being emitted by 'radio-electric sources' that radiate electromagnetic waves of a different wavelength from that of stellar light.

For the clear and orderly picture of the universe painted by the astronomers of 1900–25, their successors have substituted a dark, incoherent composition in which the drawing is indistinct and the subject lost in a mass of lines—a canvas that would certainly be discouraging if those sketching it in were not animated by the joy of discovery.

It would be a great deal more discouraging if this book could claim to be a final summing-up and the conquest of the universe were to be regarded as now complete.

Contrary to what was believed at various periods in the course of the ages, astronomy is far from being a finished science. We find to our bewilderment that it has scarcely begun, since our certainty extends only just beyond our immediate sidereal vicinity. It is a workshop still filled with productive disorder, but perhaps that is precisely why so many people labour there with such enthusiasm. For the conquest of the skies by human intelligence offers the double attraction of giving access to a realm literally incommensurable with our physical smallness and, at the same time, of disclosing the scientific laws that enable us to extract the maximum advantage from our terrestrial habitat.

It is perhaps also because there is little in astronomy that can be regarded as a permanent acquisition, because its hypotheses are perpetually being challenged, because obscurity is no sooner dissipated at one point than it gathers elsewhere, that the discovery of the skies appears to us the most marvellous and the most inspiring of all discoveries and astronomy the science in which rigorous pursuit of truth accords most easily with poetic flights of the imagination. What epic of literature can rival the prodigious poem written by the universe-hunters, Herschel, Shapley or Hubble?

Imagination guided by knowledge! 'Beyond the present outposts of science,' wrote John Tyndall, 'spreads a vast field in which imagination can run riot. But it is only the privileged spirits, those able to enjoy freedom without abusing it, who can fruitfully work in it.'

Index

347

INDEX

DATE DUE

AP 21 '70			
MAR 8 1982			
APR 2 8 '86			
MAY 1 9 '86			
MAY 31 '93			
MAY 31 '94			
MAY 0 1 1998			
			PRINTED IN U.S.A.